CW01023945

ANIMAL GENETICS

AN INTRODUCTION TO THE SCIENCE OF ANIMAL BREEDING

BY

F. A. E. CREW, M.D., D.Sc., Ph.D., F.R.S.E.

Lecturer in Genetics in the University of Edinburgh, and Director of the Animal Breeding Research Department

TO

JAMES COSSAR EWART

EDITORS' PREFACE

THE increasing specialisation in biological inquiry has made it impossible for any one author to deal adequately with current advances in knowledge. It has become a matter of considerable difficulty for a research student to gain a correct idea of the present state of knowledge of a subject in which he himself is interested. To meet this situation the text-book is being supplemented by the monograph.

The aim of the present series is to provide authoritative accounts of what has been done in some of the diverse branches of biological investigation, and at the same time to give to those who have contributed notably to the development of a particular field of inquiry an opportunity of presenting the results of their researches, scattered throughout the scientific journals, in a more extended form, showing their relation to what has already been done and to problems that remain to be solved.

The present generation is witnessing "a return to the practice of older days when animal physiology was not yet divorced from morphology," Conspicuous progress is now being seen in the field of general physiology, of experimental biology, and in the application of biological principles to economic problems. In this series, therefore, it is intended that biological research, both pure and applied, shall be represented.

F. A. E. C.
D. W. C.

INTRODUCTION

STOCK-BREEDING is an adventurous experimental study in applied biology. The stock-breeder is concerned with the maintenance of the desirable qualities of his stock and with the improvement of these qualities generation by generation. He has drawn up his own standards of perfection, often in entire ignorance of the scientific principles which undoubtedly underlie his practice, often indeed in direct defiance of these principles, and has set himself the task of attaining them. And he has done wonderful things. Down the ages has come a traditional craft of animal-breeding based upon the accumulated experience of countless generations of husbandmen, and out of his methods of trial and error the breeder has developed his wonderful art. But in this country at least the unit in animal-breeding is no longer inexpensive, stock-breeding is now a business enterprise besieged with difficulties and the breeder is turning more and more to the scientifically trained man for help in the elucidation of his many and varied problems.

The export returns bear witness to the claim that until recently the animal-breeders of Great Britain have held a pre-eminent position as improvers and distributors of live-stock. This export demand nurtured the stock-breeding industry and enabled it to develop into one of vast national importance. But the more recent returns show that the export of pure-bred live-stock generally is diminishing. The reason for this undoubtedly is that the countries which formerly imported from Britain and elsewhere have used their importations to build up stocks of their own as good as that which now exists in Britain. America, for example, has made the Poland-China, the Duroc-Jersey, and the

Chester-White pigs, the American Merino sheep, the Wyandotte and the Rhode Island Red fowl; New Zealand the Corriedale sheep; Australia the Merino and the Australorp. The milking Shorthorn of Australia and New Zealand, the Holstein-Friesian, the Guernsey and the Jersey of America, Canada and South Africa, the Percheron of America—these are as good as their ancestral stocks in Europe. The great new animal-breeding countries are fast becoming independent of Britain; her erstwhile customers are now her competitors. The case of the Australorp is illuminating; the Orpington fowl was imported into Australia from England; it is now being imported from Australia into Britain as the Australorp, an improved Orpington and a veritable boomerang. Force of circumstances has insisted in many instances that the British stock-breeder should model his stock to suit overseas conditions. It does not necessarily follow that the characterisation which suits one environment should suit another; in certain cases it can be maintained that the demands of the farms of Britain have been neglected. There is room for improvement in all kinds of stock that populate the home farms and it will be to the benefit of the breeder and of the nation if the same attention that in the past has been given to the demands of the overseas markets is now given to those of Britain herself. It behoves the British stock-breeder to inquire whether he may gain some reinforcement to his craft.

Of the several sciences which may serve the breeder, genetics is the one which bears upon his breeding practices. It is the science which seeks to account for the similarities and dissimilarities in characterisation exhibited by individuals related by a common ancestry and to define the exact relation between successive generations. It deals with the physiology of heredity—the mechanism by which resemblance between parent and offspring is conserved and transmitted—and with the origin and significance of variation—the mechanism by which such resemblance is modified and transformed. The central problems of this systematical study of the principles and causes which underlie the origin of the individual are these: (1) to define the manner in which the hereditary characters of the individual are represented in the fertilised egg in which it has its beginning; and (2) to demonstrate the way in which these characters become expressed as the development of the individual proceeds. Genetics as a recognised science has but recently come of age, yet already a very great deal is known of the principles of heredity and variation. As would be expected, the geneticist has studied those characters the hereditary transmission of which promised to be comparatively straightforward, and the materials used for genetical study have been, among animals, such inexpensive, quickly-maturing, highly fecund forms as the fruit-fly (*Drosophila melanogaster*), moths, the mouse, rat, guinea-pig, and rabbit.

But out of this work interpretations and theories have arisen which, there is every reason to believe, can account for the phenomena of hereditary transmission met with in the course of practical stock-breeding. The theories derived from experimental breeding work with laboratory animals have indeed been applied to certain known facts of heredity and variation in the fowl, sheep, pig, dog, horse, and cattle, and in all cases the same general principles have been shown to hold true. The fundamental conception of genetics postulates that the hereditary constitution of the individual, established at the time of the union of the ovum and the sperm, decides in great part the future characterisation of the individual, that those qualities alone are inherited which are innate in the germ-cells; this conception is being more and more confirmed as the results of experimental breeding work, of experimental morphology and of cytology accumulate. The geneticist is justified in his conviction that the phenomena of heredity have a definite knowable basis, that indeed in this matter there are no real mysteries but only a present lack of knowledge.

The science of genetics has made great strides during the last twenty years, and it has been assumed at times that coincident with this advance in our knowledge of the fundamental laws of heredity there has been an equal and parallel advance in the practical art of breeding. It is indeed commonly accepted that any advance in a pure science necessarily involves a corresponding advance in the practice of an associated art or craft. This perhaps is true in many instances, but it certainly is not so in the case of the relation of genetics and stock-breeding. The art of animal-breeding is far in advance of the applied science; the geneticist is not in a position to produce or to instruct anybody else how to produce finer specimens of farm-stock that those which foregather at the shows. In fact, a century before the science of genetics was born there existed animals which were intrinsically as fine and as productive as any existing to-day, if it is recognised that standards change and husbandry has improved. But it is of importance to note that the methods used by the geneticist in the investigation of his peculiar problems to-day are exactly those which were employed empirically, and yet with such phenomenal success by the great "improvers" in their deliberate fashioning of new breeds. Bakewell, the brothers Colling, Booth, Bates, Francis Quartly, Coke of Holkham, Amos Cruikshank, Hugh Watson of Keillor, were applied biologists, whether they acknowledged it or not: heredity and variation lay at the basis of all their work. It can be affirmed confidently that their success was due to the fact that their practices were in exact conformity with the underlying biological principles concerned. Experience was followed by the elimination of those methods which were not attended by success, that is, of such as were not in accord with basic biological principles. The geneticist claims no monopoly; the principles of heredity were in operation long before Mendel discovered them, and there can be no doubt that the success of the breeders must have been achieved by practices not violently in discord with these principles. The discovery of these principles therefore could not result in any profound change in the practice of stock-breeding.

The breeder has employed the methods of hybridisation and inbreeding associated with selection in the creation of the modern breeds; to-day he practises line breeding and selection in order to maintain the desired characters of his stock and to improve upon them generation by generation, or he seeks hybrid vigour in out-crossing. These are the very methods by which the biologist has explored the hereditary constitution of his material, the very tools with which he has carved out of his experiences the modern theory of heredity. By the use of these methods the geneticist has analysed his animals into their independently heritable characters, and now his experience, gained whilst working with the more simply organised sorts of living beings, is equipping him to engage in the character-analysis and synthesis of such complex and highly organised creatures as those with which the stock-breeder deals. The present-day knowledge of heredity and variation could never have been derived from the study of hereditary transmission in the domesticated stock: Mendel found the key to this knowledge because he chose the culinary pea for his experimental material, and if the present generation of geneticists feels that it is prepared to approach the problems of the stock-breeder, it is because there exists for guidance the accumulated work of the last twenty-five active years.

The geneticist does not delude himself and does not wish to hold out false hopes to the breeder that many of the recent developments of genetical science must prove of immediate practical economic importance. The scientist is not seeking something necessarily useful: he is seeking knowledge, and all knowledge is potentially useful. This much is certain: knowledge of the phenomena of heredity and variation in the domesticated animals will be gained, and this knowledge must be of considerable value in the education of the stock-breeder and may be applicable to the practice of breeding. It can be said with confidence that the experienced breeder who has a thorough knowledge of genetical theory can guarantee to discover in less time, other conditions being equal, the way by breeding towards those improvements, for example, so much desired by the progressive breeder of cattle—increased quantity and improved quality of milk or meat, the creation of a dual-purpose breed, or of a breed to fit a given environment —than any breeder who is ignorant of genetics though possessing an extensive knowledge of the art of breeding, provided it can be shown that size, regional distribution of muscle and of fat, differences in amount and constitution of milk, those qualities referred to as "fineness" and "vigour" are capable of genetical analysis and prove to be characters in the genetical sense. The great service to the breeder that the science of genetics offers to-day is that it provides an interpretation of his methods and of his results, so that he is enabled to discard all unessential steps in his practices and proceed confidently and more directly to his goal, to plan the steps of a breeding operation with a certainty and precision which otherwise are lacking.

The science of genetics has shown that specific characters or groups of characters are inherited as independent and definite units. It has furnished a critical appreciation of the value of selection, demonstrating that this is not a germinally creative or additive process as the breeder so often believes, but rather is one of sorting out from among a mixture of heritable characters already present in the stock. The geneticist has gained a considerable knowledge of the mechanism of sex-determination and has interpreted the phenomena of sex-linked inheritance (to the profit of the poultry breeder, incidentally), hermaphroditism and sex-reversal. He has demonstrated beyond doubt that certain diseases are truly inherited and has shown the way in which these could be obviated. He has given an exact meaning to the phenomena of inbreeding, outbreeding, and prepotency, and has shown that fecundity, fertility, longevity, and certain forms of sterility have a definite genetical basis. He has critically examined the traditional beliefs and is able, when consulted, to give an authoritative opinion as to their validity. He has given to purity in breeding and to hybridity an exact meaning and has perfected the methods by which any hereditary character, morphological or physiological, can be subjected to genetical analysis.

The geneticist has already shown that the methods of genetical research and the results of genetical investigation can be applied to the problems of stock-breeding. The breeder is not in a position to deny this until he has made himself aware of what has been done, and has provided opportunities for further experimentation. There must be extensive analysis of the characters of the domesticated stock. Analysis must precede synthesis and a completer knowledge of the material must be gained before there can be any talk of revolutionary improvement. It is for the breeder to enlist the co-operation of the biologist. It behoves the breeder to examine carefully the results of the work of the geneticist and to consider whether or not the methods of precision employed by the latter, the great body of facts he has ascertained, and the theories he has constructed, may not be applied with advantage to the study of those characters which are of importance in the practice of stock-breeding. Let the breeder examine the position and he will surely find that for the solution of his problems the assistance of the geneticist is much to be desired.

Circumstances are such that to-day research into the problems of animal-breeding is best conducted at or directed by a research institute. Research is expensive; the collection of facts and measurements, the elaboration of detail, the testing of theories, these take time and money, but if there is to be discovery there must be research. In the field of applied genetics the biologist is not primarily concerned with discovery—he is concerned with the application of a discovery to breeding practices. The facts have been collected from work with laboratory animals, the inductions have been made, and it remains to apply what is known to the problems of the live-stock industry. Experimental breeding work with farm animals is too expensive to be undertaken lightly by a private individual. Moreover, it is somewhat embarrassed by the well-established pedigree system ; it is more profitable to produce specimens of an established breed than to create anything new, for, as definitions go, anything new cannot be pure-bred and therefore cannot command the market price of an animal in whose family history there is no bar sinister. And since genetical methods of character-analysis involve hybridisation, it is not to be expected that the breeders of pedigree stock will practice crossing in the hope that eventually something better may possibly be evolved.

To-day it cannot be held that to be a successful breeder of pedigree stock a man must have a thorough knowledge of the science of genetics; it can, however, be maintained that the State cannot afford to neglect the services of the geneticist, and that the breeder who carries on his work without a sufficient knowledge of genetics is in the position of a surgeon who knows no anatomy, he cannot hope to achieve the highest success. Already the science has much to offer, and if opportunities are given to the geneticist much will be added to the knowledge which may be applied to the practices of the breeder. The extent of the usefulness of genetics to the breeder will be decided by the amount of the support the breeder gives to the institutions which have been organised by the State for his benefit.

In order to provide the breeder with a brief account of what has been and of what is being done by the geneticist, this book has been compiled. The writer makes no claim to originality save perhaps in the presentation of the subject matter. The field of genetics is being surveyed by hundreds of investigators and the greatest activity prevails. It is inevitable, therefore, that much of importance must be omitted; it is probable that much has been misinterpreted. But if in these pages the reader finds the stimulus that shall urge him to study further, this book, built around certain lectures given to students of Agriculture and of Veterinary Science, will have served its purpose. If there is to be any degree of co-operation, the breeder must become familiar with the vocabulary of the geneticist and he must not subscribe to the contention that though *Drosophila melanogaster*, the fruit-fly, may be an animal, yet it is not a "real" animal; that the experimental material and the results of the biologist are too remote to have any bearing upon the problems of the man who breeds cattle for his living. Let the breeder but make himself thoroughly acquainted with the work towards which this book is meant to be a sign-post and he will surely recognise that future advances in breeding will be made by the man who, experienced in the art of breeding, possesses a thorough working knowledge of the science of genetics. If it is admitted that the art of breeding consists in the maintenance of those characteristics or qualities of the stock which are regarded as desirable by the breeder, in the improvement of these characters generation after generation, and in the elimination of undesirable characters through breeding, then it will not be denied that any intelligent attempt to breed must be based upon a knowledge of the manner in which the qualities of a stock arise, are lost, are modified and are transmitted in inheritance.

CONTENTS

"To prevent disappointment . . . it must be at once admitted that for fanciers Mendelism can as yet do comparatively little. 'Fancying' provides the chief interest in life for thousands of persons in this country. It is an occupation with which the scientific naturalist should have more sympathy than he has commonly evinced. If the scientific world had kept in touch with the operations of the 'fancy,' much nonsense which has passed into scientific orthodoxy would never have been written. The study of Mendelian phenomena will do something to bring about a fruitful interchange of experience. But for the 'fancy' our work can as yet do two things only. First, in the study of the workings of the Mendelian system it will provide a fascinating pursuit which, if followed with assiduous care, may lead to some considerable advance in scientific knowledge. Secondly, the principles already ascertained will be found of practical assistance in the formation of new breeds, and may save many mistakes and waste of time. But applied to the business of breeding winners in established breeds they cannot materially help, for almost always the points which tell are too fine to be dealt with in our analysis."

William Bateson,
Mendel's Principles of Heredity, 1913.

ANIMAL GENETICS

CHAPTER I.

THE FACTORS AND THE GERM-PLASM

THE classification of living things by Linnæus (1758) and his fellow-naturalists of the eighteenth century was made possible by the astonishing diversity which they exhibited in details of structure. The systematic zoologist has been able to group the animals into phyla, classes, orders, families, genera, species, and races, by arbitrarily choosing certain distinguishing and true-breeding features as the group characteristics, the different groups representing the various degrees of similarity and dissimilarity, and in so doing has replaced vague impressionistic description by precise significant labelling. If those peculiarities of structure which are characteristic of a race, species, genus, family, order, class or phylum were not inherited there could be no constant group characters and a systematic classification of living things would have been impossible.

Such a systematic classification of animals and plants as this would at once call attention to certain facts: like tends to beget like; animals and plants arise from pre-existing and closely similar forms; the domesticated have arisen from the wild; the characteristics of the parents are transmitted to the offspring. "Breed the best to the best" had ever been the slogan of the breeder. Yet everywhere there is distinctive individuality: no son is the "carbon-copy" of his father: no two individuals are identical, no matter how closely related; each is the first and the last of its identical kind. If this were not so, the breeder could not have hoped to attain improvement by breeding from his best; there would perforce be a dead level in the quality of his stock. Further, it would stimulate speculation as to the mechanism of hereditary transmission and provoke experiment in attempts to ascertain the interrelationship between the species. And so it was that the idea of a common descent engaged the minds of zealous experimentalists who followed Linnæus. In his *Variation of Animals and Plants under Domestication* Darwin gives an account of their work on the crossing of species and varieties in an investigation of the species problem. Their efforts were not crowned with conspicuous success, partly because in their day the relation of parent to offspring was imperfectly understood, and partly because in their experiments in hybridisation they took for their unit the individual as a whole. While this experimental study was in full progress, *The Origin of Species* appeared and there seemed no problem left to solve. Darwin had so marshalled the evidence that it was impossible to avoid the fact of organic evolution. His explanation of the fact also seemed at the time to be beyond dispute. Experimental investigation soon ceased and the field was left to the systematist and the theorist. The systematist concerned himself with the proper labelling of the new and the re-labelling of the old; the theorist, unguided by any scientific observation of the mechanism of heredity and variation, and confused by a mass of popular tradition current among stock-breeders, proceeded to the construction of hypotheses which, when put to the test of experiment, were doomed to disrepute.

Some of the observed facts which the theorist has had to accommodate are as follows. Many characters peculiar to certain individuals were known to be inherited: *morphological* (structural) characters, such as form, structure, location, size, and colour of the different constituent parts; *physiological* characters, such as longevity, obesity, baldness, fecundity, fertility, immunity; *pathological* (unusual, abnormal) characters, such as polydactylism (extra digits), syndactylism (fused digits), brachydactylism (short digits), achondroplasia (abnormal skeletal development), deaf-mutism; *psychological* characters, such as peculiarities of temperament, of intellect, feeble-mindedness, genius, insanity. All these have been recognised as heritable qualities in respect of which offspring might resemble the parent. But a child in its characterisation might seem to be a patchwork of ancestral qualities, a mosaic of ancestral traits: such a type was defined as *particulate* as opposed to *blended* inheritance in which the characters of two dissimilar parents appeared to be blended in their offspring, as in the case of the skin colour of mulattoes. It was also suggested that a child could inherit all or nearly all his characters from one of the parents; such inheritance was termed *alternative.* A character of one generation might appear again in the grandchildren, being *latent* in the parent and *patent* in the grandparents and grandchildren. Such skipping of a generation had long been known as *atavism.* In other cases a character borne by a remote ancestor remained latent for many generations and then suddenly reappeared; such cases were known as *reversions.* Other characters were observed to be *limited* to one or to the other sex, while others were transmitted from grandparent to grandchild of the same sex, or from parent to child of the opposite sex; such cases constitute instances of *sex-linked* inheritance. In addition to these permutations in the distribution and combination of characters already exhibited by the stock, new characters unexpectedly appeared in one generation and these new characters were transmitted through inheritance to succeeding generations. Such "sports" or *mutants* were known to have been the foundation of new breeds of domesticated animals.

The theories expounded to explain the observed facts of heredity have been numerous, but since it is not intended to spend time in reading the epitaphs in the graveyard of discredited theories, only some of the more modern ones will be mentioned.

It is of importance to note that it was not until the end of the eighteenth century that it became generally accepted that each of the sexes made a definite contribution to the offspring; previous to this time, one sex was supposed to supply the seed, the other the soil in which the seed grew. Also it must not be forgotten that the fertilisation of the egg by a single sperm was not established with any degree of certainty until many years after *The Origin of Species* had appeared.

Theories of Pangenesis have suggested that the germ-cells are the centres of contributions from the different parts of the body. Darwin's Provisional Hypothesis of Pangenesis, for example, suggested that every cell of the body, not too highly and specially differentiated, threw off characteristic "gemmules" which multiplied yet retained their characters and which became especially concentrated in the reproductive organs of both sexes, so that in the union of the gametes—the egg and the sperm—and in the development of the zygote—the fertilised egg—the gemmules united with others like themselves and grew into cells like those from which they originally came, or, on the other hand, remained latent during development even through several generations.

Darwin considered all variations as being heritable. Variation in characterisation was regarded as somatic in origin, occurring in the bodily tissues of the individual and thence being transferred by means of the gemmules to the germ-cells. Every somatic variation whether induced by use or by disuse, in response to some environic stimulus or by some spontaneous tendency to variability, was supposed to give off characteristic gemmules into the blood stream which carried to the germ-cells the material representative of the varying character. There is no experimental basis for this assumption.

Up to the end of the nineteenth century, the bulk of biological opinion regarded the central problem of heredity to be that which was concerned with the mechanism by which the various heritable qualities of the individual got into the germ-cells produced by that individual. But genetic theories were gaining ground from the pangenetic, and in the end the newer theories, supported by the new facts of cytology, caused a complete restatement of the problem. The question now asked was: *How are the qualities of an individual represented in the germ-cells which in their union produce the individual?*

Genetic theories have been based upon the conception of what is termed germinal continuity and are supported by cytological facts. As early as 1849, it had been shown that in certain instances it was possible in the embryo to distinguish between the cells which were to become the reproductive organs and those which were to form the body of the individual. Haeckel (1866) had emphasised the simple yet fundamental fact of the material continuity of offspring and parent and of the distinction between the personal and the germinal, while Jäger (1879) had carried the doctrine further by his powerful teaching that through a great series of generations the germinal protoplasm retains its specific properties: in every reproduction it divides into an ontogenetic (pertaining to the individual) portion, out of which the individual is built up, and a phylogenetic (pertaining to the race) portion which is reserved to form the reproductive material of the adult offspring. Genetic theories were extended as the years passed, and biological opinion became prepared for the teaching of Weismann.

Weismann (1882, 1893) taught that the germ-cells were to be regarded merely as parts of an unbroken line of "germ-plasm," the bearer of the heritable qualities, and that this germ-plasm under certain circumstances, usually the union of two of its constituent germ-cells, frothed up and produced a great excrescence, the somato-plasm—the body of the next generation—and continued its existence in that body; that the germ-plasm was immortal, the body mortal; that the germ-plasm had existed from the very dawn of life, whereas the body was formed afresh in every generation; that the individual did not, as it appeared to do, produce germ-cells on reaching maturity; that the germ-cells were not formed afresh by each succeeding generation; and that when the fertilised egg divided, some of the resulting cells were set apart at once and took no further part in the building of the body, but later became the germ-cells of the individual into which the fertilised egg developed.

This peculiar "apartness" of the germ-cells can be actually demonstrated in several groups of living organisms but perhaps is best illustrated in the case of Ascaris,[1] as was shown by Boveri (1910). In Ascaris the cells which are destined to give rise to the somatic tissues are always clearly distinguishable from those which are to give rise to the germ-cells. In the case of the former, the chromatin of the nucleus[2] undergoes a diminution in quantity: in the case of the primitive sex-cells no such chromatin reduction takes place. The lineage of the sex-cells from embryo to adult is demonstrable and these form the material link between generation and generation. The somatic cells, busied in playing their part in the general act of living, are overtaken by that physiological exhaustion which ends in death; the germ-cells take no part in the general functioning of the body and they are in a sense immortal. In short, "the proper statement of the relation between successive generations is not to say that a hen produces another hen through the medium of an egg, but to say that a hen is merely an egg's way of producing another egg."

An individual is like its parents not because it is produced from the parent but because both offspring and parent are produced from the same stock of germ-plasm. The somatoplasm of the father and that of the son are developments at different times from one and the same continuous stream of germ-plasm (of course the germ-plasm from which the son arises in reality is not the same as that from which the parent arose, for inheritance is biparental). The resemblance of parent and offspring is called by analogy heredity though actually the heritable qualities are not transmitted to the following generation in the same way as is property. Inheritance—all that the individual possesses in virtue of the hereditary relationship—implies in the biological sense a rhythmical repetition in each species of a definite and on the whole similarly repeated series of events leading up to the production of an individual which liberates germ-cells capable of initiating the same process. Qualities as such are not transmitted, what is transmitted from parent to offspring is the germ-plasm, the common material which

[1] *Ascaris megalocephala*, a worm parasitic in the intestine of the horse.
[2] *See* Chapter III.

determines, other things being equal, the production of a similar type of structure. Weismann postulated that in each development a portion of the specific germinal plasma, which the fertilised egg contains, is not used up in the formation of the offspring but is reserved unchanged for the formation of the germinal cells of the following generation; that what is actually continuous is the *germ-plasm* of definite chemical and specific molecular constitution, a continuity of germinal cells being rare, while a continuity of intact germinal plasma being the rule.

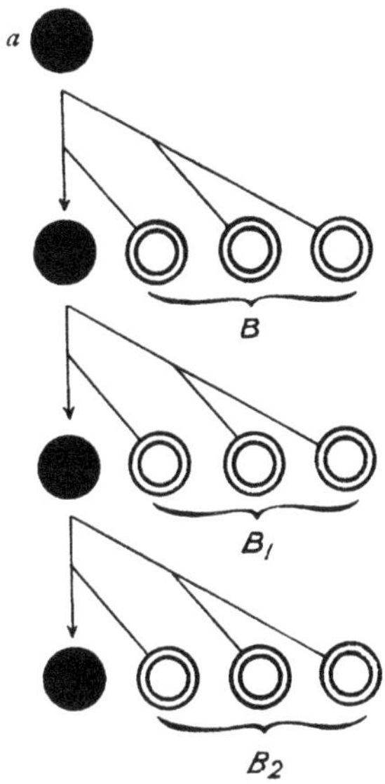

FIG. 1.—(*a*) The germ-plasm, the line of inheritance. (*B*) The somato-plasm, the line of succession. (*After* Wilson.)

Bateson in 1894 further compelled biologists to revise their ideas of the significance of variation by showing that discontinuity in variation was widespread, that there were great numbers of cases in which by sharp sudden steps offspring differed markedly from their parents. Later (1901) came the Mutation Theory of de Vries, which postulated that new varieties could arise quite suddenly from the older ones by a single leap instead of coming into being by the slow accumulation of minute differences. During this time also the Darwinian hypothesis had been subjected to biological as well as to the theological criticism and in many ways had been found to be somewhat incomplete. Darwin had not explained the mode of evolution though through him the general fact of evolution—that the present is the child of the past and the parent of the future—had come to be accepted. He had offered an explanation for the survival of the fittest, but had not demonstrated the mode of their origin. He had based certain of his interpretations upon the assumption that acquired characters were transmitted through inheritance to following generations. The transmission of such characters had not been conclusively demonstrated. It was found that in a given limited habitat a considerable number of species could thrive side by side, and it became difficult to conceive how the various specific characters could have been evolved in the course of a struggle for existence when these characters appeared to be not adaptive characters at all, being in themselves apparently quite useless to their possessors. Many of the variations in characterisation which "bred true" appeared to be so minute that it was hard to grant that they possessed any life-and-death value. The subject of inter-specific sterility had not been disposed of finally, and sex-dimorphism had not been completely explained. The need for further experimental investigation of the problems of heredity and variation came to be recognised and the study of the origin of species gave place to the study of the processes by which individuals came into existence, since it seemed probable that the principles and causes of the origin of individuals would be found to apply also to the evolution of species. The stage was set for the re-entry of Mendel in 1900.

When the records of the work of Gregor Johann Mendel were brought to light during the course of similar work by Correns (1900) (Germany), de Vries (1910) (Holland), and Tschermak (Austria), it was seen that in Mendel's facts and theory there was confirmation and extension of Weismann's own. Mendel, Prälat of the Königskloster at Brünn, communicated to the Brünn Natural History Society in 1865, the results of eight years' experimental breeding. The paper *Versuche über Pflanzen-Hybriden* was published in 1866 in the Transactions of that Society, but from that date until 1900 it lay unheeded for the reason that during the controversy which the promulgation of Darwinism in 1858 had aroused, biologists generally were too much occupied to consider the merits of the interpretation which Mendel placed upon his results. Moreover, this was entirely opposed to current biological opinion of the period when the paper appeared: the teaching of Weismann, Bateson and de Vries was necessary before the immense value of Mendel's work could be appreciated. Besides, no mechanism in animals or plants was known which would explain how such processes as were invoked by him could be brought about. In 1900 cytological advances were disclosing this mechanism and an appeal to the hypothetical was no longer so necessary.

In any experimental biological inquiry it is necessary at the outset to consider: (1) the definition of the scope of the inquiry; (2) the planning of the method of inquiry in such a way that at the end of each step a "yes" or "no" answer may be expected; (3) the choice of the most suitable material. Mendel took for his problem the question as to the exact manner in which the definite and true-breeding varieties within a species are related to one another. For his experimental material he chose the culinary pea, and in this choice he was most fortunate and wise. The pea is normally self-fertilised, male and female reproductive organs and products being present together in every flower, so that when a plant is left to itself the ovules of a flower are fertilised by the pollen-grains of the same flower. Of the pea there are many varieties: one is characterised by having a red flower, another by a white; one has a relatively short stem, another a long one; in one the unripe pods are green, in another they are yellow, and so on. The many investigators in cross-breeding who had preceded Mendel had considered the individual as a whole as the unit for study and they had concluded that hybrids, *i.e.*, individuals which were begotten by dissimilar parents, must be intermediate in type. This conclusion had engendered the notion that the back-crossing of the hybrid to the parental form must involve a dilution of the new type, culminating after a number of generations in the swamping of it out of existence. When the individual was regarded in its entirety, all the hereditary resemblances and dissimilarities were averaged. But in genetics, as in anatomy, the individual must be dissected and each component part considered by itself and in its relation to the others. Mendel, unlike his predecessors, did not deal with a complete individual, did not consider an individual as a unit, but concentrated upon pairs of what seemed to be distinctly contrasted characters, a character being the mode of exhibition of one of the different details of anatomical structure and physiological function. Each pair was related to the same property and the same structure. Ultimately he dealt with seven pairs of characters: round and wrinkled seed, orange and green cotyledon, inflated and wrinkled seed-coat, grey and white seed-coat, green and yellow unripe pod, axial and terminal position of flowers, long and short stem. The method used by Mendel was that of hybridisation. He transferred the pollen-grain from a flower of one true-breeding variety to the stigma of a flower of another, the stamens of the artificially pollinated flower being removed before they were ripe. The result in every case was that the cross-bred offspring constituting the first filial generation (or shortly, as suggested by Punnett the F_1) exhibited one and only one of the two alternative characters which distinguished its parents. The character which in this way prevailed Mendel called the Dominant, that which was suppressed—the Recessive. The seeds from each individual plant were harvested separately and sown separately the following year. The F_1 individuals were allowed to become self-fertilised and a second filial generation —F_2—was thus produced. This generation was mixed, consisting of individuals exhibiting the dominant character and individuals exhibiting the recessive, and in every 4 on an average there were 3 with the dominant character to 1 with the recessive. It will be noticed that the 3 : 1 ratio was never actually obtained, but the extension of Mendel's work was greatly simplified by his regard for a "round" number.

The yellow and green pod colour mating was repeated by Correns, Tschermak, Hurst, Bateson, Lock (1908), Darbishire (1911) and White at different times. Their results combined give an F_2 of 195477 individuals, 146802 yellow and 48675 green, or a ratio of 3·016 : 1.

The individuals of the F_2 generation were allowed to fertilise themselves when it was found that every one of those which had exhibited the recessive character bred true for this character, whereas of those which had exhibited the dominant character in every 3 on the average there was 1 which bred true and 2 which, being of similar factorial constitution to the F_1 individuals, repeated the production of a 3 : 1 ratio. In every one of the seven pairs of characters dealt with by Mendel, the mode of inheritance was essentially the same. Two organisms differing in respect of a single pair of characters produced, when mated, a hybrid which manifested the so-called dominant member of the pair to the more or less complete exclusion of the recessive, and an F_2 showing a 3 : 1 ratio.

Structure.	Property.	Characters.		Ratio in F_2.
		Dominant.	Recessive.	
Seed . . .	Form	5,474 round	1,850 wrinkled	2·96 : 1
Reserved material in cotyledons .	Colour	6,022 yellow	2,001 green	3·01 : 1
Seed-coats . .	Form	882 inflated	299 wrinkled	2·95 : 1
Seed-coats . .	Colour	705 grey	224 white	3·15 : 1
Unripe pods .	Colour	428 green	152 yellow	2·82 : 1
Flowers . .	Position	651 axial	207 terminal	3·14 : 1
Stem . . .	Length	787 tall	277 dwarf	2·84 : 1
		14,949	5,010	2·98 : 1 or 3 : 1

It is now known that dominance is an unessential feature of Mendelian inheritance: *what is essential is the orderly reappearance of the characters of the parents of the hybrid, and of the hybrid itself, in the second hybrid generation in definite numerical proportions.*

The theory put forward by Mendel to explain the facts which he had observed was an attempt to explain the phenomena of inheritance upon a rigid statistical basis and is probably a very close approximation to the true one. It certainly is true to such a point that it is possible by means of it to predict the results of the simpler types of mating which the practical breeder is likely to want to make.

Each new individual had its origin in the union of of an ovule and a pollen-grain. Mendel concluded that there must have been something in the reproductive cell taken from a flower on a tall plant which made the offspring of a dwarf plant fertilised by this pollen develop into a tall plant. His theory was that there must have

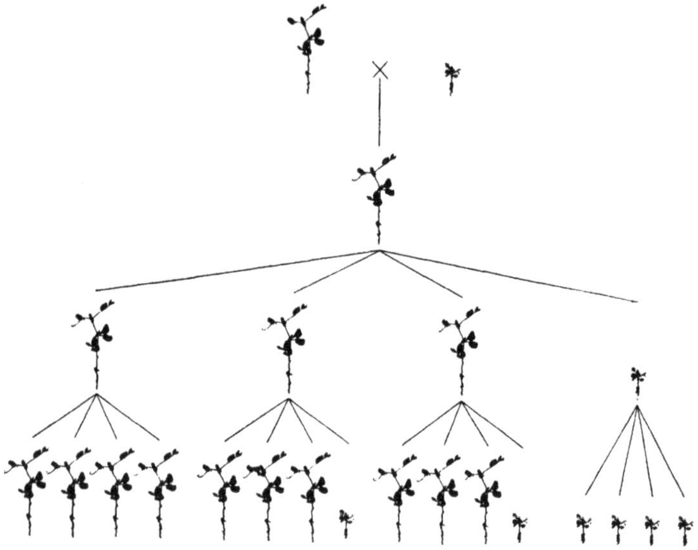

FIG. 2.—Tall and Dwarf. (*After* Darbishire.)

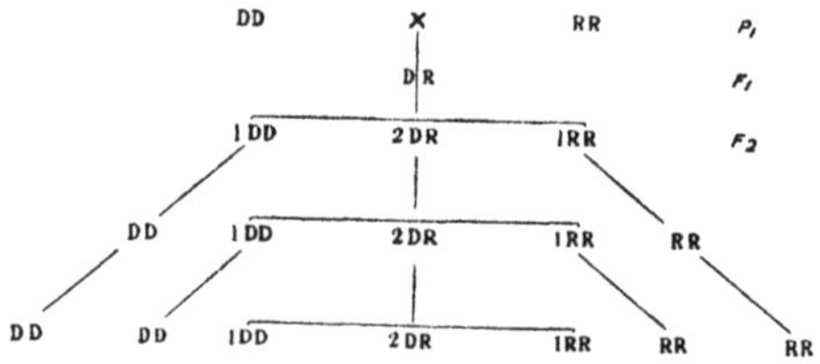

FIG. 3.

been in every one of these germ-cells, or gametes, something which is capable of giving rise to the character tallness. He did not know what that something was—for that matter neither do we to-day—so that it does not really matter what that something is called. The terms that have come into general use are *factor*, *gene*, or *differential.* Every germ-cell of the tall pea of the parental generation (P_1) carried the factor for tallness, those of the dwarf—the factor for dwarfness. When a tall pea is self-fertilised, therefore, a male germ-cell containing the factor for tallness unites with a female germ-cell containing the factor for tallness to form a new individual which exhibits the character tallness and which is pure for this character and will breed true. Similarly, when a male gamete containing the factor for dwarfness unites with a female gamete carrying the same factor, a zygote results which in its development will exhibit the character dwarfness and will be pure for this character. But Mendel found, as has been seen, that when a gamete bearing the factor for tallness united with a gamete bearing the factor for dwarfness, a tall pea was produced. The fertilised egg—the zygote—in this case possessed in respect of the stem-length character two factors, one from each parent, but one of them was a factor for tallness, the other that for dwarfness. For some unknown reason the factor for tallness in this combination was the only one which played any appreciable part in determining the character of the stem-length. It made no difference to the results which parent was the male and which the female, the reciprocal crosses were found to give identical results.

To account for the 3 : 1 ratio in the second cross-bred generation, Mendel supposed that half of both male and female gametes provided by the F_1 hybrid contained the factor for the dominant character, the other half—the factor for the recessive. The factor for the dominant is not adulterated by its association with the factor for the recessive, nor that for the recessive by its intimacy with that for the dominant. At the time when the germ-cells of the hybrid ripen, the factors *segregate*, so that half of the female gametes come to contain the factor for the dominant character and the other half the factor for the recessive character. A similar process takes place in the case of the male gametes of the hybrid, half come to contain the one factor of the pair, the other half—the other factor. The two kinds of factors occurring in equal numbers among the germ-cells of the hybrid are as pure, in respect of the characters they represent, as the same two factors existing in the germ-cells of the pure-bred parental forms, according to this theory. In the case of the gametes of the F_1 individual in Mendel's experiment, there are equal numbers of ovules bearing the factor for the dominant character and that for the recessive; similarly, there are equal numbers of pollen-grains bearing the factor for the dominant character and that for the recessive. There may, or may not, be equal numbers of ovules and of pollen-grains; this is a matter of no importance, since any one ovule can be fertilised by but one pollen-grain.

Consider the case of the ovules with the factor for the dominant character. They have an equal chance of becoming fertilised by a pollen-grain bearing the factor for the dominant character as by a pollen-grain bearing the factor for the recessive. The following associations in the F_2 zygotes will be approximately equally frequent:—

Factor for the Dominant Character : Factor for the Dominant Character
,, ,, ,, : ,, ,, Recessive ,,

Consider now the case of the ovules with the factor for the recessive character. These again have an equal chance of being fertilised by a pollen-grain with a factor for the dominant character as by one with the factor for the recessive character, so that the following associations in the zygote will be equally frequent:—

Factor for the Recessive Character : Factor for the Dominant Character
,, ,, ,, : ,, ,, Recessive ,,

There are therefore four kinds of factor associations and these are on the average equally frequent. F_2 will thus contain the following associations:—

Dominant : Dominant, 25 per cent.	"Pure" Dominant . .	1	3
Dominant : Recessive, 25 ,,	"Impure" Dominant or Hybrid . . .	2	
Recessive : Dominant, 25 ,,			
Recessive : Recessive, 25 ,,	"Pure" Recessive . .	1	1

or, 25 per cent. like one grand-parent, 25 per cent. like the other, and 50 per cent. like the parents. This theory is in complete accordance with the facts. Schematically the situation can be illustrated so—

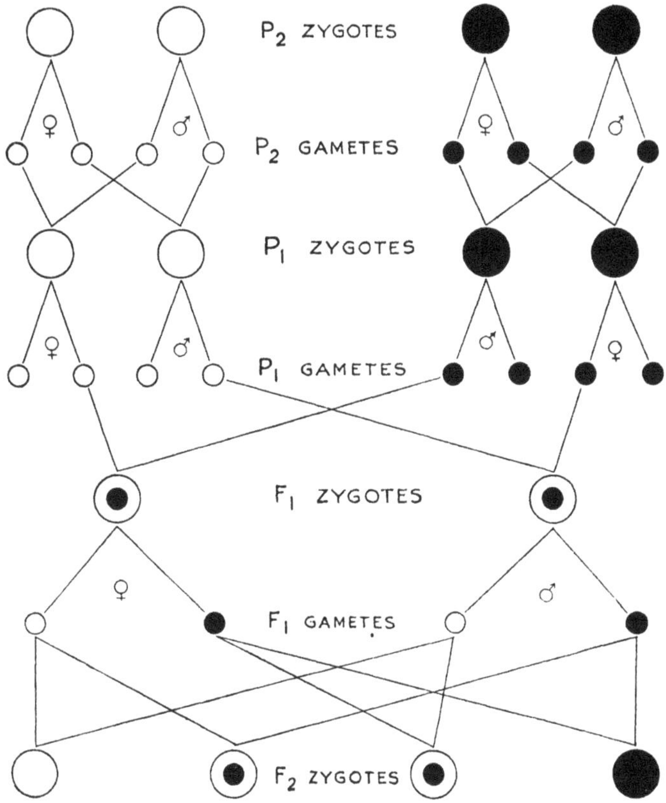

○ = Dominant. ● = Recessive.
♂ = Male. ♀ = Female.

FIG. 4.

The significance of the facts of Mendel's results is profound. Out of them arose the conception of the *unit-character*, a unit because it acted as such in inheritance. A second conception was that of the *purity of gametes*. Purity of type acquired a precise meaning being dependent on gametic segregation. Purity depends upon the meeting of two gametes bearing similar factors for the one character, and so an individual may be pure in respect of one character and impure or hybrid in respect of others. The hybrid condition cannot be represented in a single reproductive cell, it can only be produced by the union of male and female reproductive cells which are dissimilar with regard to the factor in question. Further, each reproductive cell, male or female, contains a complete set of factors for determining the characters of an individual. The third conception was that *the zygote had a double structure* and so therefore had the individual which developed from it. A zygote may be formed by the union of gametes each bearing similar factors with regard to one or more characters. In this case the individual is said to be a *homozygote* or *homozygous* (Bateson) with respect to the character or characters concerned, and in the zygote in which this individual had its origin the factor for each of these characters was present in the duplicate or *duplex* condition. On the other hand, a zygote may result from the union of two gametes which bear factors for dissimilar alternative characters, when the individual developing from such a zygote is said to be a *heterozygote* or *heterozygous* with respect to these characters, and in the zygote the factors for these characters were present in the *simplex* condition. *Homozygosis* is the state of being homozygous, the condition of an individual in which any given genetical factor is present in the duplex condition, due to the fact that the two gametes forming in their union the zygote from which the individual had its origin were alike with respect to the factor in question. Such an individual in turn produces gametes of only one kind with respect to the given factor. *Heterozygosis* is the state of being heterozygous, the condition of an individual in which any given factor has been derived from only one of the two gametes which in their union formed the zygote in which the individual had its origin. The gametes liberated by such an individual are typically of two kinds, half of them containing the factor in question, the other half lacking this factor. An individual homozygous for a given character or characters is one which had its origin in the union of gametes which in respect of the character or characters concerned were factorially identical. An individual heterozygous for a given character or characters is one which had its origin in the union of gametes which in respect of the character or characters concerned were factorially dissimilar. A homozygote is an individual which when mated to another, factorially similar or dissimilar, produces offspring all factorially alike; a heterozygote is an individual which when mated to an individual, factorially similar or dissimilar,

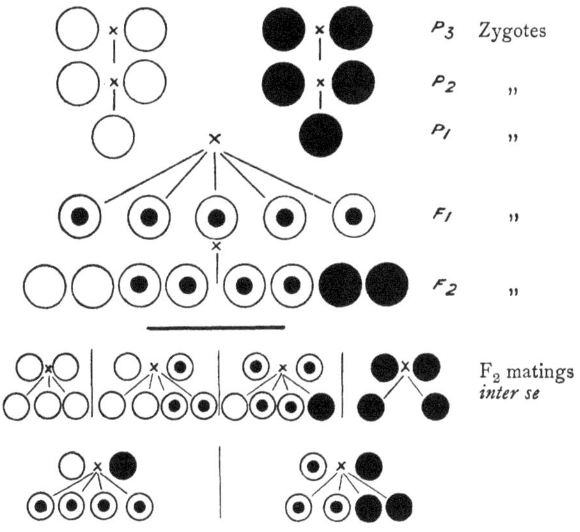

○ = the dominant; ● the recessive.

FIG. 5.

produces offspring factorially dissimilar *inter se*. Finally, the most important conception was that *the germ-plasm had a definite structure*. If it is derived from a hybrid parent it may have either of two structures with regard to any one character, but it cannot be any vague or indefinite mixture of the two.

Such is the generally accepted theory of Mendelian inheritance. Its validity can be tested by other matings, as for example by a back-cross between the F_1 hybrid and the parent exhibiting the recessive character. It would be expected that equal numbers of offspring exhibiting the dominant and the recessive characters respectively should appear, and that every one of those exhibiting the dominant character should prove to be a hybrid. This is exactly what happens.

Other matings are shown in Fig. 5. In every case the results conform to the actual experience of the hybridiser. The most convenient way of representing the supposed causes of Mendelian segregation is to make use of Punnett's chess-board table. Along the top of the table are written the letters representing the kinds of factors which occur among the male gametes and along the left side of the table the letters referring to the equivalent series of the female gametes. The squares alongside each other constitute a row, those superimposed one above the other, a column. In the square formed by the intersection of a row with a column is written the factorial constitution of the zygote which results from the union of the factor at the head of the column with the factor at the left of the row. A square of this sort indicates that equal numbers of all the different kinds of gametes are involved in fertilisation. Bateson introduced the use of the letters *D* and *R* to signify the factors for the Dominant and Recessive characters respectively.

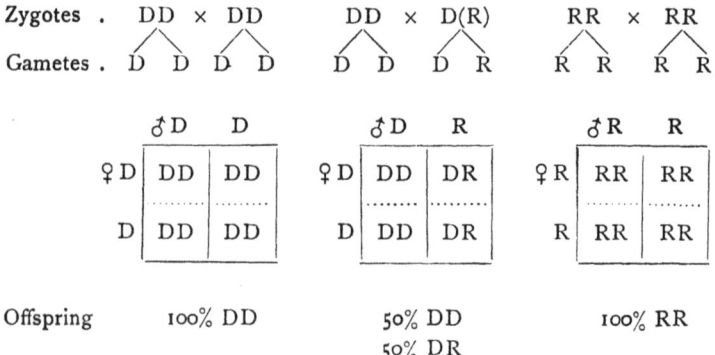

Zygotes .	DD × DD	DD × D(R)	RR × RR
Gametes .	D D D D	D D D R	R R R R

	♂D	D
♀D	DD	DD
D	DD	DD

	♂D	R
♀D	DD	DR
D	DD	DR

	♂R	R
♀R	RR	RR
R	RR	RR

Offspring	100% DD	50% DD 50% DR	100% RR

Zygotes .	DD × RR	D(R) × D(R)	D(R) × RR
Gametes .	D D R R	D R D R	D R R R

	♂ D	D
♀ R	DR	DR
R	DR	DR

	♂ D	R
♀ D	DD	DR
R	DR	RR

	♂ R	R
♀ D	DR	DR
R	RR	RR

Offspring	100% DR	50% DR 25% DD ; 25% RR	50% DR 50% RR

Or tabulated :—

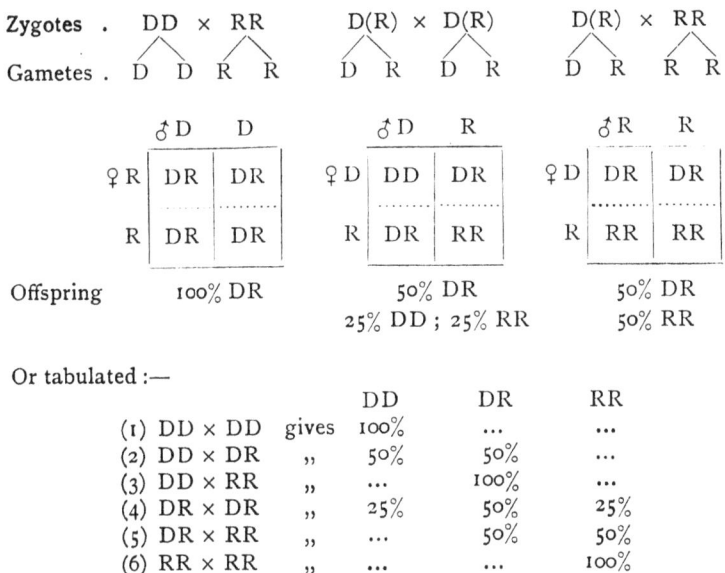

		DD	DR	RR
(1) DD × DD	gives	100%	...	...
(2) DD × DR	,,	50%	50%	...
(3) DD × RR	,,	...	100%	...
(4) DR × DR	,,	25%	50%	25%
(5) DR × RR	,,	...	50%	50%
(6) RR × RR	,,	...	...	100%

It will be noted that if, for example, in the mating DR × DR the two sorts of male gametes are elaborated in the proportion of 3 D-bearing to 1 R-bearing, the size-relations of the classes among the offspring will not be 25% DD, 50% DR, 25% RR, but 37·5% DD, 50% DR, 12·5% RR, and the ratio not 1 : 2 : 1 but 3 : 4 : 1.

	♂ D			R
♀ D	DD	DD	DD	DR
	DD	DD	DD	DR
R	DR	DR	DR	RR
	DR	DR	DR	RR

It is useful to consider this scheme working backwards. For example, the occurrence in a generation of equal numbers of individuals exhibiting the recessive character which is being dealt with in the experiment and of individuals exhibiting the dominant can mean only one thing, that the parents of these offspring are DR × RR—heterozygous dominant and a recessive. If all the offspring show the dominant character then the parents might have been DD × DD, DD × DR, or DD × RR. If it is known that one parent bore the recessive character then the other parent must have been a homozygous dominant, DD. Here then is an acid test by which the homozygous and heterozygous dominants may be identified in those cases in which dominance being complete, the F_1 individual appears indistinguishable from the parent with the dominant character. The homozygous dominant mated to the recessive gives only heterozygous dominants (which in these cases look like the homozygous), whereas the heterozygous dominant similarly mated will produce as nearly as possible equal numbers of heterozygous dominants and of recessives. In order that in such a test it may be certain (= extremely probable) that among the individuals exhibiting the dominant character there shall be one homozygote, it is necessary to take at least twelve such and mate them with the individuals exhibiting the corresponding recessive character.

Mendel gives the following table showing the numbers as calculated theoretically and as verified experimentally of the different classes of offspring in any generation of a monohybrid mating followed by self-fertilisation:—

Generation.	DD	DR	RR	Ratios.
F_2 . . .	1	2	1	1 : 2 : 1
F_3 . . .	6	4	6	3 : 2 : 3
F_4 . . .	28	8	28	7 : 2 : 7
F_5 . . .	120	16	120	15 : 2 : 15
F_6 . . .	496	32	496	31 : 2 : 31
F_n . . .	...	...	...	$2^n - 1 : 2 : 2^n - 1$

The method of experimental breeding in essence became the analysis of the experimental material into its component unit characters. From this point of view animals may be regarded as definite orderly combinations of independently heritable unit characters which may be dissociated and recombined. Genetics thus became an instrument by which the nature of the living organism might be explored.

As an example of a monohybrid experiment with animals, the Rosecomb × Singlecomb mating in fowls may be cited; the results are shown in the following diagram. Rosecomb is dominant to single. Further consideration will make it clear that the singlecombed bird which occasionally appears among the progeny of a (rosecombed) Wyandotte mating is the result of the mating of two heterozygotes and will point to the infusion of White Leghorn "blood."

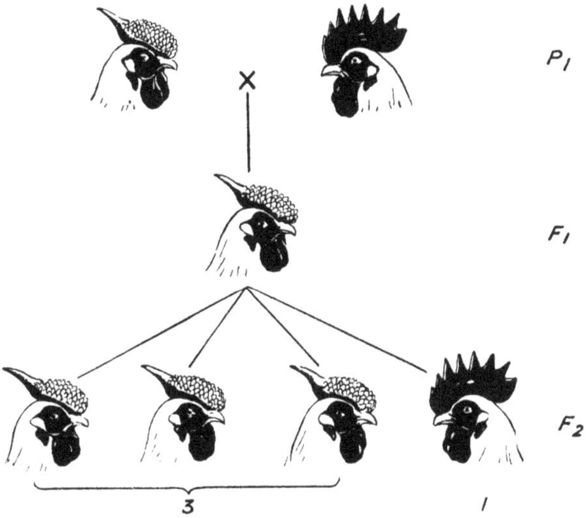

FIG. 6.—Rosecomb and Single. (*After* Darbishire.)

Another case would seem to be that of the mating Black and Red coat colour in cattle; black is dominant, and if this is so the occasional occurrence of a red calf in a black herd is readily interpreted. Such a red calf can only occur when two heterozygous blacks are mated. This question of colour-inheritance in cattle is one of considerable importance to the breeder, for the appearance of a red calf in a breed in which the standard and fashionable colour is black may lead to suspicion concerning the "purity" of the herd, to misunderstanding and indeed even to legal action. The fact that a red calf does appear occasionally in an Aberdeen-Angus herd, in a Galloway herd, or among Holstein-Friesians or Kerries can be accounted for if it can be shown that during the formative periods in the history of these breeds a red individual was employed. This unfortunately is usually impossible, for the history of most breeds is beset with mystery. It is known, however, that all the modern breeds have been produced by a gradual evolution in the hands of the breeder from some common local stock. In founding a new breed out-crossing was at first practised freely in order to collect the desired characteristics in the same stock. Then out-breeding was followed by in-breeding and the breed was modelled to fit certain arbitrarily chosen standards. The breed became a group of individuals all of which exhibited certain well-defined hereditary characters. Finally came registration. In certain cases it is known that the maker of the breed introduced a red strain into his stock at a time when coat-colour was a matter of no great concern to him. In other cases in which there is no accurate record of the employment of red stock it can be assumed that such was used since the appearance of red in any modern breed in which black has come to be the fashionable colour is amenable to the same interpretation.

If red was introduced and if black was chosen later as the standard coat-colour, a beast may be a homozygous or a heterozygous black and when the latter kind are present an occasional red calf is inevitable. It will be noted that if the breeder had chosen red as the standard there could have been no off-colour calves.

There have been red Aberdeen-Angus herds, and as far as is known a red Aberdeen-Angus is as typical a specimen of the breed as is a black. The red is as "pure-bred" and as valuable as its black relative. The same is true of the Galloway. Fashion and prejudice have condemned the red, and though this is a matter of no great importance in the case of the beef breeds it is a most reprehensible state of affairs that in the milk breeds a potentially most valuable specimen should be disposed of secretly or sold for veal just because it happens to be born with the unfashionable coat-colour. There is no reason to suggest that a Holstein-Friesian is not so good a Friesian because its coat is red-and-white instead of black-and-white, yet a red-and-white is not eligible for registration in the American Herd Book. It is a fact that up to about 1850, before the importation of black-and-white Jutlands, the majority of Holstein-Frieslands were red-and-whites. It was later that the black-and-white coat-colour became fashionable. In Holland red-and-whites are still eligible for registration and are relatively common. Surely when a more liberal minded attitude shall follow the spread of genetical knowledge such a red-and-white calf will be disposed of to a dairy farmer to whom colour is a matter of secondary importance and will be no longer regarded as an indication of "impurity."

It may be necessary to devise a method of distinguishing between the homozygous and the heterozygous black. Possibly this may be done by micrological and chemical examination of the hair of the black male calf. As yet the only method which can be suggested is one which would seem to be impracticable. The bull should be mated during one and the same season to at least a dozen red cows. If no red calf appears then it may be accepted that the bull is a homozygous black.

One modification of Mendel's original views has already been referred to: that dominance is an unessential feature of the scheme. The case of the Blue Andalusian fowl, described by Bateson and Saunders (1901) and by Bateson, Saunders and Punnett (1906), may be considered in illustration of this. The plumage-colour of this fowl is a slaty blue-grey. A similar case would seem to be that of the Blue Mendel fowl.

If two such birds are mated, it will be found that they do not breed true, for in addition to the more numerous blue-plumaged offspring there will be produced a number of black, and of white with black flecks. On the average, the number of blue offspring equals the total of blacks and whites, while these latter are produced in more or less equal numbers, so that the ratio 1 : 2 : 1 appears. This in itself is suggestively reminiscent of the ratio in the F_2 of a Mendelian monohybrid experiment. At once the question arises as to what happens when a white and a black Andalusian are interbred. The offspring of such a mating are without exception blue, and blue birds obtained in this way, when mated together, produce a generation of 1 black, 2 blues, and 1 white in every 4 on a average. The suggested interpretation of these facts was that the Blue Andalusian is a monohybrid in the Mendelian sense, the

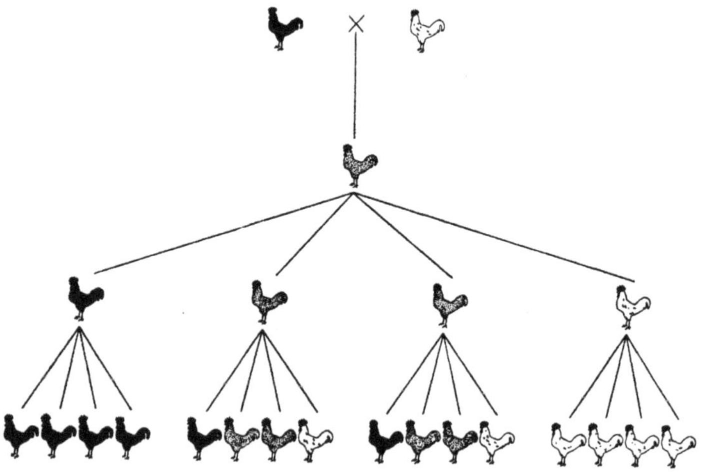

FIG. 7.—The Blue Andalusian. (*After* Darbishire.)

offspring of parents which differed one from the other only in respect of one pair of unit characters, but a hybrid which possessed an easily observable character of its own which distinguished it from both parents. In this way it differs from the hybrid pea in Mendel's own experiments, in which case, for example, the hybrid tall pea only differs from the pure tall by its breeding properties and not by any outward characteristic of its own, as far as can readily be estimated. The blue of the Andalusian may be considered for the moment as an intermediate between the black and the white of its parents, and it is not unreasonable to refer to black as the *imperfect dominant*, imperfect because it is legitimate to regard the differences between the result of crossing the

FIG. 8.—Red × White in the Shorthorn. (*After* Finlay.)

[*Face page 25*

black and the white Andalusian and the tall and the dwarf pea as being only a matter of degree. The blue colour is due to a fine but uneven sprinkling of black pigment through the feathers; on some, such as those of the breast, the black pigment forms a distinct edging or "lining." The blue of the Blue Andalusian is thus a mosaic of black and white. In any case the phenomena as exhibited by the two cases of the pea and the fowl are perfectly analogous, the only difference between them being the degree of dominance, and this not an essential feature of Mendelian inheritance. It is probable that actually there are always differences between homozygous and heterozygous dominants, but that commonly there is no sufficiently precise method other than further breeding by which these may be detected.

It is of interest to consider the practice of the breeder of Andalusians, who, always mating blue to blue, is obliged to cull his wasters, the blacks and the whites, in every year, and to contrast this with that of the breeder who has a knowledge of the facts outlined above and who therefore breeds black to white and thus gets in every hatch 100 per cent. blues. The Blue Andalusian interpreted thus is an excellent example of an unfixable variety which has defied the art of the breeder. More recently Lippincott (1918) has advanced considerable evidence to show that the case of the Blue Andalusian is not susceptible to so simple an interpretation. To his work reference will be made later. The case is used at this point because of its historical interest, and because, interpreted in terms of a simple monohybrid example, it serves to make it clear that dominance is an unessential feature of the Mendelian scheme of inheritance. A similar case among cattle is red-roan, which in the majority of cases behaves as though it were a hybrid between the red and the white as regards coat-colour; yet another is blue-roan such as follows a black (Galloway) and a white (Shorthorn) mating. The blue-grey colour is the result of an intermingling of black and of white hairs, and is found in cattle, horses, and rarely in swine. It is most commonly seen in the progeny of a white Shorthorn bull and black Aberdeen-Angus or Galloway cows. This cross-bred has, since the first quarter of the nineteenth century, been held to possess many desirable qualities to an exceptional degree—vigour, rapid growth, and so on and these qualities in time came to be regarded as being indissolubly associated with the particular blue-roan coat colour. So popular did the cross become that white Shorthorns were bred largely for this purpose, and the Aberdeen-Angus was looked upon merely as a means of obtaining its more profitable cross-bred offspring. The subject was clearly suitable for examination under satisfactory experimental conditions. Lloyd Jones and Evvard (1916) took the matter up, using white Shorthorns and Galloways, and carrying on with the work for thirteen years. Their results were such that while black and red, polled and horned behaved as simple allelomorphs (alternative characters), the nature of the roan character was not finally established. They were inclined to suggest that a roaning factor was present, but agreed that the assumption that blue-grey was the heterozygous condition between black and white explained the results almost equally as well. Among sheep there are reasons for believing that the white, blue and black fleece colours constitute a similar series in the Wensleydale.

An example of a measurable difference between the degree of expression of a quantitative character is that of the mating "earless" and "long ears" in sheep. There are Norwegian sheep with no external ears and others with the usual ear-length of 4½ inches. The short-eared and the earless conditions are found also in the Karakul sheep of Bokhara. Wriedt (1914) and Ritzmann (1916) both found that the inter-mating of the former produced sheep with an ear-length of 2¾ inches, *i.e.*, intermediate between the ear-lengths of the two parental stocks. Earless × earless give none but earless; short ear × long ear give equal numbers of shorts and longs. The long ear character is based on homozygosis, the short ear on heterozygosis. The interpretation of such a case as this appears to be that the factor concerned, if present in the duplex state, results in a degree of expression of the corresponding character twice as great as that which results from the action of this factor when present only in the simplex state. The degree of dominance of a character will vary with the "efficiency" of the corresponding factor and with the threshold of response to the action of this factor on the part of the tissues involved in the assumption of the character. A factor in the simplex state may be as "efficient" in the rôle it plays in determining the corresponding character as are two, and then the degree of expression of the character exhibited by the individual homozygous for this character and that exhibited by the heterozygote will be the same. In other cases the factor in the simplex state may result in a certain degree of expression of the corresponding character, whereas this factor in the duplex state may yield a degree of expression twice as great. The mating "polled" × "horned" in cattle is of interest in this connection. The F_1 individuals are polled but develop "scurs"—rudimentary horns. In the F_2 there are in every 4, on the average, 1 fully-polled, 2 with scurs, and 1 with horns. It should be mentioned that the extent of the growth of horns is affected by the presence of a functioning testis, and in thus mating "polled" and "horned" while the heterozygous female may be entirely hornless the heterozygous male usually has scurs. Both carry the factor for horn-growth but this is only appreciable in the one which has the testis.

So much misunderstanding has resulted from the misconception that dominance is an essential feature of the Mendelian scheme that too much emphasis cannot be placed upon this point: the degree of dominance, though very helpful in the course of a breeding experiment in that it provides some idea of the factorial constitution of an individual, is not at all an essential feature of the Mendelian scheme of inheritance; what is essential is the production of a characteristic ratio among the classes constituting the generations.

The examples so far dealt with have been concerned with organisms cross-bred with respect to a single character, with *monohybrids*, the parents of which are supposed to be similar except with respect to a single unit character. The Mendelian ratio for a monohybrid in those cases in which the homozygous and heterozygous dominants are indistinguishable, is 3 : 1, that is in the F_2 there are two sorts of individuals judging by superficial appearance—two phenotypes—those which exhibit the dominant character and those which exhibit the recessive—the ratio of the former to the latter is 3 : 1. (It has been seen that the 3 : 1 ratio is really a 1 : 2 : 1 ratio disguised.) A *phenotype* is a group of individuals all of which look alike irrespective of their factorial constitution. The term is also used to indicate the sum of all the characters displayed by an individual. It is now possible to study the cases in which the parental organisms differ from each other with respect to two different pairs of unit characters, one of each pair being dominant and the other recessive. It can be stated at once that the two pairs of factors which represent these characters segregate independently of each other and give character combinations in F_2 exactly as would be expected on the basis of chance factor distribution. Mendel's second law applies to the independent behaviour in inheritance of two or more pairs of alternative characters (termed "allelomorphs" by Bateson). Mendel crossed a variety of pea with a round seed and yellow cotyledons with another variety having a wrinkled seed and green cotyledons. The F_1 individuals were all yellow rounds and when these were selfed a generation was produced in which in every 16 individuals on the average there were:—

9	with	yellow	cotyledons and	round	seeds	—the two dominant characters.
3	"	yellow	"	wrinkled	"	—one dominant, one recessive.
3	"	green	"	round	"	—one dominant, one recessive.
1	"	green	"	wrinkled	"	—the two recessives.

The 9 : 3 : 3 : 1 ratio follows from the mere combination of the two 3 : 1 ratios and is characteristic of a Mendelian dihybrid F_2, a dihybrid being an individual which results from the mating of two parental forms which differ one from the other in respect of two pairs of allelomorphic characters. The F_2 phenotypes are shown in the chessboard diagram and the genotypes—the actual factorial constitutions—are defined in the combinations of letters, representing the factors, in the squares. The term *genotype* is also used to define a group of individuals all of which possess the same factorial constitution.

The P_1 individuals will possess the factorial constitution YYRR and GGWW respectively, if Y,G,R and W are taken to represent the factors corresponding to the characters Yellow and Green cotyledon colour and Round and Wrinkled seed-form. The F_1 individuals will all have the constitution

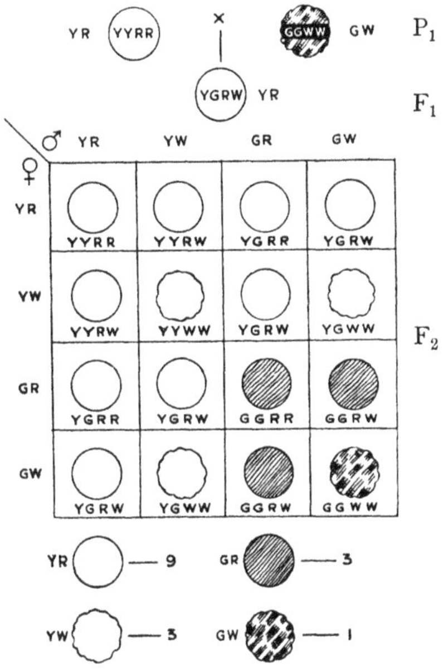

FIG. 9.—Yellow-Round Green-Wrinkled.

YGRW as far as these characters are concerned; they will all be heterozygous for the Round and Yellow characters which they exhibit, and simplex for the factors Y,G,R and W. When these F_1 individuals elaborate their gametes, on the understanding that the factors Y and G, R and W cannot be present together in one and the same mature germ-cell, they will liberate 4 sorts in equal numbers, so:—

$$\begin{matrix} Y & & G \\ | & \times & | \\ R & & W \end{matrix} = \text{YR, YW, GR, GW,}$$

and of these 4 sorts of gametes there will be 2 series, the

male and the female, so that fertilisation will yield the phenotypes and the ratio stated.

The dihybrid experiment can be well illustrated by the mating Black Hamburgh and White Leghorn among fowls. The white-plumage colour of the exhibition White Leghorn is dominant to the black of the Hamburgh, and the rosecomb pattern of the Hamburgh is dominant to the single comb of the Leghorn. The term "breed" or "strain" has no biological significance whatsoever. These classifications refer solely to phenotypes and are not based upon any knowledge of the genotypes included therein. For this reason it would have been safer to have defined this experiment as the mating of a certain Black Rosecomb with a certain White Singlecomb. There are two pairs of allelomorphic characters involved, so that 4 factors are concerned. The possible number of their combinations is 4×4 or 16, and this is the monohybrid figure squared $(3 + 1)^2$. Of course it does not follow that there will be exactly 16 or some multiple of 16 individuals in the F_2, but the greater the number of individuals in this generation the nearer will the proportions of the phenotypes therein approach the typical dihybrid ratio of 9:3:3:1. All the F_1 individuals will exhibit the two dominant characters, they will be White Rosecombs, and for the moment we are not concerned with the exact degree of the whiteness or with the perfection of the rose, it is enough to state that they will have white plumage as opposed to black, and rosecombs as opposed to singles. When these F_1 individuals are interbred, among the offspring there will be in every 16 on the average:—

9 White Rosecombs : 3 White Singlecombs : 3 Black Rosecombs : 1 Black Singlecomb.

It is seen that in F_2 all possible combinations of the characters of the P_1 individuals appear. The two characters Black and Rosecomb are not transmitted in conjunction—they become separated and recombined with members of the other pair during the course of the experiment. The outstanding feature of this result is the segregation and recombination of characters which occurs when the F_1 individuals are interbred and in no other way. The F_1 individual may appear a veritable "mongrel" to the eye of the fancier, but had he been desirous of creating a black-plumaged singlecombed individual out of the material available in P_1 then the only way he could have done this deliberately would have been to have raised an F_1 and interbred these individuals. The 9 : 3 : 3 : 1 ratio follows from the co-existence of two 3 : 1 ratios in the F_2 resulting

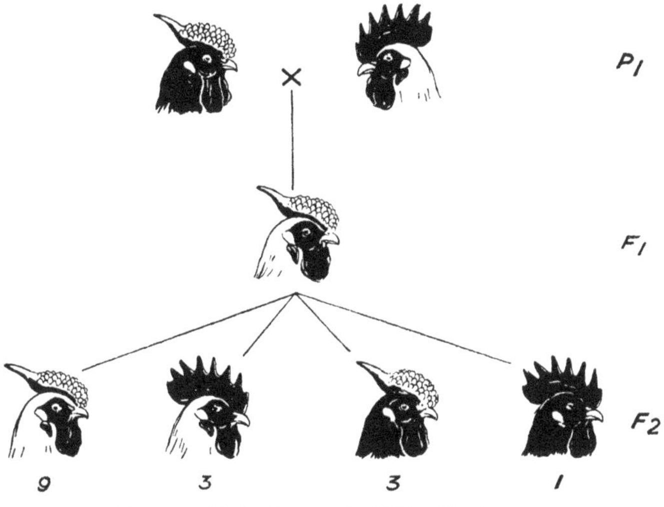

FIG. 10.—Black Rosecomb × White Singlecomb.

from a single cross. The characters White and Black, Rosecomb and Singlecomb are distributed in their own proportions of 3 : 1 at random over the individuals composing the second filial generation. By "at random" is meant that the colour of the plumage is not affected one way or another by the pattern of the comb, or the pattern of the comb by the colour of the plumage. If Whites, Blacks, Rosecombs and Singlecombs occurred in equal numbers in F_2 then it would be an even chance that a white bird had a rosecomb or a singlecomb or that a rosecombed bird were white or black; but in every four birds of F_2 there are three whites to each black and three rosecombs to each singlecomb. The actual proportions of the four classes of combinations of characters in F_2 can be arrived at by multiplying together the ratios in which each of the characters in a combination occurs separately:—

White and Rosecomb .	$3 \times 3 = 9$	Black and Rosecomb .	$1 \times 3 = 3$
White and Single .	$3 \times 1 = 3$	Black and Single . .	$1 \times 1 = 1$

But from what we have seen in the case of the typical monohybrid experiment the individual of F_2 which exhibits the dominant character may be homozygous or heterozygous for that character and the proportion of homozygotes to heterozygotes is 1 to 2. In the F_2 of this experiment, therefore, there will be homozygous Whites and Rosecombs and heterozygous Whites and Rosecombs and the combinations of the 4 characters will be as follows:—

White Rosecombs.			
Homozygous White and Homozygous Rosecomb .	$1 \times 1 = 1$		
Homozygous White and Heterozygous Rosecomb .	$1 \times 2 = 2$		
Heterozygous White and Homozygous Rosecomb .	$2 \times 1 = 2$		
Heterozygous White and Heterozygous Rosecomb .	$2 \times 2 = 4$	$= 9$	
White Singlecombs.			
Homozygous White and Singlecomb	$1 \times 1 = 1$		
Heterozygous White and Singlecomb	$2 \times 1 = 2$	$= 3$	
Black Rosecombs.			
Black and Homozygous Rosecomb	$1 \times 1 = 1$		
Black and Heterozygous Rosecomb	$1 \times 2 = 2$	$= 3$	
Black Singlecomb.			
Black and Singlecomb	$1 \times 1 = 1$	$= 1$	$= 16$

There are 4 phenotypes and 9 genotypes, and the individuals exhibiting a recessive character are inevitably homozygous for that character.

Using the chess-board plan, these results can be illustrated as follows:—

Let W represent the factor that corresponds to the dominant character White plumage.

" w represent the factor that corresponds to the recessive character Black plumage.

" R represent the factor that corresponds to the dominant character Rosecomb.

" r represent the factor that corresponds to the recessive character Singlecomb.

The conventional use of a capital and the corresponding small letter for the factors of the dominant and recessive members respectively of a pair of contrasted characters, the letters usually being the initial letter of the name of the character the inheritance of which is being investigated, has proved very helpful. The factorial constitution of the Black Hamburgh will then be wwRR in so far as these particular characters are concerned; that of the White Leghorn WWrr. The gametes produced by these will be factorially wR and Wr and the F_1 individual will therefore be WwRr. When such an individual, or rather when such a genotype, in its turn produces gametes, since W and w, R and r cannot be present in the same gamete there will be 4 sorts:—

W < R—WR
W < r—Wr

w < R—wR
w < r—wr

and there will be 2 equivalent series of these, male and female, and within these the 4 sorts will be present in equal numbers.

♀	♂ WR	Wr	wR	wr
WR	WWRR 1	WWRr 2	WwRR 3	WwRr 4
Wr	WWRr 5	WWrr 6	WwRr 7	Wwrr 8
wR	WwRR 9	WwRr 10	wwRR 11	wwRr 12
wr	WwRr 13	Wwrr 14	wwRr 15	wwrr 16

1. Phenotype WR = White Rosecomb—							
	Genotype	1 WWRR	Square	1	Total	1	
	,,	2 WWRr	,,	2, 5	,,	2	
	,,	3 WwRR	,,	3, 9	,,	2	
	,,	4 WwRr	,,	4, 7, 10, 13	,,	4	
						—	9
2. Phenotype Wr = White Singlecomb—							
	Genotype	5 WWrr	Square	6	,,	1	
	,,	6 Wwrr	,,	8, 14	,,	2	
						—	3
3. Phenotype wR = Black Rosecomb—							
	Genotype	7 wwRR	Square	11	,,	1	
	,,	8 wwRr	,,	12, 15	,,	2	
						—	3
4. Phenotype wr = Black Singlecomb—							
	Genotype	9 wwrr	Square	16	,,	1	
						—	1
							—
							16

If a diagonal is drawn from the top right-hand corner of the chess-board to the bottom left it will cut through all the zygotes which are heterozygous for both the characters which they exhibit, whereas a diagonal from top left to bottom right will cut through all that are homozygous for the characters which they display. This is of help in the filling-in of the chess-board, for in squares cut by the first diagonal the symbols WwRr can be filled in without any reference to the letters above and at the side and the squares cut by the other diagonal can be quickly filled by referring only to the symbols at the side, each being written in duplicate. It is only necessary to consider carefully the constitution of the remaining zygotes. It will also be noted that the gametic series provides a list of the phenotypes.

It is now possible to examine the scheme of inheritance as one must in the actual conduct of a breeding experiment. So far it has been more or less assumed that the genotype of the P_1 individual has been known and that the problem has been to anticipate the genotypes of the F_2. Actually the problem often is to identify the factorial constitution of the P_1 individuals, having a knowledge of the phenotypes and possibly also of the genotypes in F_2. A consideration of the genotypes in the F_2 of the above experiment will allow an anticipation of the results of their intermatings to be made and the results of such intermating will define the genotypes of the individuals taking part, thus leading to a recognition of the factorial constitution of the original P_1 birds.

There are four sorts of White Rosecombs in the F_2 of the experiment: (1) one that is homozygous for both its exhibited characters, and of this kind there is but one in every nine on the average; (2) one that is homozygous for its white-plumage colour character and heterozygous for its Rosecomb character, and of these there are two in every nine on the average; (3) one that is heterozygous for its colour and homozygous for its comb-form, and of these there are two in every nine on the average; and (4) one that is heterozygous for both characters, and of these there are four in every nine on the average. The Black Rose-combed birds are homozygous for their colour, but as regards comb-form there are two sorts, some homozygous and others heterozygous for the character they exhibit and on the average in every three there are one of the former and two of the latter. The White Singlecombed birds are in like case, they are homozygous for their comb-pattern character but as regards their plumage-colour some are homozygous and others heterozygous and on the average there are one homozygote and two heterozygotes in every three. The Black Singlecombed individuals are homozygous for both the expressed characters and when interbred will throw none but Black Singlecombed offspring. From these results it is possible to state with certainty that the F_1 individuals possessed the factorial constitution represented as WwRr and that the parental forms were respectively WWrr and wwRR, White Singlecomb and Black Rosecomb (or else WWRR and wwrr, White Rosecomb and Black Singlecomb). The behaviour of characters in inheritance is an indication of the factorial constitution of the individuals from which they were received, a parent is judged by its offspring: the breeding pen is to the geneticist what the test-tube is to the analytical chemist.

	Factorial Constitution of Offspring.									Factorial Constitution of Parents.
	WWRR.	WWRr.	WwRR.	WwRr.	WWrr.	Wwrr.	wwRR.	wwRr.	wwrr.	
White Rosecomb matings	100%	...	...	...	...	...	...	...	...	= WWRR × WWRR
	50	50%	...	...	...	...	...	...	...	WWRR WWRr
	50	...	50%	...	...	...	...	...	...	WWRR WwRR
	25	25	25	25%	...	...	...	...	...	WWRR WwRr or WwRR WWRr
	12½	25	12½	25	12½%	12½%	...	...	...	WWRr WwRr
	12½	12½	25	25	...	...	12½%	12½%	...	WwRR WwRr
	6¼	12½	12½	25	6¼	12½	6¼	12½	6¼%	WwRr WwRr
	25	50	...	...	25	...	...	...	...	WWRr WWRr
	25	...	50	...	...	...	25	...	...	WwRR WwRR
Black Rosecomb matings	...	...	...	...	...	...	100	...	...	wwRR wwRR
	...	...	...	...	...	...	50	50	...	wwRR wwRr
	...	...	...	...	...	...	25	50	25	wwRr wwRr
White Singlecomb matings	...	...	...	...	100	...	...	...	...	WWrr WWrr
	...	...	...	...	50	50	...	...	...	WWrr Wwrr
	...	...	...	...	25	50	...	...	25	Wwrr Wwrr
Black Singlecomb mating	...	...	...	...	...	...	...	...	100	wwrr wwrr
	White Rosecomb.				White Single.		Black Rose.		Black Single.	

The surest and quickest way to a recognition of the factorial constitution of any bird of the P_1, F_1, or F_2 generations is to mate it with the double recessive, a Black Singlecomb from the same stock. This method is the routine procedure in testing for homo- and heterozygosis.

White Rosecomb × *Black Singlecomb* (wwrr).

Phenotypes and genotypes of offspring.				Genotype of the other parent.
White Rosecombs. WwRr.	White Singles. Wwrr.	Black Rosecombs. wwRr.	Black Singles. wwrr.	
100%	...	...	...	WWRR
50	50	...	...	WWRr
50	...	50	...	WwRR
25	25	25	25	WwRr
		White Singlecomb × *Black Singlecomb.*		
...	100%	...	...	WWrr
...	50	...	50	Wwrr
		Black Rosecomb × *Black Singlecomb.*		
...	...	100%	...	wwRR
...	...	50	50	wwRr
		Black Singlecomb × *Black Singlecomb.*		
...	...	...	100%	wwrr

The classes of offspring and their proportions provide a sure indication of the factorial constitution of the parents. The genotype of the double recessive is known for such a Black Singlecomb can be accepted at face value, and the unknown is tested against the known.

As a further instance of a dihybrid mate the following may be cited. Wellmann (1916) mated a male basset-hound with a fox-terrier bitch. In F_1 there were 5 black-and-tans with white spots on chest and legs, and with a stature recalling that of the basset sire. He therefore concluded that the black-and-tan and shape of the basset are dominant over the coloured spots and shape character of the terrier. He obtained an F_2 of 32 of which 11 died and 21 grew up. Of these 16 had the basset body (one had very short legs indeed) and 5 had the terrier body characters.

There were

12 black-and-tan basset shaped,
4 spotted „
3 black-and-tan terrier shaped,
2 spotted „

a result closely approaching the typical 9 : 3 : 3 : 1 ratio.

In the case of a trihybrid experiment in which the individuals homo- and hetero-zygous for the dominant characters which they exhibit are indistinguishable, the F_1 individuals will every one possess the three dominant characters whilst their genotypic constitution will include six factors, the three for the dominant characters and the three for the corresponding recessives. The ratio obtained in the F_2 is 27:9:9:9:3:3:3:1. Each pair of unit characters, through their respective factors, segregate independently of each other and give character combinations in F_2 exactly as would be expected on the basis of chance factor distribution. For example, if a tall variety of pea with round and yellow seeds is crossed with another variety with dwarf stem, wrinkled and green seeds, all the F_1 individuals will exhibit the characters tall, round, yellow, and in F_2 there are 64 possible combinations of the six characters concerned, and the following classes appear:—

27 tall round yellow—the 3 dominant characters.
9 „ „ green—2 dominants and 1 recessive.
9 tall wrinkled yellow—2 dominants and 1 recessive.
9 dwarf round yellow—2 dominants and 1 recessive.
3 tall wrinkled green—1 dominant and 2 recessives.
3 dwarf wrinkled yellow—1 dominant and 2 recessives.
3 „ round green—1 dominant and 2 recessives.
1 „ wrinkled green—the 3 recessives.

The trihybrid mating is well illustrated by Castle's guinea-pig experiment (1916). A cross between a short-coated, smooth-coated, coloured guinea-pig and one which was long-haired, rosetted, and albino, produced an F_1 which was short-coated coloured, and rosetted, and when these individuals were interbred an F_2 was produced which included eight phenotypes, one like the one P_1 individual, one like the other P_1 individual, one like the F_1 individuals, and five quite new. The largest of the groups was the one which, like the F_1, exhibited the three dominant characters, the smallest the one which exhibited the three recessive characters in combination.

Let S represent the factor for the dominant character Short coat and s that for the corresponding recessive long.

" C represent the factor for the dominant character Coloured coat and c that for the corresponding recessive albino.

" R represent the factor for the dominant character Rough coat and r that for the corresponding recessive smooth.

These 6 factors can combine to form 8 gametes, so—

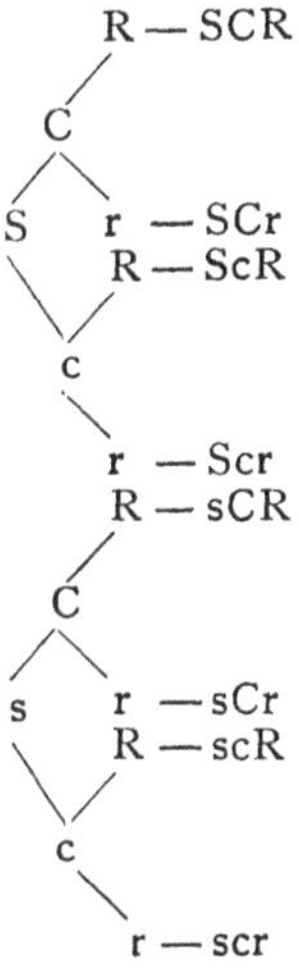

3 dominants	SCR	3 × 3 × 3 = 27
2 dominants and 1 recessive	SCr	3 × 3 × 1 = 9
	ScR	3 × 1 × 3 = 9
	sCR	1 × 3 × 3 = 9
1 dominant and 2 recessives	Scr	3 × 1 × 1 = 3
	sCr	1 × 3 × 1 = 3
	scR	1 × 1 × 3 = 3
3 recessives	scr	1 × 1 × 1 = 1
		64

and since there are male and female individuals concerned there will be 2 equivalent series, and the possible combinations of these gametes in the formation of zygotes will be 8 × 8 = 64.

♀ \ ♂	SCR	SCr	ScR	sCR	Scr	sCr	scR	scr
SCR	1 SSCCRR	2 SSCCRr	3 SSCcRR	4 SsCCRR	5 SSCcRr	6 SsCCRr	7 SsCcRR	8 SsCcRr
SCr	9 SSCCRr	10 SSCCrr	11 SSCcRr	12 SsCCRr	13 SSCcrr	14 SsCCrr	15 SsCcRr	16 SsCcrr
ScR	17 SSCcRR	18 SSCcRr	19 SSccRR	20 SsCcRR	21 SSccRr	22 SsCcRr	23 SsccRR	24 SsccRr
sCR	25 SsCCRR	26 SsCCRr	27 SsCcRR	28 ssCCRR	29 SsCcRr	30 ssCCRr	31 ssCcRR	32 ssCcRr
Scr	33 SSCcRr	34 SSCcrr	35 SSccRr	36 SsCcRr	37 SSccrr	38 SsCcrr	39 SsccRr	40 Ssccrr
sCr	41 SsCCRr	42 SsCCrr	43 SsCcRr	44 ssCCRr	45 SsCcrr	46 ssCCrr	47 ssCcRr	48 ssCcrr
scR	49 SsCcRR	50 SsCcRr	51 SsccRR	52 ssCcRR	53 SsccRr	54 ssCcRr	55 ssccRR	56 ssccRr
scr	57 SsCcRr	58 SsCcrr	59 SsccRr	60 ssCcRr	61 Ssccrr	62 ssCcrr	63 ssccRr	64 ssccrr

It is possible, as has been seen, to so combine the factors that 8 types of individuals in the F_2 generation can appear.

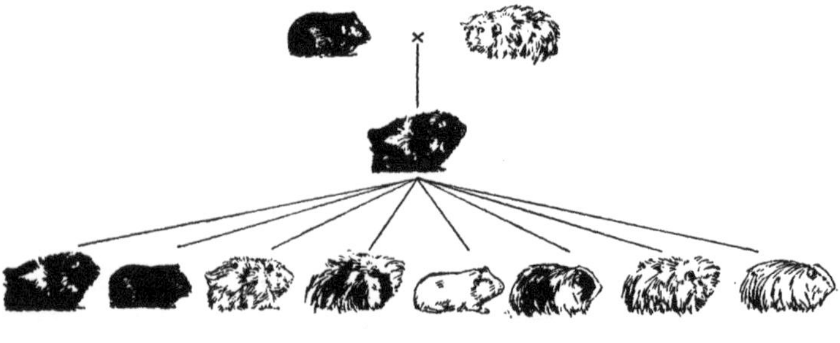

FIG. 11.—Short, Smooth, Coloured × Long, Rosetted Albino. (*After* Castle.)

	Phenotypes.
(1) Guinea-pigs with short hair, coloured and rosetted coats .	SCR
(2) „ „ short hair, coloured and smooth coats . .	SCr
(3) „ „ short hair, albino and rosetted coats . .	ScR
(4) „ „ long hair, coloured and rosetted coats . .	sCR
(5) „ „ short hair, albino and smooth coats . .	Scr
(6) „ „ long hair, coloured and smooth coats . .	sCr
(7) „ „ long hair, albino and rosetted coats . .	scR
(8) „ „ long hair, albino and smooth coats . .	scr

Within each phenotype there will be several genotypes :—

	Genotypes.	Square.	Total.	
Phenotype SCR (short hair, coloured, rosetted).	1 SSCCRR	1	1	
	2 SSCCRr	2, 9	2	
	3 SSCcRR	3, 17	2	
	4 SSCcRr	5, 11, 18, 33	4	
	5 SsCCRR	4, 25	2	
	6 SsCCRr	6, 12, 26, 41	4	
	7 SsCcRR	7, 20, 27, 49	4	
	8 SsCcRr	8, 15, 22, 29, 36, 43, 50, 57	8	
			—	27
Phenotype SCr (short hair, coloured, smooth).	9 SSCCrr	10	1	
	10 SSCcrr	13, 34	2	
	11 SsCCrr	14, 42	2	
	12 SsCcrr	16, 38, 45, 58	4	
			—	9
Phenotype ScR (short hair, albino, rosetted).	13 SSccRR	19	1	
	14 SSccRr	21, 35	2	
	15 SsccRR	23, 51	2	
	16 SsccRr	24, 39, 53, 59	4	
			—	9
Phenotype sCR (long hair, coloured, rosetted).	17 ssCCRR	28	1	
	18 ssCCRr	30, 44	2	
	19 ssCcRR	31, 52	2	
	20 ssCcRr	32, 47, 54, 60	4	
			—	9
Phenotype Scr (short hair, albino, smooth).	21 SSccrr	37	1	
	22 Ssccrr	40, 61	2	
			—	3
Phenotype sCr (long hair, coloured, smooth).	23 ssCCrr	46	1	
	24 ssCcrr	48, 62	2	
			—	3
Phenotype scR (long hair, albino, rosetted).	25 ssccRR	55	1	
	26 ssccRr	56, 63	2	
			—	3
Phenotype scr (long hair, albino, smooth).	27 ssccrr	64	1	
			—	1
				64

So that the 64 individuals will belong to 27 genotypes and to 8 phenotypes.

It is again to be noted that only one member of each phenotype is homozygous for all its characters and will breed true for these. Thus, no matter how many factors are involved it is possible in F_2 to obtain a homozygous race possessing any of the possible combinations. It is apparent from this case that it is infinitely easier to obtain homozygous individuals from the classes represented in the smallest numbers.

It must not be forgotten, however, that in order to be "certain" of getting the smaller phenotypes many more than 64 individuals must be obtained in F_2 of such an experiment as this. If it is desired to get, for example, the triple recessive, since there is no such thing as certainty in these matters, at least 292 individuals must be reared.

A trihybrid mating with cattle would be that involving the cross Aberdeen - Angus × Hereford — Black, Polled, coloured face × red, horned, White face.

The ratios for more than a trihybrid were computed by Mendel, but the experimental test for more than a quadruple hybrid has never been carried out since it involves extremely complicated proportions. For example, the F_2 of a quadruple hybrid includes 256 (or $(3+1)^4$) possibilities instead of 64 (or $(3+1)^3$) as in the case of the trihybrid. And in a case where the parents differed in 10 unit-characters, there would result among the F_2 generation $(3+1)^{10}$ or 1,048,576 possibilities. It is obvious that the correct method is to deal with but two or, better still, with one unit-character at a time until it is segregated out in a homozygous condition before proceeding to deal with the others. The following table gives the mathematical relations which obtain in the production of gametes in F_1 individuals and in their union to form the F_2 zygotes. It is assumed throughout that one character of each pair of allelomorphs is dominant.

No. of pairs of factors . .	1	2	3	4	5	6	n
„ different kinds of gametes	2	4	8	16	32	64	2^n
„ combinations of gametes	4	16	64	256	1024	4096	4^n
„ homozygotes in F_2 . .	2	4	8	16	32	64	2^n
„ heterozygotes in F_2 .	2	12	56	240	992	4032	$4^n - 2^n$
„ kinds of genotypes in F_2	3	9	27	81	243	729	3^n
„ homozygous genotypes in F_2	2	4	8	16	32	64	2^n
„ heterozygous genotypes in F_2	1	5	19	65	211	665	$3^n - 2^n$

CHAPTER II

EXTENSIONS AND MODIFICATIONS OF THE MENDELIAN HYPOTHESIS

It was fortunate for biological science that in 1900 there were men who immediately grasped the significance of Mendel's work when this was brought to light. From their experiments undertaken in ignorance of Mendel's paper, de Vries, Correns, and Tschermak were at once able to confirm his results in the case of plants and Bateson to demonstrate that inheritance in animals obeyed the same general rules. From this time onwards experimental breeding was more and more undertaken as a method of inquiry into the problems of inheritance, and the results which have been obtained have shown clearly that the scheme which Mendel enunciated to explain his own results can be applied to a multitude of others, many of which at first seem to be exceptional. In the case of animals there has been much talk of Mendelian and non-Mendelian inheritance of characters: it has been held that there are these two kinds. For the present it is better to hold that there are those characters which in their mode of inheritance have been shown to obey the neo-Mendelian scheme and there are those of which the mode of inheritance has not yet been fully demonstrated. Naturally enough as time passed and experimentation multiplied, the original scheme was subjected to various modifications. The experimental material which Mendel chose gave him clear-cut results and he was able, without qualification, to postulate that for each unit-character there was a corresponding factor, one for the dominant and another for the recessive, of every pair of allelomorphs, and that the characters of any given pair were alternative for the reason that no gamete could possibly carry both of the factors which corresponded to them. The results were so definite that, when once recognised, the finding of the key to the riddle of heredity became merely a matter of time. It was indeed fortunate that Mendel chose the pea, for as will be seen it is by no means the rule for the results of experimental breeding to be so readily interpretable. Dominance disclosed the key, yet as has been shown dominance itself is not an essential feature of the scheme. Dominance and a 3 : 1 ratio gave the clue; the 1 : 2 : 1 ratio without dominance marked a great extension in the application of the theory; and then it became possible to entertain the conceptions of factor interaction, accessory modifying factors, and of linkage.

One of the first cases which seemed to fall outside the Mendelian scheme was that of the Rosecomb × Peacomb characters in the domestic fowl investigated by Bateson and Punnett (1905, 1906). Rosecomb and Peacomb are both dominant to the Singlecomb character. According to the original Mendelian conception, therefore, Rose is to be regarded as alternative to Single and so also is Pea. But at once the question arose—What is the interrelation of Rose and Pea? Without spending any time in speculation, the question was put to the test of experiment and Rosecomb and Peacomb were mated up. The result was startling, for all the F_1 individuals had Walnut combs, a comb character which is possessed by certain breeds such as the Malay and the Orloff. These F_1 birds were interbred with the result that in the following generation a 9 : 3 : 3 : 1 ratio appeared and the classes were Walnuts, Roses, Peas, and Singles. The proportions of the classes were understandable, but the appearance of a Single in F_2 was disconcerting for it had not been possessed by either of the P_1 individuals.

To interpret these results the following hypothesis was constructed. The case was that of a dihybrid, but two (not four) factors were concerned, R the factor corresponding to the character Rosecomb pattern and P the factor for Peacomb. All combs fundamentally are Singles: a Rosecomb is a Single transformed into a Rose by the action of the factor for Rose; that is to say, the factor for Rosecomb may be either *present* or *absent* in the factorial constitution of a bird; if it is present, the bird exhibits the Rosecomb character; if it is not, the Singlecomb character. Similarly in the case of Pea. When both R and P are present synchronously in the factorial constitution of a bird that bird exhibits the Walnut character: when neither is present then the comb is a Single. According to this *Presence and Absence hypothesis* (first suggested by Correns but later worked out in detail by Bateson and others), the two members of a pair of contrasted characters are not based

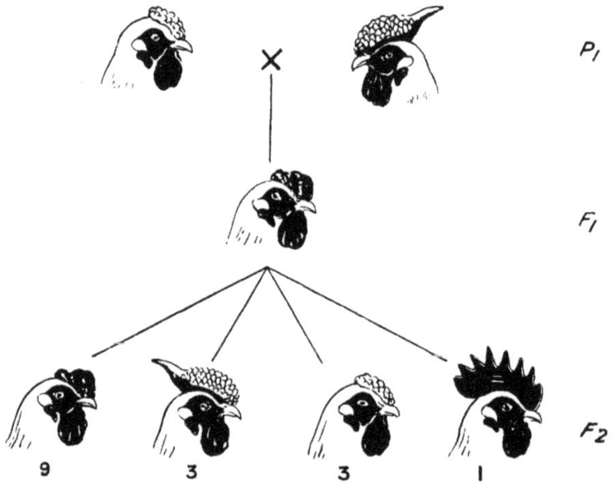

FIG. 12.—Rosecomb × Peacomb.

upon two distinct factors but upon the only two possible states of one and the same factor—its presence and its absence in the genotype.

According to this hypothesis the Singlecomb is based upon the constitution rrppSS, the absence of the factors R and P; the Rosecomb upon RRppSS or RrppSS, the presence of the factor R and the absence of the factor P; Peas upon rrPPSS or rrPpSS; and the Walnut character upon RRPPSS, RRPpSS, RrPPSS, or RrPpSS. It is to be noted that these formulæ imply that the factors R and P are accessory *modifying* factors and that their action can only result in a visible effect when the factor S is present, as it is since all fowls are supposed to possess it in the duplex state. Since SS is present in all genotypes it can be omitted in the formulæ for the other forms of comb. The mating of homozygous Rose and Pea therefore is RRpp × rrPP;

GAMETIC SERIES OF F_1.

R ⟨ P—RP, p—Rp

r ⟨ P—rP, p—rp

	♂ RP	Rp	rP	rp
♀ RP	1 RRPP	2 RRPp	3 RrPP	4 RrPp
Rp	5 RRPp	6 RRpp	7 RrPp	8 Rrpp
rP	9 RrPP	10 RrPp	11 rrPP	12 rrPp
rp	13 RrPp	14 Rrpp	15 rrPp	16 rrpp

F_2 Zygotes.

Phenotypes.	Genotypes.	Square.	Total.	
RP, Walnut . .	RRPP	1	1	
	RRPp	2, 5	2	
	RrPP	3, 9	2	
	RrPp	4, 7, 10, 13	4	
			—	9
Rp, Rose . . .	RRpp	6	1	
	Rrpp	8, 14	2	
			—	3
rP, Pea . . .	rrPP	11	1	
	rrPp	12, 15	2	
			—	3
rp, Single . . .	rrpp	16	1	
			—	1

the gametes produced by these respectively will be Rp and rP and the constitution of the F_1 individuals with respect to the comb-pattern character will be RrPp. Capital letters are used to signify the presence, small letters the absence of the factors which they represent. It should be noted that it is no more difficult to postulate that the small letters represent factors for recessive characters allelomorphic to those based on the factors represented by the corresponding capital letters than to regard them as indicative of the absence of factors. Recessivity of a character does not signify the absence of its factor and dominance is not merely an indication of the presence of a factor.

The case of the comb pattern opened up the important question as to the extent to which different factors could interact one upon the other, and soon it became clear that certain characters depended for their manifestation upon the simultaneous activity of more than one factor in the zygote, any one of which alone produces a different effect or else none at all, and each of which is transmitted quite independently. The results of early experiments in crossing two distinct white fowls both of which (as opposed to the white of the plumage of the White Leghorn previously mentioned) were first shown to be recessive to colour, bear upon this question. Incidentally, it is seen from this example that different white fowls do not necessarily owe their plumage-colour to the same cause, that such fowls may have different genotypic constitutions. Bateson and Punnett (1908) mated a White Silkie fowl to a White Dorking. The birds of F_1 were *all coloured*, and when these were interbred the F_2 generation consisted of coloured and white birds in the ratio 9 : 7. This ratio is in reality 9 : 3 : 3 : 1, but the last three terms are indistinguishable owing to the special circumstances, namely, that neither factor can produce a visible effect without the other. This case was interpreted in terms of the presence and absence of two factors. It was suggested that in this case colour resulted from the interaction of two factors and that unless these were both present in the genotype the colour could not appear. Each of the white birds carried one of the two factors whose interaction was necessary for the production of colour, and so a cross between them brought these *complementary* factors together in the F_1 generation and therefore every individual in this generation was coloured. Denoting these two colour factors by A and B, the constitution of the P_1 individuals may be expressed as AAbb and aaBB respectively, and their gametes will be Ab and aB. The F_1 birds must therefore be AaBb and will produce four kinds of gametes: AB, Ab, aB, and ab, in equal numbers—

♀ \ ♂	AB	Ab	aB	ab
AB	AABB	AABb	AaBB	AaBb
Ab	AABb	AAbb	AaBb	Aabb
aB	AaBB	AaBb	aaBB	aaBb
ab	AaBb	Aabb	aaBb	aabb

F_2 Phenotypes.	F_2 Genotypes.	Square.	Total.
AB (coloured) . . .	AABB	1	1
	AABb	2, 5	2
	AaBB	3, 9	2
	AaBb	4, 7, 10, 13	4
			— 9
A (white)	AAbb	6	1
	Aabb	8, 14	2
			— 3
B (white)	aaBB	11	1
	aaBb	12, 15	2
			— 3
ab (white) . . .	aabb	16	1
			— 1
			— 7

Coloured, 9 ; White, 7.

The only phenotypes in this experiment the genotypes of which are known are the two P_1 individuals—AAbb and aaBB, and the F_1—AaBb; and against these the F_2 individuals may be tested. (See table on page 50).

Genotype AABB possesses both A and B in the duplex state and all the gametes produced must contain both of these factors. AABb has the factor A in the duplex state and B in the simplex; all of its gametes will contain A, but only half of them will contain B, *i.e.*, it will produce equal numbers of gametes AB and Ab, and two such series of gametes coming together must give a generation consisting of n(AABB) + $2n$(AABb) + n(AAbb), that is, coloured and white birds in the ratio 3 : 1. The zygotes having the constitution AaBb are identical with their parents produced from the mating of the two whites and therefore when bred together must give coloured and whites in the ratio 9 : 7. AAbb × aaBB, both whites, have the same constitution as the original P_1 white and therefore the result of this mating should be all coloured. aabb × any other white from the various genotypes should give nothing but whites, since a white of the constitution aabb cannot furnish the complementary factor necessary for the production of colour. Aabb × aaBb should give both coloured and whites and the whites should be three times as numerous as the coloured.

F_2 Individuals.	× AAbb.		× aaBB.		× AaBb.	
	Coloured.	White.	Coloured.	White.	Coloured.	White.
	Offspring.		Offspring.		Offspring.	
Coloured—	%	%	%	%	%	%
AABB . .	100	...	100	...	100	...
AABb . .	50	50	100	...	75	25
AaBB . .	100	...	50	50	75	25
AaBb . .	50	50	50	50	56¼	43¾
White—						
AAbb . .	...	100	100	...	50	50
Aabb . .	...	100	50	50	37½	62½
aaBB . .	100	...	...	100	50	50
aaBb . .	50	50	...	100	37½	62½
aabb . .	...	100	...	100	25	75

The experiment gives results closely in accordance with the theoretical explanation. From the evidence afforded it is impossible to avoid the conclusion that the appearance of colour in the above mating depends upon the *interaction* of two factors. In other cases it has been found that the simultaneous presence of a greater number of factors than two is necessary for the manifestation of characters.

From the above experiment it is seen that as a result of factorial interaction the typical 9 : 3 : 3 : 1 ratio in the F_2 of a dihybrid mating may be modified to become a 9 : 7.

In a dihybrid experiment two factor pairs are involved,

for example, A : a; B : b. In the genotypes of F_2 the following factor combinations are possible: (1) A+B, (2) A+b, (3) a+B, and (4) a+b. In the typical dihybrid F_2 the ratio is 9 A+B, 3 A+b, 3 a+B, 1 a+b, and these four classes appear because the four different factor combinations yield four distinguishable characterisations. Variations of this 9 : 3 : 3 : 1 ratio follow, however, when two or more of the factor combinations lead to the development of the same characterisation. The following table illustrates certain of these variations of the typical 9 : 3 : 3 : 1 ratio:—

No. of Phenotypes in F_2 of a Dihybrid Experiment.	Ratio in F_2.	Reason.
4	9 : 3 : 3 : 1	Combinations 1, 2, 3, 4 (above) lead to distinct characterisations.
3	9 : 4 : 3	Combinations 2 and 4, or 3 and 4 yield characterisations which are indistinguishable.
3	12 : 3 : 1	Combinations 1 and 2, or 1 and 3 yield characterisations which are indistinguishable.
2	13 : 3	Combinations 1, 2 and 4, or 1, 3 and 4 yield characterisations which are indistinguishable.
2	9 : 7	Combinations 2 and 3 and 4 yield characterisations which are indistinguishable.
2	15 : 1	Combinations 1 and 2 and 3 yield characterisations which are indistinguishable.
2	3 : 1	= Linkage (see on).

See also page 141.

So far it has been suggested that white was due to absence of colour, in accordance with the Presence and Absence hypothesis, and this being so, colour had proved to be dominant to white, Presence dominant to Absence. But that this is not always so, was shown by the fact that the white plumage of the White Leghorn proved dominant to colour—as was seen in the illustration of a typical dihybrid when a Black Hamburgh was mated with a White Leghorn and the F_1 generation consisted of white individuals. But if a White Leghorn is mated with a pure Black Leghorn, the F_1 generation consists of individuals which are white with black flecks, so that the dominance is not quite perfect. It becomes so at the time of the first moult and the complete dominance of white is therefore only *delayed.* In such a case as this, where white is dominant to colour, the absence of colour was interpreted as being due to the action of a factor whose property it is to *inhibit* the production of colour in what would otherwise be a pure coloured bird. It is to be noted that the absence of a character does not imply the absence of its corresponding factor: the *absence of a character* from a phenotype may be due to the *presence of a factor* in the genotype. The white bird in this case is a coloured bird + a factor which inhibits the development of colour. This view can be put to the test of experiment.

It has already been stated that the white of the White Silkie and the White Dorking is recessive to colour and that the whiteness of these varieties is due to the fact that they lack a factor for the development of colour. Denoting this factor by C and the postulated *inhibiting* factor in the dominant white bird by I, the constitution of the recessive white bird can be represented as ccii, that of the dominant, CCII. The results of a cross made between these two pure white breeds, White Leghorn and White Dorking, may now be contemplated. The constitution of the F_1 birds will be CcIi, and possessing both C and I in the simplex condition they will produce in equal numbers the 4 different sorts of gametes: CI, Ci, cI, ci.

♀	♂ CI	Ci	cI	ci
CI	CCII	CCIi	CcII	CcIi
Ci	CCIi	CCii	CcIi	Ccii
cI	CcII	CcIi	ccII	ccIi
ci	CcIi	Ccii	ccIi	ccii

F_2 Zygotes

Any zygote containing the inhibiting factor I will develop into a white bird: if there is a double dose, II, then the bird will be pure white; if one I, there will be some few coloured ticks or flecks in the plumage. Any formula containing C and not I will be a coloured bird. A formula containing neither C nor I—the double recessive—will indicate a white bird.

Squares containing I	1, 2, 3, 4, 5, 7, 9, 10, 11, 12, 13, 15	12 *whites*—
(Duplex) . .	1, 3, 9, 11	4 pure
(Simplex) . .	2, 4, 5, 7, 10, 12, 13, 15	8 ticked
Squares containing C and not I .	6, 8, 14	3 *coloured*
Squares containing neither C nor I .	16	1 *white*
	13 white; 3 coloured.	

The results thus theoretically deduced were found to accord with the actual facts of experiment. The F_1 birds were all ticked whites, and in the F_2 came white and coloured birds in the expected ratio. In this case, then, the dominant white is a coloured bird in which the absence of colour is due to the action of a colour-inhibiting factor.

From the above it becomes evident that a character which is dominant in one breed may be recessive in another. Similarly, a character which is dominant in one species is found to be recessive in another.

Bateson and Punnett in 1906 made a most important and far-reaching discovery. They encountered the phenomenon of linkage (called by them gametic coupling). They found that when a sweet pea with the factors for purple flowers and long pollen-grains was crossed with a pea with the factors for red flowers and round pollen-grains, the two factors that entered the cross together, being inherited from one parent, tended to remain together in their transference from generation to generation. Free assortment did not occur; characters could be inherited in groups, the members of a group being linked.

In most of the cases dealt with so far, the F_2 generation consisted of individuals which resembled the parental forms. But the nature of the F_2 generation may be much more complex, and in cases in which factors interact upon one another it may even present the appearance of a series of intermediate forms grading from the condition found in one of the original parents to that which occurred in the other, particularly in cases in which quantitative rather than qualitative characters are concerned. A typical example of this is furnished by Castle's (1911) work on the rabbit's ear. A female Belgian hare with an ear-length of 118 mm. was crossed with a male lop-eared rabbit with an ear-length of 210 mm. The average of these two ear-lengths is 164 mm. Five offspring of this pair had ear-lengths when adult approximating to this average, as follows: 170 (three), 166 (one), 165 (one). Two were females and 3 males. A female from this litter with ear-length 170 mm. was crossed with her brother with ear-length 166 mm. Two litters were produced in which the individuals when adult attained ear-lengths of 160, 166, 168, 168, 172, 176. It is obvious that the evidence of any segregation, *i.e.*, any return to one or the other of the parental types is wanting and that there is no definite suggestion of blending. Seventy different litters containing 341 individuals were examined and crosses were made in which lop-ears of various fractional lengths were obtained as desired, including $\frac{1}{8}$, $\frac{1}{4}$, $\frac{3}{8}$, $\frac{1}{2}$, $\frac{5}{8}$, $\frac{3}{4}$ and $\frac{7}{8}$ lengths. All these fractional lengths bred approximately true. Ears of half lop-length were obtained in three ways: 1, full-lop × short-eared, as in the first cross; 2, half lop-length × half lop-length; and 3, one-quarter lop-length × three-quarters lop-length. Here there is definite suggestion that blending has occurred, but had more individuals been raised, it would have been possible to arrange them in an apparently continuous series of gradually increasing ear-lengths with a length equal to that of the lop-eared parent at one end and an ear-length equal to that of the other parent at the other.

The case is one in which complete segregation of the different factors takes place and the apparently continuous series of intermediates is the result of the interaction of several "ear-length" factors one with another. The existence of such cases showing a series of intermediate stages between the characters has sometimes been brought forward in opposition to the view that the characters of organisms depend upon specific factors which are transmitted according to the Mendelian rule. But it can be shown that neither the existence of such a continuous series of intermediates, nor the fact that some of them may breed true, is incompatible with the Mendelian principle of segregation. The explanation is to be found in the conception of *Multiple Factors*—a series of factors each associated with the same end-result. This idea owes its origin to Nilsson-Ehle (1909), who when investigating the inheritance of red and white colour in the grain of wheat found that while the red was incompletely dominant and the F_1 was of a pale red colour, intermediate between the parental red and white, in the F_2 generation all shades of red were found, from the very pale to about the same depth of colour as the parent race. The very palest of the individuals were looked upon as whites, and the rest as reds of different shades of colour. In one case reds and whites occurred in F_2 in a 3 : 1 ratio; in another in a 15 : 1 ratio; in another they occurred in the proportion of 63 reds to 1 white. These results can be explained on the assumption that there are three independent factors each of which can produce independently the red effect. It will be remembered that the interpretation of the blue-roan coat colour in cattle suggested that the duplex conditions of a factor could result in the expression of a certain degree of colour—black—whereas the simplex condition led to the development of a *dilute* black—blue-roan. In this interpretation lies the germ of the idea of the cumulative or additive action of factors. This conception was elaborated by Nilsson-Ehle. Only three assumptions are involved: (1) that dominance does not exist in a particular case; (2) that the duplex state of a factor has twice the effect of the simplex; (3) that the independent yet similar factors are cumulative in operation.

Let R, S, and T represent these three factors. The genetic formula of a race of wheat which owes its red colour to the presence of all three will be RRSSTT. Let the reds of the families which show the 3:1 ratio have a formula which contains any one of the three factors in the simplex state, so: Rrsstt, or rrSstt, or rrssTt; the reds which give a 15 : 1 ratio will be: RrSstt, or rrSsTt, or RrssTt; and the reds which give the 63 : 1 ratio will be so: RrSsTt. A white grained plant only arises from the union of two gametes having the constitution rst, and the genetic formula of the resulting zygote will be rrsstt, nulliplex that is in respect of all three factors. In those cases where the three factors are all present the inheritance is as that of the typical trihybrid.

	RST	RSt	RsT	Rst	rST	rSt	rsT	rst
RST	1 RRSSTT (18)	2 RRSSTt (15)	3 RRSsTT (15)	4 RRSsTt (12)	5 RrSSTT (15)	6 RrSSTt (12)	7 RrSsTT (12)	8 RrSsTt (9)
RSt	9 RRSSTt (15)	10 RRSStt (12)	11 RRSsTt (12)	12 RRSstt (9)	13 RrSSTt (12)	14 RrSStt (9)	15 RrSsTt (9)	16 RrSstt (6)
RsT	17 RRSsTT (15)	18 RRSsTt (12)	19 RRssTT (12)	20 RRssTt (9)	21 RrSsTT (12)	22 RrSsTt (9)	23 RrssTT (9)	24 RrssTt (6)
Rst	25 RRSsTt (12)	26 RRSstt (9)	27 RRssTt (9)	28 RRsstt (6)	29 RrSsTt (9)	30 RrSstt (6)	31 RrssTt (6)	32 Rrsstt (3)
rST	33 RrSSTT (15)	34 RrSSTt (12)	35 RrSsTT (12)	36 RrSsTt (9)	37 rrSSTT (12)	38 rrSSTt (9)	39 rrSsTT (9)	40 rrSsTt (6)
rSt	41 RrSSTt (12)	42 RrSStt (9)	43 RrSsTt (9)	44 RrSstt (6)	45 rrSSTt (9)	46 rrSStt (6)	47 rrSsTt (6)	48 rrSstt (3)
rsT	49 RrSsTT (12)	50 RrSsTt (9)	51 RrssTT (9)	52 RrssTt (6)	53 rrSsTT (9)	54 rrSsTt (6)	55 rrssTT (6)	56 rrssTt (3)
rst	57 RrSsTt (9)	58 RrSstt (6)	59 RrssTt (6)	60 Rrsstt (3)	61 rrSsTt (6)	62 rrSstt (3)	63 rrssTt (3)	64 rrsstt (0)

If for purposes of illustration, since each of the three factors for colour is of equal value, each "dose" of each factor be supposed to equal 3 units of colour, the totals shown in the brackets will be found. These totals indicate the depth of colour of each plant which will result from the various strengths of the doses of the factors. RRSSTT = 18, and rrsstt = 0. The different totals and the number of individuals in each class will be as follow:—

Total.	No. of Individuals.	Squares.
18	1	1
15	6	2, 3, 5, 9, 17, 33
12	15	4, 6, 7, 10, 11, 13, 18, 19, 21, 25, 34, 35, 37, 41, 49
9	20	8, 12, 14, 15, 20, 22, 23, 26, 27, 29, 36, 38, 39, 42, 43, 45, 50, 51, 53, 57
6	15	16, 24, 28, 30, 31, 40, 44, 46, 47, 52, 54, 55, 58, 59, 61
3	6	32, 48, 56, 60, 62, 63
0	1	64

A frequency curve can be constructed thus:—

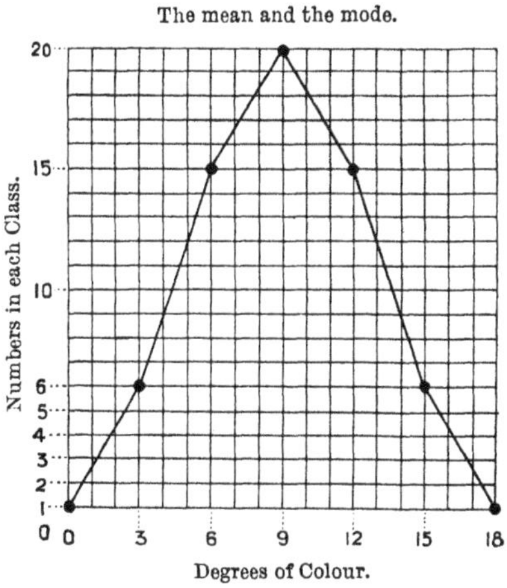

FIG. 13.

The intermediate shade of red produced in the F_1 generation would fall into group 9, since the formula for the hybrid will be RrSsTt. The varying shades of colour depend on the cumulative effect of the colour factors which have an additive effect, *i.e.*, two factors produce twice the depth of red colouration that one can produce and all six are necessary for the production of the full colour of the parent red wheat. Consequently, there are six shades of red in F_2, a population possessing various frequencies with respect to the proportionate number of individuals which display a particular shade of colour, as shown in the diagram. Factors which display summation effects have been conveniently called cumulative factors.

It remains to apply the Nilsson-Ehle explanation to the case of the lengths of the rabbits' ears. If the average ear-length of a full-lop ear is placed at 220 mm. and of an ordinary ear at 100 mm., then the difference due to the factor for extra ear-length is 120 mm. If, however, the first hybrid generation is a trihybrid in respect to ear-length then this excess is shared by three factors and each is responsible for 20 mm. There are 64 possibilities in F_2, but since the average litter of rabbits is about 5, the chances are that these 5 will have ear-lengths more or less like their parents. Of the 64 individuals in F_2, 20 will be quite intermediate, and 50, or 75 per cent., will have ear-lengths between 140 and 180 mm., thus approaching a blend sufficiently to be classified as such upon a casual inspection. The chance that the F_2 individuals would closely resemble the grandparents with respect to this character is extremely slight, since in 64 only 1 individual is like either grandparent, and, as has already been stated, in order to be certain of getting such, at least 292 individuals must be raised.

The mode of inheritance of a quantitative character is exactly similar to that of a qualitative character. Size in an animal is the expression of the interaction of a large number of factors, in a plant it results from the interaction of a relatively small number of factors but the mode of inheritance is the same. The number of classes in the F_2 generation and the frequency of the reappearance of the P_1 characters will indicate the nature of the size factor complex. If but one factor difference is involved, then the

F_1 will be intermediate and in the F_2 there will be three classes of which two will exhibit the P_1 and one the F_1 characters, *i.e.*, the P_1 characters will be exhibited by 50 per cent. of the F_2 individuals. If two factor differences distinguish the P_1 individuals, then the F_1 will again be intermediate in size; in the F_2 there will be five size classes and in every 16 individuals only 2 will exhibit the respective P_1 size characters. If three factor differences are concerned, then there will be seven size classes in the F_2 and the P_1 sizes will each appear only once in 64. If four factor differences are involved, there will be nine size classes in F_2 and the P_1 sizes will each appear but once in 256, and so on, so that if eight factor differences were involved each P_1 size character would reappear in F_2 only once in 65536 times—in other words, they would never appear.

Example:—An individual 16 inches tall is crossed with another 24 inches tall, these length-differences being true Mendelian characters.

(1) One "size" factor difference—

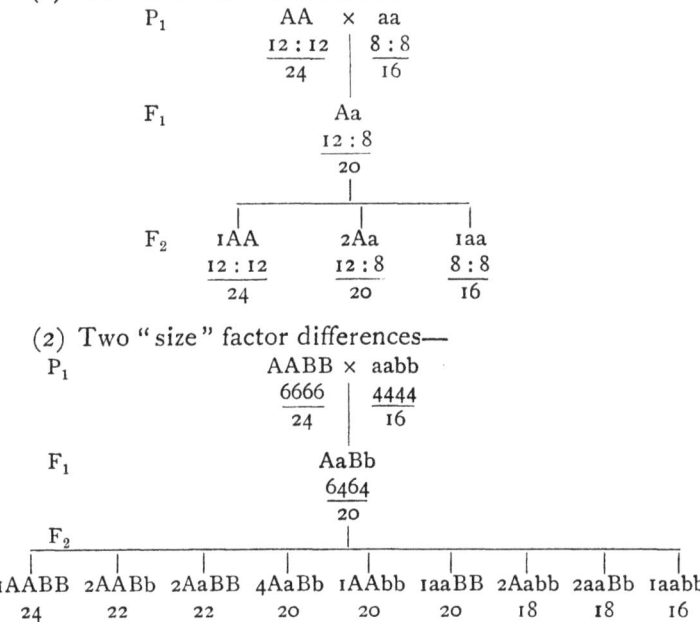

P_1 AA × aa
$\frac{12:12}{24}$ | $\frac{8:8}{16}$

F_1 Aa
$\frac{12:8}{20}$

F_2	1AA	2Aa	1aa
	$\frac{12:12}{24}$	$\frac{12:8}{20}$	$\frac{8:8}{16}$

(2) Two "size" factor differences—

P_1 AABB × aabb
$\frac{6666}{24}$ | $\frac{4444}{16}$

F_1 AaBb
$\frac{6464}{20}$

F_2

1AABB	2AABb	2AaBB	4AaBb	1AAbb	1aaBB	2Aabb	2aaBb	1aabb
24	22	22	20	20	20	18	18	16

The expression of a character, quantitative or qualitative, depends primarily upon the presence and action of a corresponding factor or upon the coincident presence and action of several factors, which may be multiple factors, affecting the degree of expression of the character, or may be modifying factors. Since so many of the characters of the larger domesticated animals appear to be multifactor in nature, it is desirable to consider further examples of such factors as have been defined as inhibiting, intensifying, dilution, restriction, extension factors, accessory modifying factors acting in conjunction with the principal factors and resulting in some alteration in the form or degree of development of the corresponding character. It follows that a modifying factor cannot produce any effect if the factor for the development of the character is not also present and active—it is only when there is a developing single-comb that the modifying "rose" can fashion it into a rosecomb. It is important to recognise that variation in the expression of a character may be an instance of *modification*, a result, that is, of the impress of extrinsic environmental forces, and there is no question that environment, using the term in its widest sense, can modify and even condition the expression of a character, or it may be due to the action of independently heritable *modifying factors* present in the genotype. But in either case there must be a character to be modified. It is important also to recognise quite clearly that the principal factor and the one or several modifying factors are transmitted from generation to generation quite independently. An individual may possess the modifiers but not the principal, or the principal but not the modifiers, so that when two such are mated, there will be produced an F_1 with a character markedly unlike either of the P_1 types, and an F_2 which will include classes with different groupings of modifiers, either alone or in association with the principal. In this way an F_2 which contains classes showing different grades in the exhibition of a character concerned can be obtained in the same way as in the case of multiple factors. If modifiers are not involved, the mating of P_1 individuals which are homozygous in respect of the characters being investigated will produce an F_1 as uniform as themselves and any variation in the exhibition of the characters will be due to environmental agencies. ($AA \times aa = Aa$). The F_2 population likewise will be similar in the matter of variability, but will show greater diversity than the F_1, and if the numbers are sufficient will include P_1 types. Such a result follows segregation and recombination. ($Aa \times Aa = 1AA + 2Aa + 1aa$). If modifiers are present then there will be marked diversity in F_2, for as a result of recombination individuals with a greater or a lesser degree of modification in characterisation will appear.

Few attempts have been made as yet, for reasons that can well be understood, to apply to the larger and more expensive domestic animals the principles of genetics which have been worked out as the result of countless breeding experiments with the usual laboratory material. Direct experiments with horses and cattle are prohibitive because of the expense, but many observations have been made as to the nature and transmission of characters in these animals from studies of the breed registers. Coat colour is the character most fully recorded. Frances Pitt (1919) has dealt with the genetic analysis of the characteristic Hereford colour pattern. The Hereford is a red beast with a white face and the white extends in a greater or lesser degree along the mid-line of the back and of the underparts in such a way as to more or less encircle the animal in the median plane. Ramm (1901) describes some seven continental breeds which possess the same fundamental pattern of coloured body, white face, feet and tail-end with a dorsal and ventral white line. Cattle of this general pattern were kept in Hereford in the seventeenth century and formed the foundation stock out of which the modern Hereford has been made. A study of the carefully kept records of a large herd has led Miss Pitt to the conclusion that five factors are concerned in the constitution of the modern Hereford. These hypothetical factors are as follow:—

(1) A "whitening" factor, responsible for the *recessive* character "extension of white," or "restriction of pigment." This factor modifies what otherwise would be a typical Hereford coat-colour pattern, 0, to grades -1 to -4.

(2) A "dark-neck" factor, responsible for the *dominant* character "extension of pigment." This factor modifies

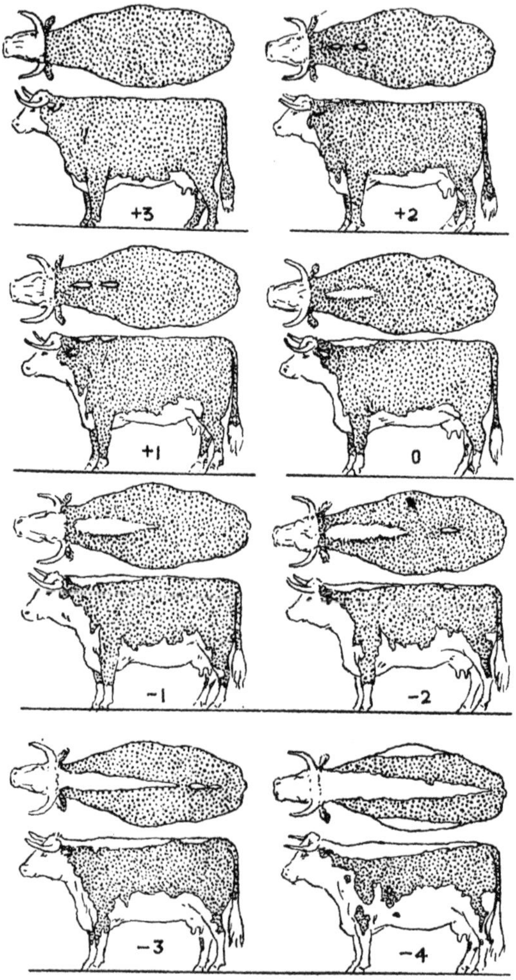

FIG. 14.—Coat-colour pattern in the Hereford.
(By permission of the Editors of the *Journal of Genetics*.)

grade 0 to grade +2 or +3. The greatest effect is seen in the obliteration of the white area on the crest, but all the white areas are reduced.

(3) A "red-eye" factor, responsible for a ring of red around the eye, a *dominant* of some interest to the breeder, for some maintain that pigment round the eye is associated, with immunity to attacks of flies and certain eye diseases.

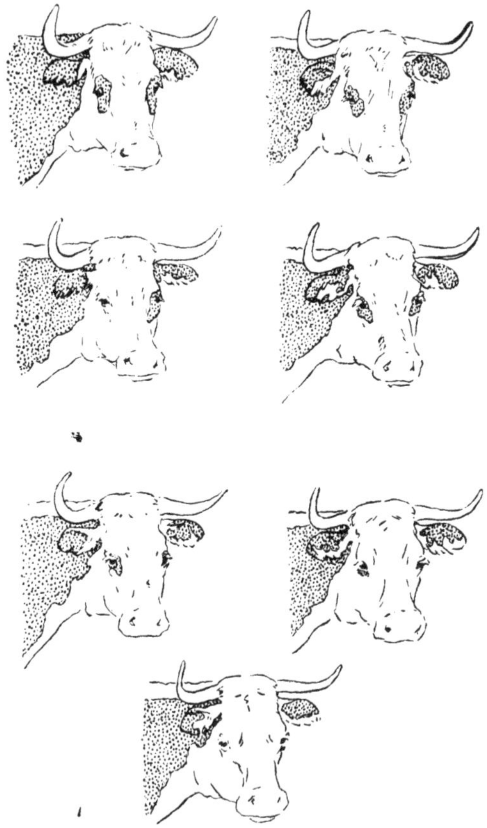

FIG. 15.—Grades of the Red-Eye character in the Hereford.
(By permission of the Editors of the *Journal of Genetics*.)

(4) A "dirty nose" factor, responsible for the presence of spots of brown and black pigment on the nose, a *dominant* character greatly disliked by the breeders.

(5) A "claret" factor, responsible for the desired *recessive* character claret colour as opposed to the pale-brown known as yellow.

This preliminary analysis is an interesting contribution, but there are reasons for expecting that fuller information will necessitate a modification of the scheme. If, for example, the undesired character "dirty-nose" is a simple dominant, then by steady elimination of all "dirty-noses" a clean-nosed herd could be built up. Yet though the dirty noses are rejected the character still appears. Further, 1 and 2 could be regarded as allelomorphs, but as the degree of the expression of these characters is very variable most probably many modifying factors are involved. Coat-colour pattern may or may not constitute a character of importance in the eyes of the breeder, but since it is not *known* as yet whether certain patterns are actually correlated with such characters as immunity or milk yield, it will be well if the breeders of parti-coloured stock keep photographs or descriptive diagrams of each and every beast used along with their other records.

Sewall Wright (1917-1918) has worked out in a masterly fashion the factorial significance of the various colour patterns met with in mammals. The pigment present in the skin, hair, and eyes of mammals is melanin, and the most intense coloration is found in the colour black in which the pigment has the form of dark sepia-brown granules. This condition may be diluted to form the browns or the blues (the maltese). The latter dilution seems to be of the same nature as the blue-roans in which there is an intermingling of jet black hairs and white hairs, for in the maltese pattern there are dense black pigmented areas alternating with colourless spaces within the hair. Another series of colours is the reds in which the pigment granules appear orange-yellow, and as yet it is not definitely decided whether there is an essential chemical difference between these and the sepia brown. Red undergoes dilution to yellow and cream, while a light red is equivalent to the maltese dilution of black. By combining the different kinds of dilution with the different kinds of intergrades between sepia and yellow an infinite variety of colour is produced. Sewall Wright suggests that melanin is produced by the oxidation of certain products of protein metabolism by the action of specific enzymes and that the different colour characters result from differences in the enzyme element in this reaction. Colour depends on the rates of production or potency of 2 enzymes, enzyme 1 being essential to the production of any colour but alone producing yellow; enzyme 2, being supplementary to 1, producing no effect alone but with 1 producing sepia. The combination 1 and 2 is more efficient than 1 alone, also in that it produces sepia pigment when 1 alone is at too low a potency to produce yellow. Above the level at which enzyme 1 produces its effect, 1 and 2 in association complete the oxidation of chromogen, and chromogen oxidised by enzyme 1 to yellow pigment is incapable of further oxidation to sepia. The various factors concerned in the production of coat-colour characters act as if on enzyme 1 or 2.

(1) There are factors affecting the *distribution* and *intensity* of colour (acting on enzyme 1), (*a*) those which affect the *distribution of colour* in contrast with white, and (*b*) those which affect the *intensity of colour* in the pigmented areas.

(2) There are factors which affect the *distribution and intensity of differentiation* from yellow to black (acting on enzyme 2), (*a*) those affecting the *distribution of a dark colour* (sepia series) in contrast with red, and (*b*) those which affect the *intensity of the dark colour*.

Thus, the factors in class 1 (*a*) determine patterns of colour and white; those in class 2 (*a*) determine the pattern of dark and light colours in the coloured areas, while the kind of dark colour and of light colour is determined by factors of classes 1 (*b*) and 2 (*b*). The factors which determine the white face of the Hereford are examples of class 1 (*a*), and since this white face appears in Hereford, Aberdeen-Angus × Hereford, and Hereford × American Bison cross-breds, the factor acts on colour in general regardless of its quality. The same is true in the case of the Dutch belted cattle, in black-and-white Holsteins and in roan and in white Shorthorns, and in the case of the belted Hampshire pig. The common white patterns of horses, dogs, and cats are similarly independent of the ground colour of the animals.

The maltese factor which produces alternative bands of pigment and colourless spaces in the hair is provisionally placed by Sewall Wright in class 1 (*a*). Recessive factors affecting simultaneously the maltese type of dilution of the sepia and the homologous kind of dilution of yellow have been demonstrated in dogs, cats, mice, and rabbits. Of the factors in class 1 (*b*), affecting the intensity of the colour in the coloured areas, those which produce correlated dilution of the sepia and the yellow are common. There seems to be such a factor difference between the dun, mouse, and cream-coloured horse, and the bay, black and chestnut respectively. Of the factors in class 2 (*a*) which affect the relative distribution of the sepia and the yellow areas, many have been determined. The factors by which red cattle, red pigs, bay horses, tabby and yellow cats, bi-colour and red dogs, agouti, tortoise and yellow guinea-pigs differ from the black in each species, are examples. The factors in class 2 (*b*) which reduce the intensity of the sepia series without affecting the yellow series form a well-defined group. The difference between liver-coloured and black dogs is of this kind.

There is more than one kind of white coat colour in cattle. That of the white Shorthorn is not a perfect white for the face carries red hairs. It is not the white extreme of the red and white condition but is probably due to the action of a recessive extension factor as suggested by Lloyd Jones and Evvard (1916). A white which is the extreme of the spotting condition is encountered in the Ayrshire and Friesian. The white Park cattle (with coloured extremities) constitute a third kind of white about which little is known. (Pitt 1921; Wallace 1923.)

Red exists in different shades and the exact relation of shade to shade is not yet revealed. The distribution of red is affected by the action of a dominant extension factor and also by the roaning factor. Black is dominant to red in self- or parti-coloured breeds and its distribution is affected by the extension and roaning factors mentioned above. Little is known as yet concerning the exact relation between the above colours and yellow, dun, light dun, and brown.

Reference may be made to the following experimental results—Parlour (1913) reports on Jersey × Aberdeen-Angus crosses undertaken in order to test the possibility of combining in one and the same race the milking qualities of the Jersey with the beef qualities of the Angus. In P_1 an Aberdeen-Angus bull and four Jersey cows were employed. In F_1 there were three males, nine females, all black save one female which showed a patch of white near the udder. There were traces of the Jersey in the udder (yellow, well-shaped and silky) and on the inside of the thighs and ears (covered with hair). The females were all polled but the males developed scurs (usually). A number of the F_1 cows produced calves, and all but one were as good milkers as their dams. The steers were only slightly larger than Jerseys; they fattened readily. In the F_2 there was considerable variation in characterisation; two black hornless females of Aberdeen-Angus type, one black and white female with strong horns, one black female with fawn showing through (Jersey type), one black male with strong horns, one orange-fawn with white muzzle and hornless, and one fawn (dark muzzle), sex not given.

The Shorthorn roan coat colour in most cases, as has already been stated, behaves as the hybrid between red and white. This mating indeed does yield a high proportion of roan offspring but calves with red and white coat colours appear also. The difficulty has been that in the recording of coat colour the greater popularity of one colour can bias the judgment of the observer, and that the degree of the mixture of red and white and the regional distribution of these two colours can vary so much in different cases that what to one observer would be a red-and-white to another is a roan. The accurate statistical analysis of the inheritance of coat-colour characters is thereby rendered difficult. White × white in the Shorthorn yields whites, red × red yields reds, though exceptions are known, but as to the actual nature of roan, and of red and white there has been considerable doubt. Duck (1923) has suggested genetic formulæ for the 4 phenotypes satisfactory in many ways but not accommodating certain recognised exceptions. R represents the factor corresponding to red coat colour, r – to white, E – the roaning factor.

Reds.	Whites.	Roan.	Red and White.
RREE	rrEE	RrEE	Rree
RREe	rrEe	RrEe	
RRee	rree		

It is the RrEe genotype that has been so often regarded as the Rree, since the roaning effect is not evenly distributed. Using these genetic formulæ it is possible to interpret the results of different matings and to recognise the genotypes of the parents.

The only advantage this theory has over the simple monohybrid interpretation is that it accommodates certain exceptional results, such as red offspring out of a Red by White mating. On the other hand it demands that no white shall carry the roaning factor, that a red may do so, that homozygous roans shall be common and that all red and whites shall be heterozygous. These are demands that cannot be granted since they require the Shorthorn to be genetically different from other breeds.

Possibly Black and Red are the only fundamental coat colours in cattle (Campbell, 1924). All Shorthorns may be reds. If this is so, it is necessary only to postulate a series of modifying factors affecting (1) the extension or restriction and (2) the regional distribution of the colour to get roans and also parti-coloured beasts. A white would thus be duplex for the restriction factor, a roan one that is simplex. The factors affecting regional distribution can act on a roan as well as on a solid colour.

Funkquist (1922), dealing with the Ayrshire, Shorthorn, and Swedish Red-and-White suggests that the flesh-coloured muzzle is dominant to dark and that the difference is a multifactor one. Smith (1924) observes that black-tipped horn is dominant to clear.

Reviewing the whole question of colour inheritance in cattle Smith suggests the following scheme for phenotypes :—

		Basic colour	Spots	Others
Highland (tawny)		DRCBF	Six	TMP
	or	cb	sIX	p
Highland (light)		DrCBf	Six	TMP
	or	bf		

		Basic colour	Spots	Others
Wild White		drCBf	sIX	TMKp
	or	bf	Six	tmkP
Guernsey		DrcbF	sIX	tmK
	or		Six	Tk
Jersey		drcbF	SIx	TMK
	or		siX	mk
Galloway (dun)		DrcBF	Six	M
	or	RC		
(black)		drcBF	Six	M
(belted)		drcBF	LSix	M
Aberdeen Angus		drcBf	Six	M
	or	F	I	
Holstein-Friesian		drcBf	sIX	TM
Blue Albion		drcBf Ww	SIX	TM
	or		six	
Devon		drcbf	Six	TmK
	or			k
Sussex		drcbf	SiX	TmK
	or			k
Red Poll		drcbf	SiX	TmK
	or			k
Shorthorn (solid red)		drcbf WW	Six	tmKP
	or		IX	Tkp
(red and white)		drcbf WW	six	tmKP
	or		IX	Tkp
(roan, even)		drcbf Ww	Six fl	,,
	or		IX fl	
(roan, spotted)		drcbf Ww	six fl	,,
	or		IX fl	
(white)		drcbf ww	six fl	,,
	or		SIX fl	
Hereford, (standard)		drcbf	HSIX	tmKe
	or			TK
(eye-circle)		drcbf	HSIX	tmKE
Ayrshire (standard)		drcbf	sIX fl	tmK
	or		ix	TMk
(mahogany bull)		drcbf	(Ay) (Ay) fl	,,
			(Ay) (ay)	
(mahogany cow)		dcrbf	(Ay) (Ay) fl	,,

Basic colour-factors. Dominants—D = Dun, R = Brindle, C = Wild-type white (as in park Cattle), B = Black, b = red. Recessives—f = fawn, o = albino. Ay = the sex-linked intensification in the Ayrshire (page 195) —possibly identical with R = brindle. Spotting factors—H = the white face as in the Hereford, L = white belt as in the Lakenfeld, I = white inguinal spot, X = white switch, s = pied as opposed to S = Solid, fl = flecking as in the Ayrshire and acting on s. Other factors.—T = Black-tipped horns as opposed to t = clear horns, M = Black muzzle as opposed to m = clear, k = smoky muzzle as opposed to K = clean, p = pencil round the muzzle as opposed to P = no pencil, E = eye-circle as opposed to no circle.

Scott Watson (1921) found that in the Angus × West Highland cross the horned and polled conditions formed a simple Mendelian pair. Polled is completely dominant in the female but in the heterozygous male horn-development may be only partially suppressed. Black coat colour proved dominant to red and these colours behaved as a simple Mendelian pair. Dun proved to be dominant to black but the results did not show whether the dominance in this case was due to a simple epistatic factor or to a factor modifying colours other than black. (See page 140.)

Hooper (1919) records that in the case of the Jersey, solid colour is dominant to mottling, black tongue to white, black switch to white, and that the association of these three dominants is common. Roan was dominant to solid colour.

Nabours (1912) reports that Zebu bulls imported into Texas were crossed with Hereford and Durham cows, and that in the F_1 the individuals exhibited the coat colour of their respective mothers, and the hump, deep dew-lap, and sheath of the Zebu. They were immune to cattle tick and were 50 per cent. heavier than the ordinary range beast. In one herd twenty-eight F_1 Zebu × Durhams were mated with F_1 males of similar origin; of the eighteen calves produced, six were white and resembled the Zebu grandfathers, while the rest mostly resembled the Durhams; the F_1 produced by Zebu bulls and native Texas cows lacked uniformity in characterisation; Nabours suggests that this is probably due to the fact that in the Texas cattle there are traces of Zebu blood.

Wriedt (1919), working with the Telemark breed of the Norwegian cattle, concludes that in this breed brindle is a simple dominant to red, but that homozygous brindles are rare. He refers to one such homozygous brindle which when mated to brindle and to red cows begot none but brindles.

The Dutch belted cattle are of striking appearance,

being black with a broad belt of white. The belting has no relation to the ground colour, for heterozygous blacks produce a red calf with the characteristic white belt. The extent of the belt varies, however; some calves have no belt at all, and often the belt is but poorly marked. Belting is a dominant character, but it is suggested that several modifying factors are concerned in the determination of the actual degree of its expression (Kuiper 1920.) This applies also to the cases of the Belted Galloway and Belted Welsh.

Considering the economic importance of the question, the inheritance of the milk yield character has been but meagrely investigated. Wilson (1911) showed that there may be wide difference between the milk production of a dam and her daughter, and produced evidence to show that the milk yield character is transmitted in Mendelian fashion. Parlour (1913) made the Jersey and Aberdeen-Angus cross, and found that the F_1 heifers had a milk yield almost equal to that of the Jersey dams. Kildee and M'Candlish (1916) crossed "scrub" heifers to Guernsey and Jersey and Holstein-Friesian bulls. The results showed that the daughters of the Friesian bulls had a milk yield of 5561·6 lb. of milk compared to the 3300-3900 lb. of their dams. Gowen (1920) continued the breeding work of Pearl on the study of inheritance in crosses of dairy and beef breeds of cattle, and has been able to show that the high milk yield character is incompletely dominant to a low milk yield, and that the factors for high milk yield could be transmitted by the male. The milk yield of the F_1 is intermediate between the high and low parent, but approached most nearly that of the high milk yield parent. The character is certainly based on multiple factors.

The transmission of the high or low butter-fat percentage character has been held to be transmitted solely by the sire, by the dam, and by both. Gowen investigated the question extensively and concluded that the butter-fat percentage is controlled by multiple factors and that both sire and dam play a very considerable rôle in deciding the butter-fat percentage of their offspring. It was demonstrated that in the cross beef-type × dairy-type the former characterised the

F_1 though these were intermediate actually when contrasted with the P_1 forms.

In the case of Holstein × Guernsey reciprocal matings in which the F_1 individuals were interbred, it was found by workers at the University of Illinois that the percentage fat content of the milk produced by the F_1 individuals varied about a mean which was the average of the parent forms with a distribution corresponding closely to a normal probability curve. In F_2 there were suggestions of segregation but the data were insufficient to permit an estimate of the number of factors involved.

It may be said that a beginning has been made and that in time no doubt evidence will be shown that will demonstrate clearly the mode of inheritance of the grades of milk yield. It is a most complex problem, but the indications are that it will be solved. A useful experiment would be the reciprocal mating of Jersey and Aberdeen-Angus and the mating of the F_1 males thus produced to Aberdeen-Angus cows.

The analysis of the hereditary constitution of the horse has, so far, necessarily been limited to a survey of the Stud Books. There are reasons for holding that the trotting character is dominant to pacing. As regards coat colour, the following factors play their part: A dominant factor corresponding to black and a recessive corresponding to the alternative chestnut; the simplex state of the factor for black yields the mahogany brown; a dominant restriction factor confining the expression of black to the tail, mane, and extremities, and leaving the rest of the body a bay colour. A chestnut can carry this factor though its action will not be expressed. A black horse which carries this factor in the simplex condition is a bay with black patches in the flanks. A dominant greying factor acting on black: the foal is black at birth but becomes grey later. A dominant roaning factor acting on any colour and so producing grey roans, chestnut roans, red roans (a roaned bay), blue roans (a roaned black). Grey roans are grey at birth. A dominant diluting factor acting on any colour and turning black into mouse-colour, bay into dun, chestnut into yellow dun, and sorrel (a shade of chestnut) into cream. A dominant spotting factor leading to extreme spotting and so yielding a white.

Chestnut × chestnut gives none but chestnuts. Sorrel, according to M'Cann (1916), is distinct from chestnut and is recessive to all colours. Wentworth (1915) suggests that lighter mane and tail, often met with in sorrels, is recessive to the darker coloration. Black is a simple dominant to chestnut, but the data are unreliable because of the difficulty of getting different observers to agree as to what exactly constitutes a black, a brown, a chestnut, and a bay. Grey is dominant irrespective of the ground colour. In the Clydesdale grey is not fashionable, so all grey males are castrated, and grey mares are mated to sires of some other colour with the result that the progeny of such matings include 50 per cent. greys and 50 per cent. not greys. Grey × grey produces greys, bays, browns, blacks, and chestnuts, the actual colour depending on whether the parents are greyed blacks, chestnuts, and so on. If nothing but greys are wanted both parents must possess the greying factor in the duplex state.

The analysis is by no means complete. A survey of the Stud Books is not sufficient; actual experimentation is necessary, but even now it can be shown that the inheritance of coat colour in the horse obeys the Mendelian schemes.

In the case of the pig very little genetical work has been undertaken, and therefore very little is known. Yet the pig must prove to be a most useful genetical material. The following table gives an outline of the present state of its character analysis; many of the statements cannot yet be accepted as being conclusive:—

Dominant.	Recessive.
Litter size—	
Small (wild pig) . . .	Large (Tamworth), Lush (1921) Simpson (1912) Wentworth and Aubel (1916)
Ear form—	
Erect (Berkshire) (Tamworth) (wild pig) } multi-factor	Lop (Duroc Jersey), Simpson (1912)

Dominant.	Recessive.
Face shape—	
Long, narrow (Tamworth) .	Short, dished (Berkshire), Simpson (1909)
Straight, no forehead prominence (wild pig) . . .	Prominent forehead, Simpson (1909)
Wide forehead (Berkshire) .	Medium forehead (Duroc Jersey), ,,
(Tamworth × Yorkshire gives an F_1 of intermediate characterisation)	
Coat colour—	
Self white	All colours, Simpson (1914)
Belt (2-factor)	Self colour, ,,
Self black	Red (Tamworth), ,,
Black (Hampshire) . . .	Red (Duroc Jersey), Lloyd Jones and Evvrard (1919)
White (improved German pig)	White and black (Hanoverian), Fröhlich (1913)
	Black (Berkshire), ,,
	Grey black (European wild), ,,
	Grey black (Cornwall), ,,
	Red (Tamworth), ,,
	Black (Caucasian wild), ,,
Grey black (European wild) .	Red (Tamworth), ,,
Black and white (Hampshire)	Red (Tamworth), ,,

Lush and Simpson further state that the white of the Berkshire appears to be a diluted red and that the black of the Berkshire and of the Poland China when crossed with red breaks up into spots on a red sandy or white ground. Severson (1917) states that:—

Berkshire × Tamworth—F_1 is red with black spots.
,, × Duroc Jersey—F_1 is red with black spots, or black with white spots (rare).
,, × Yorkshire—F_1 is white, or white with black spots (rare).
Yorkshire × Tamworth—F_1 is white with a reddish tint.
,, × Duroc Jersey—F_1 is white with a reddish tint.
,, × Chester white—F_1 is white, or white with black spots.

In sheep, black fleece colour is certainly recessive to white in many breeds as has been shown by Davenport (1905), but there are suggestions that the Black Welsh is a dominant as is that of the Karakul.

The Karakul sheep is indigenous to the great Kara-Kun desert of Central Asia. The males have four horns, the females two. At birth the lambs are black, and the fleece—

Persian lamb—has a wonderful lustre and takes the form of tight curls. The adult Karakul has a coarse greyish fleece, which is used extensively in the manufacture of the various sorts of Oriental felt rugs. For years the natives have slaughtered the lambs with the best fleeces and have endeavoured to keep up the supply of Persian lamb by using Karakul sires on the ewes of other herds. The Karakul lamb fleece-characters are dominant, though — probably because some of the sires used have been heterozygous—many of the cross-bred lambs have a much more open fleece—the so-called Astrakhan fur which is much less valuable.

Karakul rams have been used in crossing with long-wooled European domesticated sheep—Lincolns, Leicesters, Cotswold, and Blackface, and the F_1 lambs have the desired black curly Persian lamb fleece. In one extensive experiment there were two exceptions—two lambs were red, one was out of a Leicester, the other out of a Lincoln, by the same Karakul sire. Duck (1921), who has investigated the matter, has suggested there are two factors involved—B, that for black lamb fleece colour, and R, that for red, and he suggests that there is correlated (linked?) with the factor for black the factor which determines the Persian lamb character. He suggests the following genotypes:—

Black Karakuls .	BBRR, BBRr, BBrr, BbRR, BbRr, Bbrr.
Reds . . .	bbRR.
Reds or spotted .	bbRr.
White . . .	bbrr.

A further point of interest concerning the Karakul is that there is on record a six horned ram out of a four horned male × two horned female mating. This ram when mated with Karakuls produced normal four horned male and two horned female offspring, and when crossed with Lincoln ewes produced hornless lambs of both sexes.

The Corriedale sheep was made deliberately to take the place of the Merino, which does not readily endure restraint. A New Zealand breeder, James Little, wanted a sheep with the wool of the Merino and with a form somewhat between the Lincoln and the Down—a dual-purpose sheep. He set out to make it, and the result is named after his property—

Corriedale. In 1865 he made the first mating—a Lincoln ram and a Merino ewe. This mating was repeated and selection among the offspring practised. In-breeding and careful selection followed. The same method was taken up by other breeders and there are now some twenty-two registered flocks. (In one case an English Leicester was introduced.)

It is commonly held that the half-bred sheep, produced regularly by the mating Cheviot ram on Border-Leicester ewes, breeds true when interbred, that there is no segregation in the F_2. If, however, sufficient numbers of F_2 individuals are raised evidence of segregation presents itself, and there is a range of characterisation from Cheviot to Border-Leicester. Report has it that the half-bred is not interbred commonly, because it is still more prone to braxy than is either P_1 form. If the P_1 forms differ one from the other in a considerable number of factors, it can be understood that only very rarely indeed would a P_1 characterisation be obtained in the F_2 and that the great bulk of the F_2 individuals would resemble the F_1.

Pucci (1915) examined the inheritance of profile in the sheep, using Rambouillet Merinos (straight line of nose and forehead) and Italian ewes (convex profile). These Italian ewes have an open fleece, and the head, throat, belly, and limbs are bare of wool. The convex profile proved to be a simple recessive. It appeared that straight profile was associated with extension of fleece. In F_2 the ratio 3 straight profiles to 1 convex was obtained.

These scanty references to the character-analysis of the domestic stock will at least serve to show how fragmentary is our present knowledge of inheritance in these forms. It is not secure with respect to any character of economic importance. The fact is that up till very recently the study of inheritance in live stock has been forced to take the form of a genetical study of Herd Book and Stud Book records—research has not been experimental but interpretative, and the records upon which this interpretation has been based are definitely unreliable. In this matter if there is to be exact scientific knowledge there must be experiment, and it behoves the breeder to see that opportunity for such is provided.

CHAPTER III

THE MATERIAL BASIS

IN reviewing the hybridisation experiments so far dealt with it is possible to infer from their analysis, if one accepts the hypothesis that there is a material basis of heredity—the germ-plasm within the gametes—that there must be some unit which is structurally continuous through all the cell divisions from the fertilisation of the egg to the liberation of the gametes by the resulting zygote; that these units must be present in duplicate in the fertilised egg; that they must segregate into maternal and paternal components at some point before the functional gametes are formed; and that they must be present in the zygote in pairs which correspond numerically with the number of character linkage groups.

It is necessary, therefore, at this stage to examine rather more closely the structure of the cells of which the individual is composed, in the hope that it may be possible to identify therein some mechanism by which these conditions may be fulfilled.

The body of an individual is built up of cells; all cells arise by the bipartition of pre-existing cells and if this process of cell-division is traced back it will be found that the individual has its origin in the zygote—the fertilised ovum, formed by the union of an ovum and a sperm (in those cases in which reproduction is sexual). Life comes from life: protoplasm "the physical basis of life" from pre-existing protoplasm. The fundamental problem of the origin of life therefore becomes that of the origin and nature of protoplasm. The segmenting zygote divides into numerous cells; these arrange themselves in different ways, assuming various functions, to become differentiated into the various tissues and organs constituting the body of the new individual. If there is a material basis of inheritance then the hereditary characters must be represented and determined by something present in the zygote, conveyed thereto by either the male or the female gamete or by both.

In the ordinary forms of asexual multiplication, reproduction is quite independent of egg and sperm or indeed of any process equivalent to fertilisation. The new life has its origin in a portion of the parent which becomes

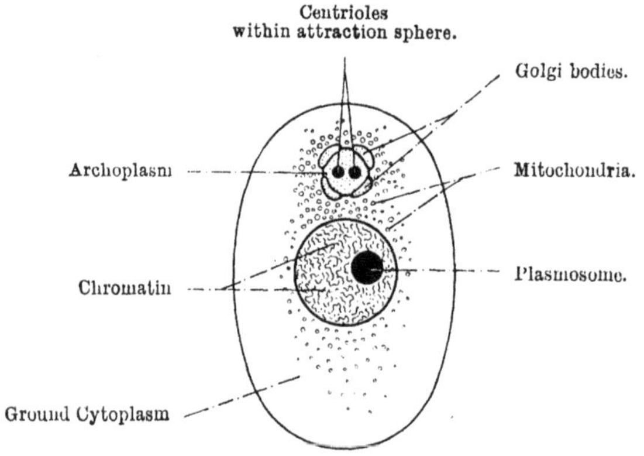

FIG. 16.—The Cell.

separated off from the rest. In such cases the resemblance between the generations tends to be complete since the portion is a representative sample of the whole. In sexual reproduction the germ-cells contain, as it were, the essence of the whole individual that liberates them. Of all the cells of the multicellular organism the gametes in their union alone have the power of developing into an individual which within limits is like the parents. These gametes are microscopical in size, the sperm often being but $\frac{1}{1000}$ the size of the ovum, yet within them must lie the mechanism of organic inheritance.

The methods of cytology, tissue culture, and microdissection have provided a faithful picture of the organisation of the living cell which consists essentially of a vesicular spherical body, the nucleus, lying in a viscous substance, the cytoplasm, in which are found granular bodies, the mitochondria and Golgi rods. The nucleus of the resting cell appears in microscopic preparations as a vesicle containing a network of delicate linin threads upon which are borne, like beads upon a tangled string, minute masses of a readily staining material called for this reason *chromatin* (from the Greek "chroma" = colour). At one side of the nucleus is a small area of cytoplasm known as the attraction sphere, the division of which into two parts heralds the inception of cell-division. As the two attraction spheres thus formed separate, they seem to draw out the surrounding cytoplasm into a spindle of fine fibrils. While this is happening, changes are taking place in the nucleus: the tangle of fine threads has resolved itself into a certain constant number of filaments of definite shape; these become progressively shorter to assume the form of stout rods—the *chromosomes*—which arrange themselves on the equator of the spindle and split longitudinally in halves (Fig. 17). The halves pass to opposite poles of the spindle. The cytoplasm of the cell divides and the chromosomes spin out again into fine threads to form the nuclei of the daughter-cells thus formed. The chromatin material of the nuclei is structurally continuous: each of the chromosomes in the nucleus of one cell-generation is structurally continuous with a corresponding chromosome in the nucleus of that of the preceding and succeeding cell-generations.

This phenomenon is true of all cell-division save that which produces the mature gametes. The spermatozoon is very different from the egg in size, structure, and appearance. It is much smaller, carries practically no nutritive matter, and most of its cytoplasm forms a locomotor tail which drives the head consisting of the nucleus before it. The relatively large food-laden passive ovum is fertilised by the infinitely small active restless sperm. But in one respect ovum and sperm are alike and in this they differ from all other cells. The penultimate division of the germ nuclei is preceded by the lateral approximation in pairs of the constituent chromosomes (synapsis), so that when the chromosomes proceed to split on the spindle, one member of each pair passes to each daughter nucleus. The succeeding

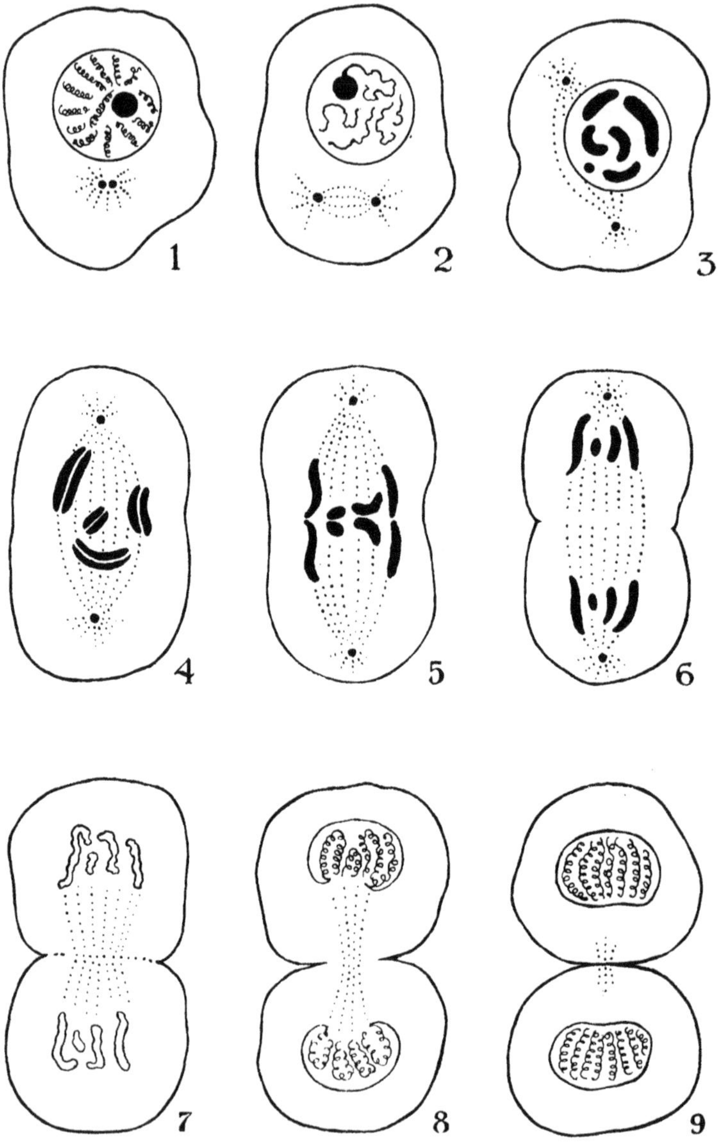

FIG. 17.—STAGES IN CELL DIVISION.

1. Resting stage of cell nucleus in "spirophase" (or interphase).
2, 3. Prophase; appearance of definitive chromosomes.
4-5. Metaphase; splitting of chromosomes.
6. Anaphase.
7-8. Telophase.
9. Resting nuclei (interphase).

division is a normal one, so that each gamete has half the number of chromosomes characteristic of the cells which constitute the body of the individual. At fertilisation, the normal number is restored and each ordinary cell of the organism has therefore a chromosome set of which half the components are paternal and the other half maternal in origin. The number of chromosomes is usually some multiple of two and is *characteristic of the species to which the individual belongs;* in certain stages of cell activity the chromosomes are arranged in pairs. In many instances the different pairs are of different shape and size—are heteromorphic—and, therefore, it is sometimes quite simple to demonstrate the fact that each gamete receives one member of each pair of homologous chromosomes which were present in the cell that, dividing, gave rise to it.

In slightly more detail the process is as follows:—

Just before the gametes become transformed into functional spermatozoa or ova the chromosomes conjugate in pairs—each paternal chromosome unites with the corresponding maternal one so that at this stage it seems as though the chromosome number had been reduced by half. But this apparent reduction is due to the intimate conjugation of the members of each pair, and each chromosome is really two lying side by side. Following this conjugation a spindle appears and each double chromosome separates into its component halves and the cell divides. In the case of the egg, one daughter cell constitutes the first polar body into which one set of chromosomes passes. Without a resting phase a fresh spindle is formed and each chromosome of each set divides lengthways. The mature egg and the second polar body are then formed, while the first polar body divides, yielding two daughter cells so that four cells result, one functional egg and three polar bodies (abortive eggs), and each is haploid containing but half the original diploid number of chromosomes. In the case of the sperm four functional gametes result.

The important points to note are the conjugation of maternal and paternal chromosomes in pairs and their subsequent separation and distribution in such a way that each germ-cell gets one or the other of each and every pair. Further, it is seen that if the chromosomes should prove to be the "germ-plasm" each and every cell of the body contains the sum total of all the hereditary elements and development and differentiation of the tissues of every

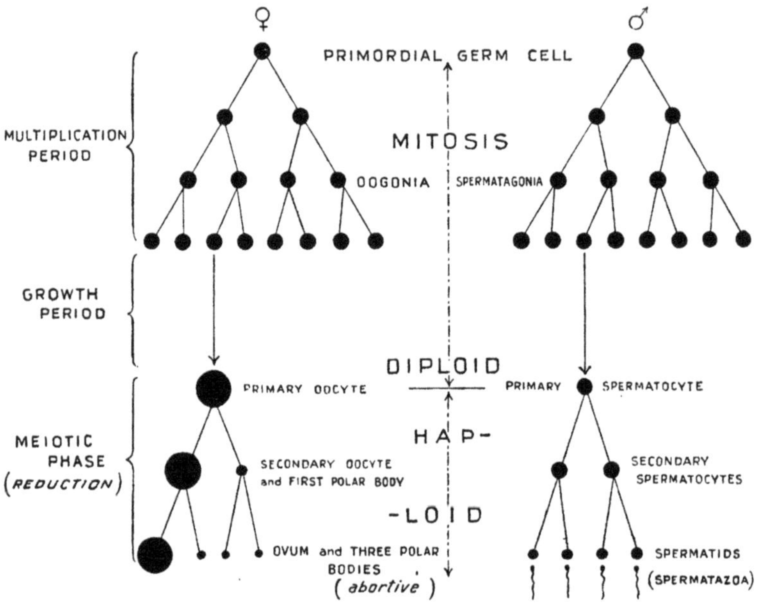

FIG. 18.—Gametogenesis. (After Boveri.)

The period of multiplication involves a much greater number of divisions than is indicated. The secondary spermatocytes give rise, by the second division of the meiotic phase, to the spermatids which are nothing else than immature spermatozoa. Four spermatozoa are produced from each primary spermatocyte. In the case of the female the growth period is more conspicuous than in the male for during this period the yolk is deposited. The division of the primary and secondary oocytes is very unequal, and of the four cells produced from the primary oocyte only one becomes a functional gamete.

part of the organism proceeds in the presence of all the hereditary material.

The search for a material apparatus for genetic segregation is ended, for the formation of gametes involves the segregation in each pair of homologous chromosomes of its paternal and maternal components. In the behaviour of the chromosomes there are realised the precise conditions of hereditary transmission demanded by the results yielded by breeding experiments. Material units preserving their integrity through all cell divisions between the fertilisation of the ovum and the liberation of the gametes by the individual thus originated, and segregating before these gametes are actually formed, so that with reference to any given pair a gamete can receive one or the other—the paternal or the maternal—but not both at the same time: these conditions are realised by the chromosomes, the only identifiable cell structure the behaviour of which conforms to the law of segregation.

Weismann had hazarded the suggestion that the germ-plasm had its seat in the nucleus, was extremely complex in structure yet nevertheless had an extreme power of persistence and an enormous power of growth; that the germ-substances proper must be looked for in the chromatin of the nucleus and more precisely in the chromosomes which contain the primary constituents of a complete organism and which are built up of vital units or determinants, each of which determines the origin and development of a particular part of the organism, but it was not until 1902 that a young student, William Sutton, whilst working in the laboratory of Professor E. B. Wilson at Columbia University, first drew attention to the possible interpretation of Mendel's laws by the application of the then known facts of cytology outlined above. The factors are borne on the chromosomes and the phenomenon of linkage suggests that factors borne upon different chromosomes segregate, whereas those borne upon the same chromosome remain linked in inheritance since they are carried upon the same structural unit. No animal or plant has yet been shown to possess a number of linkage groups in excess of the number of chromosome pairs in the dividing cell-nucleus. It is of interest to note that in the same year as linkage was first discovered Lock called attention to the possible relation between this phenomenon and chromosome behaviour.

When the genetic significance of the nucleus was first emphasised by Nageli and Weismann, the distinction between nuclear apparatus and ground cytoplasm comprised the existing state of knowledge with regard to cell organisation. The discovery, due to new technical procedure, of other cell organs has necessitated a reconsideration of the problem, especially in view of the discovery concerning fertilisation in the case of Ascaris that these structures may be carried over with the sperm nucleus which had previously been regarded as the unique link between the male parent and zygote.

Two categories of extra-nuclear cell organs are nowadays recognised. These are: (*a*) the mitochondria (chondriosomes or chondriokonts), the existence of which first attracted attention through the labours of Benda and his followers in connection with their relation to the "middle piece" of the sperm; and (*b*) the Golgi apparatus (dictyosomes) first recognised by Golgi, Kopsch, Cajal, and others as a constituent of nerve ganglion cells and later homologised through the work of Hirschler, Weigel, Nussbaum-Hilarowicz, and others with a diversity of cell organs previously described by a variety of terms (nebenkern, batonettes, acroblasts, etc.).

The mitochondria are granules, spherules, rods, or filaments scattered in the cytoplasm and often congregated eccentrically with reference to the nucleus. They are usually identifiable after fixation with reagents containing no lipin solvents (*e.g.*, acetic acid, alcohol, chloroform) as, for example, Flemming without acetic (Benda), Bichromate-osmic (Champy), and Formol-bichromate (Regaud). They readily stain *intra vitam* with Janus green. The Golgi apparatus is described as a reticulum of filaments, rods or discs often applied to the denser cytoplasm (archoplasm) enveloping the attraction sphere, though sometimes dispersed in the cytoplasm like mitochondria. As with the latter, all lipin solvents are injurious, and though in a few cases the Golgi elements are readily demonstrable with the mitochondrial technique, it is usually necessary to apply the metallic impregnation methods of Mann-Kopsch, Cajal, and Da Fano, in order to identify them satisfactorily.

The work of a large body of continental investigators, notably Duesberg, Hirschler, Terni, Weigel, and of Gatenby in this country, has now given a fairly consistent account of the behaviour of mitochondria and dictyosomes throughout the germ-cycle, in cell division, in gametogenesis and in fertilisation. Both types of cytoplasmic inclusions are self-propagating cell units; they divide and are distributed in a quite haphazard manner to the daughter-cells during cell division. Their number is inconstant in the same cell generation; there is great diversity in the configuration of the cytoplasmic inclusions within the same phylum, species, or even individual; and it is clearly established that there is no precise correspondence between the mitochondrial or Golgi components of the zygote and those of the germ-cells in the individual which develop from it.

While the case of Ascaris raised the whole question of the nucleus in relation to heredity on a somewhat different basis from previous discussion, recent work has shown that the transmission of the cytoplasmic units is very often purely matroclinal. Thus in Peripatus the entire mitochondrial content of the spermatids is sloughed off during spermateleosis, and the same is true of the Golgi elements in Paludina. In other cases, as in Annelids, where the cytoplasmic inclusions play a part in the formation of the middle piece, the latter is left outside the egg when the sperm-head penetrates it. In Echinus and in mammals the middle piece also penetrates the egg, but the mitochondrial mass ("mitosome" or "chondriome") passes wholly into one of the blastomeres and probably degenerates. In gametogenesis there is no indication of segregation. Gatenby has shown with reference to the Golgi apparatus of Limax and Wilson in the case of the mitochondria of Centrurus that the number of units present in the spermatid is one-quarter that present in the spermatogonia. According to Gatenby no mitochondria pass out into the polar bodies, so that segregation of maternal and paternal units in the female is absolutely precluded.

It thus appears that the behaviour of the cytoplasmic units fulfils none of the conditions of the material basis of inheritance inferred from breeding experiments, and the new knowledge of cell anatomy which has emerged from the impetus given by the "mitochondrial" theory of inheritance advocated by Meves' school has placed the chromosome hypothesis on a more secure foundation.

It is granted that the botanist can demonstrate that, in the case of his material, the inheritance of certain characters, such as albinism in certain plants, can be traced to the behaviour of the chlorophyll bodies in the cytoplasm which are known to divide and to be distributed to the two daughter-cells at each division independently of the nuclear division and of the maturation process in the egg. But the evidence is such that leads to the conclusion that cytoplasmic inheritance cannot play any important rôle in inheritance in the case of animals and the more highly complex plants. From what has been said it must not be inferred that the cytoplasm is an unimportant element of the zygote. Indeed it is not, for if the developmental processes are to proceed there must be cytoplasm. However, the problems of the rôle of the cytoplasm in development and of the relation twixt chromosomes and cytoplasm are not strictly problems in genetics, but in developmental physiology. In the case of unicellular organisms, bacteria and suchlike, the evidence is not such as leads to any conclusion concerning the mechanism of heredity therein.

CHAPTER IV

THE GENES AND THE CHROMOSOMES

A. *The Genes are borne on the Chromosomes*

IN 1909-1910 Professor T. H. Morgan of Columbia University first used Drosophila as experimental material with which to explore the possibility of inducing mutation by means of treatment with such agencies as different chemicals, different diets, and radium. These experiments yielded no positive

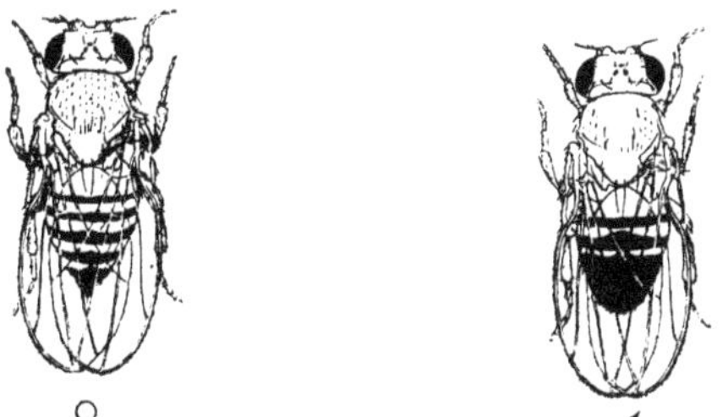

♀ 5 black bands. Black band never meets on underside. Caudal extremity relatively pointed and sharp.

♂ 3 black bands and black tip. Black caudal band extends around the underside. Caudal extremity relatively rounded and blunt.

FIG. 19.—*Drosophila melanogaster.*

results, and as a side-line Morgan undertook a selection experiment to obtain a stock in which all the individuals should have a dark trident pattern on the thorax. This was the beginning; since 1910 the investigation of the problems of heredity has increased a thousand-fold. *Drosophila melanogaster*, the pomace fly, so small that for its inspection a good hand-lens is necessary, in the hands of Morgan (1919, 1923) and his colleagues of the University of Columbia has extended our knowledge to a remarkable degree. This Dipteran with its prolific breeding habits, short life-cycle and ease of handling, has shown itself a form far superior to any other thus far investigated for the unravelling of the problems of heredity. These advantages have been thoroughly exploited by the American geneticists and have led them to formulate what is known as the Chromosome Theory of Heredity, according to which *the chromosomes form the material basis of heredity, and upon these, each in its own particular locus upon a particular chromosome, are resident the genes, the activity of which determines the expression of corresponding characters.* The theory as it stands to-day is founded on the results of countless breeding experiments; much of it is endorsed by recent advances in cytology; further understanding of its significance, it would seem, will come from future research in the realms of physico- and of bio-chemistry.

The first *mutants* in Drosophila—individuals exhibiting novel characters appearing unexpectedly—occurred in laboratory cultures of the wild flies in the spring of 1910, and since that time an ever-increasing series of novel types has been appearing. There is no absolutely definite knowledge as to whether the laboratory conditions are in any degree responsible for the frequency of mutation. They cannot as yet be produced by planned experiments. It is probable that the discovery of so many mutants is due solely to the fact that immense numbers of flies have been under observation, that mutation is as common in Nature as in the laboratory but is not so readily recognised, and that the mutant forms in many instances could not thrive in the open. The numerous mutants (400 or so) have provided unparalleled material for the experimental study of character-analysis, of variation, and of inheritance.

The chromosomes of *Drosophila melanogaster* number eight, arranged in four pairs during certain stages of cell-activity. As has already been said, this number is constant and is characteristic of the species to which the individual belongs. They are different in size and shape—hetero-morphic; there are two pairs of large curved chromosomes, one pair of very small round ones, and one pair in the case of the female of straight chromosomes about two-thirds the size of the large curved ones; in the male instead of this last pair there is a pair consisting of one straight and one large somewhat hooked chromosome: otherwise the chromosome picture in the case of the male is identical with that in the female. Because of this distinction in the chromosomal picture of male and female tissues, these last chromosomes are spoken of as the *sex-chromosomes*. The two chromosomes of the female and the similar one of the male are called the X-chromosomes, and the unequal mate of the X-chromosome of the male is known as the Y-chromosome. The large curved and the small round chromosomes are referred to as *autosomes* in contrast to the sex-chromosomes. The chromosomes themselves possess a definite individuality.

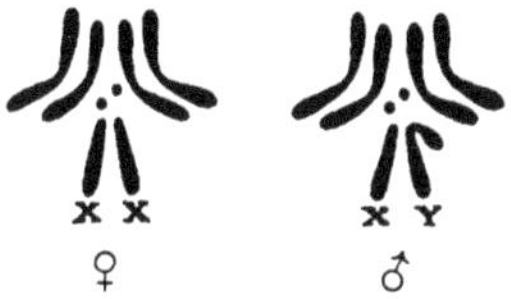

FIG. 20.—Conventional diagram of the Chromosomes of *Drosophila melanogaster*. (After Morgan.)

The characteristic paired relations which exist among the chromosomes are of general significance. During the process of gametogenesis in the meiotic phase, reduction divisions occur by means of which the chromosome number becomes reduced so that in the mature gamete there is but half the number which is characteristic of the immature gamete and of the body-cells generally. In Drosophila for instance, the mature gametes contain *only one member of each pair of homologous chromosomes*, and there is reason to believe that the distribution of the members of any one pair has no influence upon the distribution of the members of any of the other pairs. The mature gametes can, therefore, contain various combinations of chromosomes. There are eight different ways in which the chromosomes may be grouped in the reduction figures and on the basis of chance any one of these is as likely to occur as any other; as a result of this, there are sixteen possible combinations of chromosomes in the mature ovum (and spermatozoon, if one of the X-chromosomes is replaced by the Y).

In a species with two pairs of chromosomes there would be only four possible combinations; in one with three, there would be eight, and so on, so that in general the number of possible combinations is given by the expression 2^n in which n is the number of pairs of chromosomes in the individual in question, and with the increase in the number of pairs there is a rapid increase in complexity.

When gamete unites with gamete, the characteristic number of chromosomes is restored and of each pair of homologous chromosomes one has been received from the male parent, the other from the female. The mature germ-cells can be of sixteen sorts in the case of Drosophila, owing to the different possible combinations of chromosomes. As of these there are two series, male and female, it is seen that in the formation of a new zygote by the union of gamete and gamete, there is a multitude of possible combinations of chromosomes.

The chromosomes are regarded as aggregations of chromatin, which in itself has a definite and highly organised structure and consists of a definite number of individual elements called *chromomeres.* The suggestion is that a certain definite group of these elements makes up each chromosome: the individuality of the chromosome depends upon the individuality of the chromomeres of which it is composed. Each chromomere is supposed to have its own definite position upon a particular chromosome and to be identical with a certain *locus* in that chromosome.

It will be remembered that Mendel proposed a very simple hypothesis to explain the 3 : 1 ratio in the F_2 of his experiments. The P_1 parent with the dominant character contributes one element and the parent with the recessive character another element to the hybrid. When the germ-cells of the hybrid thus formed mature, these elements separate (segregate), so that half the female and half the male gametes contain the element for the dominant and the other half the element for the recessive character, and chance fertilisation of any ovule by any pollen-grain will be expected to give three genotypes, DD, DR, RR in the ratio of 1 : 2 : 1. This suggested segregation of the factors

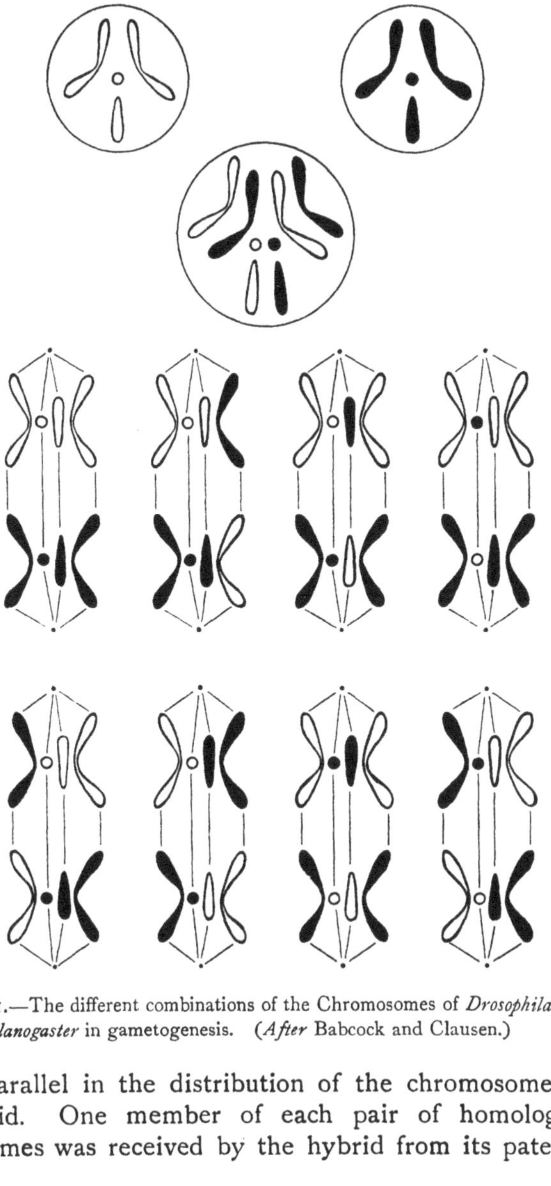

FIG. 21.—The different combinations of the Chromosomes of *Drosophila melanogaster* in gametogenesis. (*After* Babcock and Clausen.)

finds a parallel in the distribution of the chromosomes of the hybrid. One member of each pair of homologous chromosomes was received by the hybrid from its paternal parent, the other from its maternal parent. When the germ-cells of the individual mature, the members of each pair of homologous chromosomes pass into different cells—they segregate—so that as a result one-half of the gametes carry one member, the other half the other member of each pair. *The chromosomes behave like Mendel's "factors."*

As an example of a monohybrid experiment, the case of mating a pomace fly with normal wild type long wings with one with vestigial wings, may be considered. The wings of the latter are shrunken and useless and the character first presented itself among the offspring of wild type flies. (Fig. 22). The F_1 of such a mating is entirely composed of long-winged flies, the character long-wings being dominant to vestigial, and in the F_2 in every four individuals there are three long-winged to every one vestigial. The explanation of these results in terms of the chromosome theory rests upon the assumption that the factor for the character "long-winged" is resident in each member of a certain pair of chromosomes of the long-winged race of flies, and that the factor for the vestigial character is resident in each of the same pair of chromosomes in the vestigial-winged race. Apart from this one difference, the two individuals in P_1 are identical as far as their genetic constitution is concerned. Let V represent the gene for the dominant character of the wing form—long, and v the gene for the recessive character—vestigial-wing form (not the L of long-winged, since it is the inheritance of vestigial which is being studied). The name given to a mutant character is that which most clearly emphasises its contrast to the wild-type. For the corresponding gene the initial letter of the name is used, the capital if the character is a dominant, the small letter if recessive. The letter is used to indicate the character, the gene, and the locus. In order to distinguish between two genes with the same initial letter a second letter is added—so, b = black; bn = band (a thorax pattern); bx = bithorax (body segmentation). It is assumed that the genes V

VESTIGIAL

FIG. 22.

and v cannot be resident in one and the same chromosome at the same time. Of the four pairs of chromosomes of Drosophila only that pair need be considered which bears the gene V in the case of the long-winged race, or in the vestigial-winged race its allelomorph, the gene v. In the hybrid produced by crossing a long-winged and a vestigial-winged fly, one member of this pair of chromosomes bears the gene V, and the other the gene v. When the gametes of such a hybrid are maturing, the members of this pair of chromosomes become separated and distributed to different germ-cells in such a way that half of them will receive that member which bears the gene V, and half that member which bears the gene v. When two such hybrids are interbred, recombination of these chromosomes will yield the ratio 3 long-winged: vestigial-winged; so—

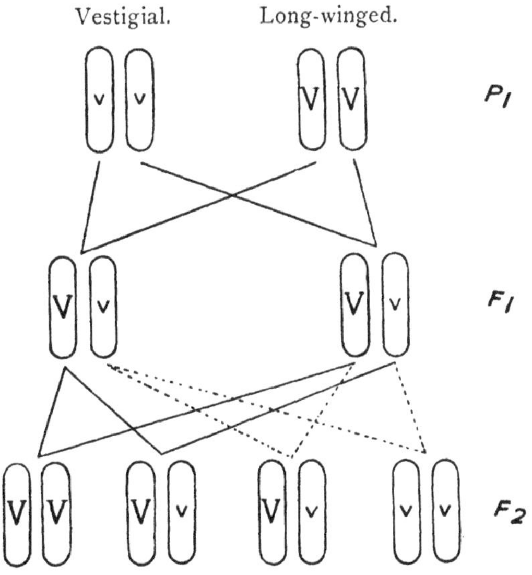

FIG. 23.

Or

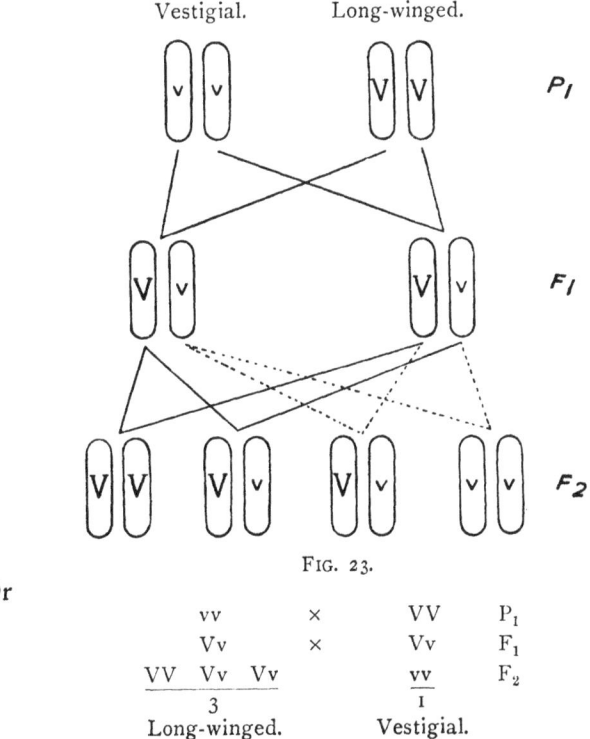

vv	×	VV	P_1
Vv	×	Vv	F_1
VV Vv Vv		vv	F_2
3		1	
Long-winged.		Vestigial.	

The genetic and cytological results agree and the behaviour of the chromosomes provides an explanation of Mendel's law of segregation.

As an example of a dihybrid may be considered the case of the crossing of a vestigial-winged, grey-bodied fly with a long-winged ebony-bodied individual. The F_1 are all long-winged grey flies, and, in the F_2 in every sixteen there are nine long-winged grey, three vestigial-winged grey, three long-winged ebony, and one vestigial-winged ebony flies. The correlation of the above facts with chromosome behaviour is again very simple. V is taken to represent the gene of the dominant character long-wing, little v that of the recessive vestigial, E the gene of the dominant

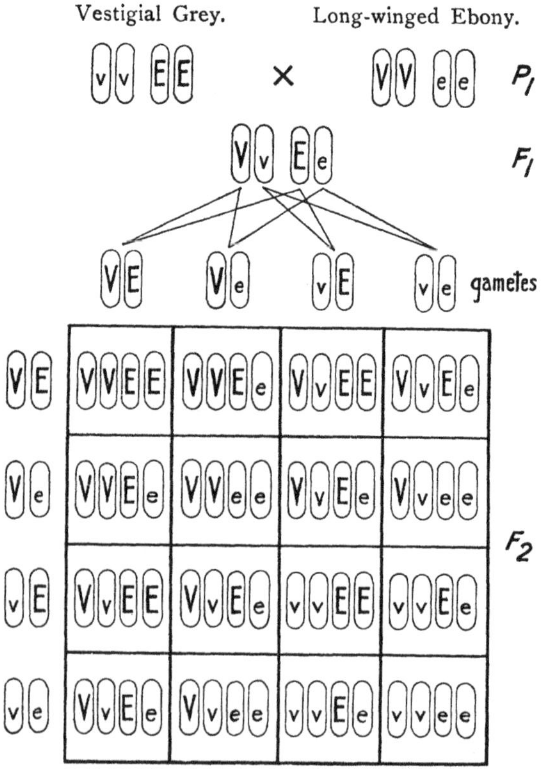

FIG. 24.

Or

vv EE	×	VV ee		P_1	zygotes
v E		V e			gametes
Vv Ee	×	Vv Ee		F_1	zygotes
VE	Ve	vE	ve		gametes

V < E, e

v < E, e

	VE	Ve	vE	ve
VE	VVEE	VVEe	VvEE	VvEe
Ve	VVEe	VVee	VvEe	Vvee
vE	VvEE	VvEe	vvEE	vvEe
ve	VvEe	Vvee	vvEe	vvee

F_2 zygotes

Phenotype.

VE.	Long-winged grey	9
vE.	Vestigial grey	3
Ve.	Long-winged ebony . .	3
ve.	Vestigial ebony	1
		16

character grey or wild-type body-colour, e that of the recessive body colour, ebony. (It is assumed that the genes V and v are resident in one pair of chromosomes, E and e in a different pair, and that E and e, V and v cannot reside in one and the same chromosome at the same time.) The two stocks of flies differ only in the matter of these two characters and their respective genes, so that the other pairs of chromosomes bear the same sets of genes and need not be considered. Each gamete of the vestigial grey parent will contain one chromosome with the gene for the vestigial character and one with the gene for the grey, each gamete of the long-winged ebony parent will carry one chromosome with the gene for the long-winged character and one bearing the gene for ebony. The hybrid will carry one chromosome with the gene for vestigial and its mate with the gene for the long-wing, and another chromosome bearing the gene for grey body-colour and its mate bearing the gene for ebony (Fig. 24).

In the maturation of the gametes of the hybrid the members of each pair separate from each other and free assortment occurs, with the result that four different kinds of gametes are produced. The chance meeting of the four kinds of ova and of the four kinds of sperm will give results as shown on pp. 94, 95.

It is to be noted that there is actual evidence that such independent assortment of chromosomes occurs. Miss Carothers (1921) has shown it to happen during the maturation divisions in several grasshoppers. Slight but constant differences in the mode of attachment of the chromosomes to the spindle enabled her to demonstrate that the sorting out of the members of the pairs is independent.

The trihybrid mating is excellently illustrated by the mating vestigial-winged, grey-bodied, normal-eyed, and long-winged, ebony-bodied, eyeless. The classes in F_2 can be accounted for if it is assumed that the genes for vestigial, ebony, and eyeless are situated each on a different chromosome.

The multiple factors explanation of Nilsson-Ehle dealt with previously is readily interpreted in terms of the Chromosome Theory and many similar instances of more than one factor producing similar or identical effects are known. For example, in the case of the Nilsson-Ehle experiments with wheat, all that is necessary is to assume that wheat has at least three pairs of chromosomes and that the genes R, S, and T, are resident upon separate ones.

B. *Certain Groups are borne on certain Chromosomes.*

In interpreting the results of the above experiments in terms of the Chromosome Hypothesis, there has been the suggestion that different genes are resident in different chromosomes.

The interpretation of the results of a breeding experiment is straightforward until a case is encountered in which there are found to be more genetical differences than there are chromosomes, when it follows, if the theory is valid, that there must be more than one gene borne on one and the same chromosome. In Drosophila, for example, several hundreds of different Mendelian characters have been investigated, and if for each of these characters there is a gene, then it follows that each chromosome must carry a very great number of these. If two genes are situated on the same chromosome it would be expected that they should always be found together in successive generations and the characters which they represent should remain *linked* in inheritance. In Drosophila the linkage relations of some hundreds of characters have been investigated and it has been clearly shown that these characters fall into four groups, the members of each group showing various degrees of linkage with each other but giving free assortment with the members of any other group. The most significant fact in regard to linkage in Drosophila is that *the number of linkage groups corresponds to the number of pairs of chromosomes* and that the relative sizes of the groups correspond roughly to the relative sizes of the chromosomes. If the genes for the characters are carried by the chromosomes, this is what one should expect to find—that there are as many groups of characters that are inherited together as there are pairs of chromosomes, provided the chromosomes retain their individuality. If at any future time the number of linkage groups should be found to be greater than the number of chromosomes, it would follow that the Chromosome Theory must undergo profound modification.

In *Drosophila obscura* there are five pairs of chromosomes, and Lancefield (1922) has shown that there are five linkage groups; in *Drosophila virilis*, which has six pairs of chromosomes, Metz (1916) has already identified five non-linked characters. In *Drosophila willistoni*, Metz (1914) has found three groups of linked characters, three pairs of chromosomes. In *Drosophila simulans*, Sturtevant (1920) has found so far three linkage groups and four pairs of chromosomes. From the evidence of comparative cytology it would appear that the difference in the chromosome pictures in these cases is the result of difference in the form and distribution of the II and III chromosomes seen in the conventional diagram of *Drosophila melanogaster*. In *D. virilis* each of these chromosomes consists of two separated halves; in *D. willistoni* or *D. obscura*, one-half of one of them has become united with what corresponds to the X-chromosome of *D. melanogaster*, leaving the other half free.

The phenomenon of linkage is excellently illustrated in the case of what are known as sex-linked characters, the genes for which are placed upon the sex-chromosomes for reasons to be stated. In Drosophila (as has been stated) the male is to be distinguished from the female by the chromosome picture. In female tissues there is a pair of X-chromosomes and in male there is one X associated with a Y-chromosome. Thus, XX designates a female, XY a male. Every egg will possess one X, the other being eliminated into the polar body; half the sperms will contain an X and the other half a Y. Any egg fertilised by an X-bearing sperm will become an XX zygote—a female; any egg fertilised by a Y-bearing sperm will become an XY individual—a male.

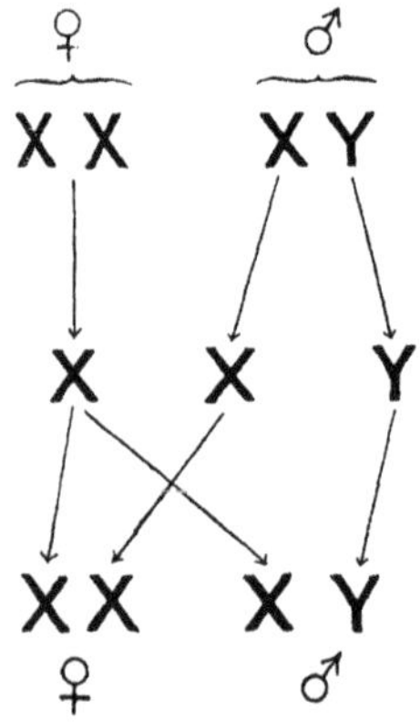

FIG. 25.—The XY Sex-Determining Mechanism.

Sex, it would appear from this, is determined by a process which automatically yields equal numbers of males and females in each generation. A son always gets his single X from his mother, a daughter gets one from the mother and the other from the father. If on the X-chromosome of the father are borne the genes for a recessive character the track of this chromosome in inheritance can be followed *if the Y-chromosome of a male carries no factors whatsoever*, and since in the case of many insects, for example, there is no Y but only a single X in the male, this assumption is not extravagant. As an example of sex-linked inheritance the case of mating red-eyed and white-eyed flies may be taken. The eyes of the wild fly are red; in one culture a mutant white-eyed fly appeared. He was mated to a red-eyed female, the offspring (both males and females) were all red-eyed. These were interbred and produced in the next generation three red-eyed to one white-eyed in every four on the average, equal numbers of males and females, but *every white-eyed individual was a male*. The white-eyed grandfather had transmitted the character white-eye to half his grandsons but to none of his granddaughters. A white-eyed female can be produced easily by mating the F_1 heterozygous red-eyed female to a white-eyed male. When a white-eyed female was mated to a red-eyed male, the reciprocal mating, that is, *all the daughters were red-eyed and all the sons were white-eyed*; when these were interbred, they gave red-eyed males and females, and white-eyed males and females in equal numbers.

This type of inheritance can be explained as follows. The gene for the recessive white-eyed character is represented by w and is borne on the X-chromosome; the gene for red-eyes, W, is borne by X-chromosome of the red-eyed race of flies. The two X-chromosomes of the female both contain the gene W and in a convenient short-hand system the genetic constitution of such a fly may be written (WX) (WX), the brackets indicating that the gene W is carried by the X-chromosome. Each egg from such a female will contain an X-chromosome with the gene W, *i.e.*, every one of them will be (WX). On the other hand, the white-eyed male will have the genetic constitution (wX) (Y) and his sperms will be of two sorts; half will have an X-chromosome with the gene w thereon, and half will have a Y-chromosome which does not bear this gene; there will be two kinds of sperms, (wX) and Y. The matings are then as follow:—

A.

P_1 Red-eyed ♀	(WX)(WX)	×	(wX)(Y)	White-eyed ♂
Gametes	(WX) (WX)		(wX) (Y)	Gametes
F_1 Red-eyed ♀	(WX)(wX)	×	(WX)(Y)	Red-eyed ♂
Gametes	(WX) (wX)		(WX) (Y)	Gametes
F_2	(WX)(WX) (WX)(Y) (wX)(WX)		(wX)(Y)	
Red-eyed	♀ ♂ ♀ / 3		♂ / 1	White-eyed

B. The Production of a White-eyed Female:—

White-eyed ♂	(wX)Y	×	(WX)(wX)	F_1 heterozygous red-eyed ♀
	(wX) Y		(WX) (wX)	Gametes

(wX)(WX)	(wX)(wX)	(WX)Y	(wX)Y
Red ♀	White ♀	Red ♂	White ♂

C. The Reciprocal Cross:—

P_1 White-eyed ♀ (wX)(wX) — (wX) (wX) | (WX)(Y) — (WX) (Y) Red-eyed ♂

Criss-cross Inheritance:—

F_1 Red-eyed ♀ (WX)(wX) — (WX) (wX) | (wX)(Y) — (wX) (Y) White-eyed ♂

F_2	(WX)(wX)	(WX)(Y)	(wX)(wX)	(wX)(Y)
	♀	♂	♀	♂
	1	1	1	1
	Red-eyed		White-eyed	

Or, diagrammatically—

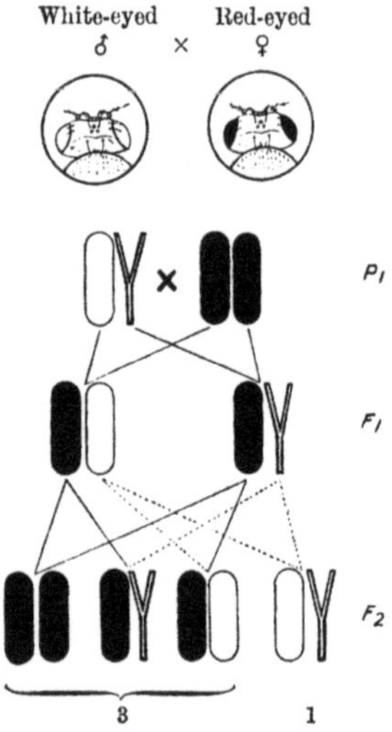

FIG. 26.—White-eyed ♂ × Red-eyed ♀.
(*After* Morgan.)

In the F_2 the numbers of males and females are equal;

all the females and half the males are red-eyed; all the white-eyed individuals are males.

Reciprocal cross—

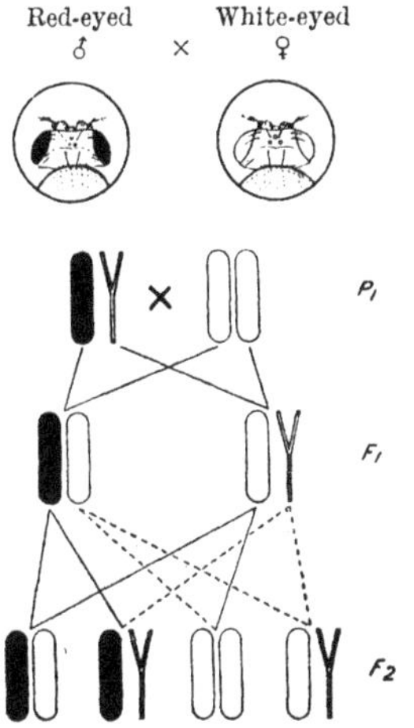

FIG. 27.—Red-eyed ♂ × White-eyed ♀. Criss-cross inheritance in F_1 (*After* Morgan.)

In the F_2 there are equal numbers of red-eyed and of white-eyed individuals, and of males and females.

The peculiar relations which exist in the inheritance of the characters red and white eye-colours can readily and logically be interpreted if it is assumed that their genes are borne upon the X-chromosome and that the Y-chromosome of the male carries no gene at all. Many other characters of Drosophila are inherited according to the above scheme. These sex-linked characters (not sex-limited since they can be exhibited by both sexes) constitute the first linkage-group and their factors are placed upon the X-chromosome, chromosome I. A larger group of characters not sex-linked, all show linkage relations with the character *black body-colour* and with each other and their genes are placed upon chromosome II, the chromosomes of the top right-hand large curved pair of the conventional diagram. As an example of linkage within this group may be considered the mating of vestigial wing-form and black body-colour with long-winged grey (wild type). F_1 consists solely of long-winged greys, but in the F_2, though two pairs of allelomorphs are involved, a monohybrid and not a dihybrid ratio is obtained, for there are three long-winged greys to every one vestigial black. These characters are linked and the genes for vestigial and black are borne on one and the same chromosome.

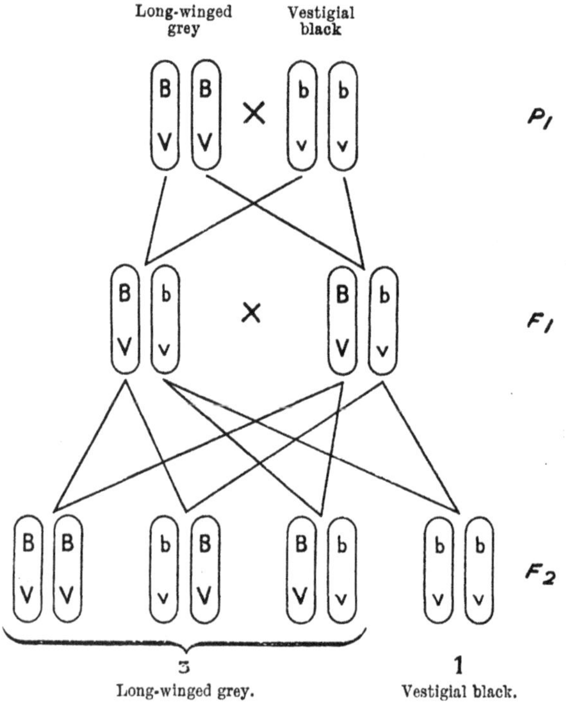

FIG. 28.—Linkage.

Or

P_1	(bv)(bv)	×	(BV)(BV)	
F_1	(BV)(bv)	×	(BV)(bv)	
F_2	(BV)(BV)	(BV)(bv)	(BV)(bv)	(bv)(bv)
	Long-winged grey	Long-winged grey	Long-winged grey	Vestigial black
		3		1

If, on the other hand, black long-winged is mated to grey vestigial, the ratio in F_2 is different, so—

P_1	(bV)(bV)	×	(Bv)(Bv)
F_1	(bV)(Bv)	×	(bV)(Bv)

(bV)(bV)	(bV)(Bv) (Bv)(bV)	(Bv)(Bv)
Black long	Grey long	Grey vestigial
1	2	1

and *no double recessive appears in the* F_2; this is regarded as trustworthy evidence of linkage.

Instead of raising an F_2, however, the usual procedure in testing linkage is to back-cross the F_1 individuals to others exhibiting both recessive characters. For example, an F_1 long-winged grey *male* (VB)(vb) is mated to a double recessive female, black vestigial (vb)(vb), when only two types of offspring are produced, long-winged greys and black vestigial, in equal numbers. The characters long-winged and grey remain together as do the characters black and vestigial.

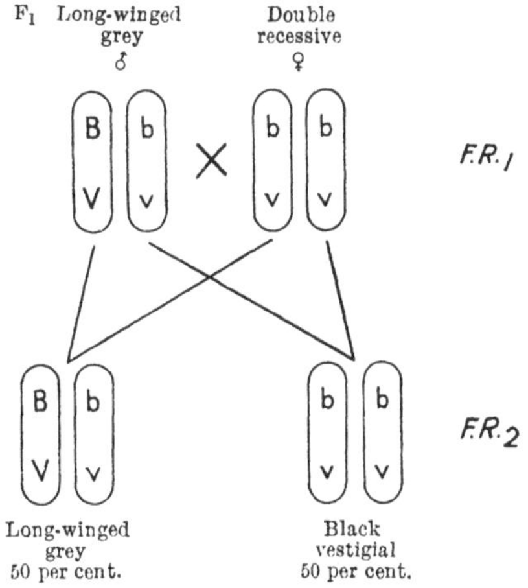

FIG. 29.—Linkage : Back-cross.

Or

F_1 ♂	(VB)(vb)	×	(vb)(vb)	♀	FR_1
Gametes	(VB) (vb)		(vb) (vb)		Gametes
	(VB)(vb)		(vb)(vb)		FR_2
	Long-winged grey		Vestigial black		
	50 per cent.		50 per cent.		

The symbols FR_1 and FR_2 may be used to indicate the back-cross of the heterozygous F_1 individual to the recessive and the offspring of this mating respectively. Similarly FD_1 and FD_2 can be used to indicate the back-cross to the dominant.

In this particular instance F_2 actually is equivalent to FR_2, but usually these generations differ—*cf.* DR × DR and DR × RR.

In the case of dihybrid in which the characters are not linked, the result of back-crossing an F_1 ♂ with a double recessive ♀ is the production of four sorts of individuals in equal numbers. Take the case of vestigial grey and long-winged ebony mating in which there is free assortment—

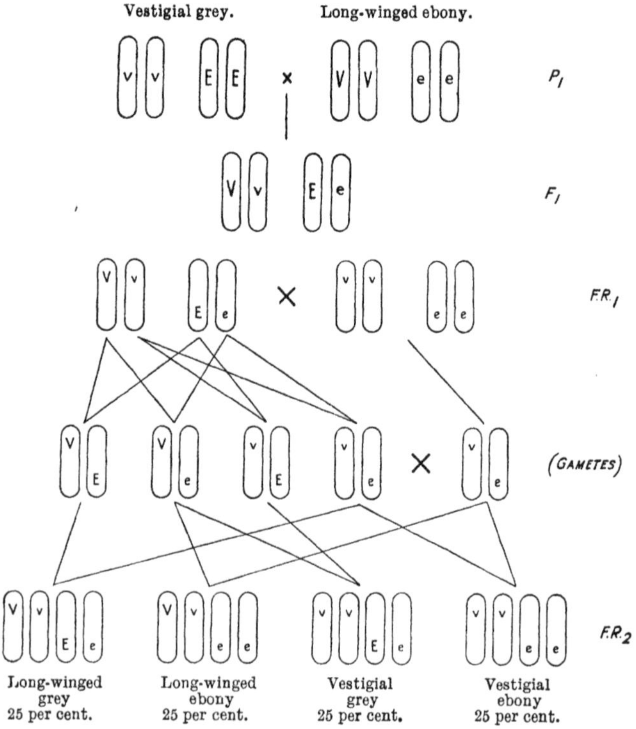

FIG. 30.—Free assortment. Back-cross.

Or

P_1	vvEE	×	VVee	P_1
F_1		Vv Ee		F_1
	♂ VvEe	×	vvee ♀	Back-cross FR_1
	VE Ve vE ve		ve	Gametes
VvEe long-winged grey 25 per cent.	Vvee long-winged ebony 25 per cent.	vvEe vestigial grey 25 per cent.	vvee vestigial ebony 25 per cent.	FR_2

Such a ratio in FR_2 is regarded as evidence that the genes for the characters concerned are resident in different chromosomes.

The members of another large group of characters exhibit linkage relations with each other and with *pink eye-colour* and the genes for these are placed upon the chromosome III, the top left-hand pair of large curved autosomes of the conventional diagram. For example, a pink-eyed grey is mated to a red-eyed ebony and the F_1 consists solely of red-eyed greys and when these are interbred the F_2 consists of pink-eyed greys, red-eyed greys, and red-eyed ebonies in the proportion of 1 : 2 : 1, but no double recessive, pink ebony, appears.

The fourth group is small, consisting as yet of some five characters only and their genes are placed on chromosome IV because they are not sex-linked and show no linkage with members of either the second and third groups.

To place any new character in its proper linkage-group the following procedure may be adopted. Pink-eyed black-bodied flies are crossed with the new mutant: black is in the second group, pink in the third, and if the new character belongs to either of these it will fail to show the corresponding double recessive forms in F_2. If it is sex-linked this is clearly demonstrated from its sex relations; and if it does not belong to groups I, II, and III, by exclusion it must belong to group IV.

Suppose, for example, that "blistered wings" was a new mutant character. A normal-winged, black-bodied, pink-eyed fly would be mated to this blistered-winged, grey-bodied, red-eyed novelty. The F_1 flies would be wild type—normal-winged, grey-bodied, red-eyed; these then would be interbred when no blistered black but blistered pink flies would appear. The mutant character "blistered" would therefore be placed in group II.

Let b=	gene for	black body colour.	B=	that for its	normal allelomorph grey body-colour.
p=	,,	pink eye.	P=	,,	normal allelomorph red-eye.
bs=	,,	blistered wing.	Bs=	,,	normal allelomorph normal wing.

(Bsb)(Bsb) pp × (bsB)(bsB) PP P_1
normal black pink | blistered grey red
(Bsb) p | (bsB) P
(Bsb)(bsB) Pp F_1

	(Bsb) P	(Bsb) p	(bsB) P	(bsB) p
(Bsb) P	(Bsb)(Bsb) PP normal black-red	(Bsb)(Bsb) Pp normal black-red	(Bsb)(bsB) PP normal grey-red	(Bsb)(bsB) Pp normal grey-red
(Bsb) p	(Bsb)(Bsb) Pp normal black-red	(Bsb)(Bsb) pp normal black-pink	(Bsb)(bsB) Pp normal grey-red	(Bsb)(bsB) pp normal grey-pink
(bsB) P	(Bsb)(bsB) PP normal grey-red	(Bsb)(bsB) Pp normal grey-red	(bsB)(bsB) PP blistered grey-red	(bsB)(bsB) Pp blistered grey-red
(bsB) p	(Bsb)(bsB) Pp normal grey-red	(BsB)(bsB) pp normal grey-pink	(bsB)(bsB) Pp blistered grey-red	(bsB)(bsB) pp blistered grey-pink

No blistered blacks, but blistered pinks; no suggestion of sex-linkage; blistered, therefore, is placed in group II.

This method has now been replaced by another. It is accepted that a non-sex-linked recessive mutant character gives a 2:1:1:0 ratio in F_2 with any other recessive of the group to which it belongs, and a 9:3:3:1 ratio with any character in any other group. But the more satisfactory method of testing for linkage is to mate the new recessive mutant to a Star Dichaete. These characters are dominants; Star is in the second group, Dichaete in the third. The F_1 Star Dichaete males from the mating are then back-crossed to a female exhibiting the new recessive mutation (or to an F_1 female heterozygous for the character). Among their offspring if the mutant character belongs to group II none of the individuals which exhibit the character Star will possess the new recessive, but of those which exhibit the character Dichaete 50 per cent. (or 25 per cent.) will do so. If the new character belongs to group III, then none of the Dichaete individuals will exhibit the new character, whereas 50 per cent. (or 25 per cent.) of those that are Star will. Suppose ebony is the new recessive character, the mating is an ebony to a Star Dichaete. Ebony shows linkage with the latter: it is placed in group III.

ss (ed)(ed) × SS (ED)(ED)

Ss (ed)(ED) × ss (ed)(ed)

Gametes			Offspring	
S (ed)	× s (ed) =		Ss (ed)(ed)	Star ebony
s (ed)			ss (ed)(ed)	ebony
S (ED)			Ss (ed)(ED)	Star Dichaete
s (ED)			ss (ed)(ED)	Dichaete

50 per cent. of the Stars are ebony.

Or, using the heterozygous ebony female—

Gametes			Offspring	
S (ed), s (ed), S (ED), s (ED)	×	s (Ed), s (ed)	Ss (ed)(ED)	Star Dichaete
			ss (ed)(ED)	Dichaete
			Ss (ED)(Ed)	Star Dichaete
			ss (ED)(Ed)	Dichaete
			Ss (ed)(ed)	Star ebony
			ss (ed)(ed)	ebony
			Ss (ED)(ed)	Star Dichaete
			ss (ED)(ed)	Dichaete

25 per cent. of the Stars are ebony.

The phenomenon of linkage was first observed by Bateson and Punnett, and to explain the results which were observed in their Sweet Peas and Primula work a theory of *Coupling and Repulsion* was developed. This is known as the *Reduplication Hypothesis* and was formulated before the greater part of the Drosophila work had been performed. It does not assume that the factors are borne upon the chromosomes, as is postulated by the Chromosome Theory of Heredity, nor that segregation occurs at the maturation phase of gametogenesis. This theory cannot provide interpretations for many of the results of the later Drosophila work, whereas the Chromosome Theory of Heredity can be applied to the cases previously explained by the Reduplication Hypothesis. But the theory advanced by Bateson and Punnett constitutes a historic milestone in the advance of genetical science, for it was the foundation upon which the Chromosome Theory has been built. The Chromosome Theory is capable of general application, and though it is clear that the Chromosome Theory is borne almost entirely by Drosophila, yet the evidence derived from the results of this work is such that it is unlikely that the theory is far from the truth. It may have to be re-expressed in terms more physiological, it is probable that it will be, but not only is it a magnificent and inspiring working hypothesis, but it rests on very sure foundation.

C. *Each Gene has its own particular Locus upon a particular Chromosome.*

It will be remembered that white-eye colour is a typical sex-linked character; yellow body-colour is another, and both characters are recessive to their normal allelomorphs—red-eye and grey body-colour. If a *female* of a yellow-bodied white-eyed strain, (ywX)(ywX), is mated to a wild-type *male* with grey body-colour and red eyes, (YWX)(Y), all the females of F_1 are like their father and the males like their mother—criss-cross inheritance. If a *female* of the F_1, having the constitution (YWX)(ywX), is mated to a *male* exhibiting the two recessive characters (ywX) Y (and since her brothers have this constitution, the F_1 individuals in this particular case may be interbred), the offspring produced will fall into four groups in the following ratio:—

Grey-reds	Yellow-whites	Grey-whites	Yellow-reds
49·25 per cent.	49·25 per cent.	0·75 per cent.	0·75 per cent.

It is seen that 98·5 per cent. of the offspring show the normal linkage relation between the eye and the body-colour, while in the case of the remaining 1·5 per cent. this linkage is broken down—the white-eye of the yellow-white strain has *crossed over* to the greys, and in exchange the red-eye of the grey-reds has *crossed over* to the yellows. The double-recessive white-yellow male parent produced two kinds of sperms, (ywX) and Y. Therefore the resulting ratio can only be explained on the assumption that the female produced four kinds of eggs in the proportions equal to those of the four groups of offspring—

(YWX)	(ywX)	(YwX)	(yWX)
49·25 per cent.	49·25 per cent.	0·75 per cent.	0·75 per cent.

The suggestion is that in a certain percentage of cases (1·5 per cent.) there occurs *an exchange of chromatin and therefore of genes between the X-chromosomes* during the maturation of the ovum, so that the gene Y becomes associated with w, and y with W. (This Y, the gene for not-yellow, must not be confused with the Y-chromosome of the male.)

The progeny resulting from the union of these ova and sperms will be as follows—

♀ (YWX)(ywX)	: (YWX)(Y) ♂	Grey-red	Non-Cross-overs
♀ (ywX)(ywX)	: (ywX)(Y) ♂	Yellow-white	
♀ (YwX)(ywX)	: (YwX)(Y) ♂	Grey-white	Cross-overs
♀ (yWX)(ywX)	: (yWX)(Y) ♂	Yellow-red	

As the sperms carry the genes for the recessive characters (the X-bearing), or else no gene at all (the Y-bearing), the characters of the zygote in such a case as this are really decided by the genetic constitution of the egg, and the kinds of eggs and their percentages determine the groups of individuals and their proportion in the FR_2 generation—

P_1	Yellow-white ♀	(ywX)(ywX)	×	(YWX)(Y)	Grey-red ♂
F_1	Grey-red ♀	(ywX)(YWX)	×	(ywX)(Y)	Yellow-white ♂
FR_1	Grey-red ♀	(ywX)(YWX)	×	(ywX)(Y)	Yellow-white ♂ (double recessive)

Gametes (ywX) (YWX) (yWX) (YwX) : (ywX) (Y)

49·25% 49·25% 0·75% 0·75%

98·5 Non-cross-over gametes — 1·5 Cross-over gametes

FR_2 ♀ (ywX)(ywX) : ♂ (ywX)(Y) — 49·25 per cent. Yellow-white
♀ (YWX)(ywX) : ♂ (YWX)(Y) — 49·25 per cent. Grey-red

98·5 per cent. Non-cross-overs.

♀ (yWX)(ywX) : ♂ (yWX)(Y) — 0·75 per cent. Yellow-red
♀ (YwX)(ywX) : ♂ (YwX)(Y) — 0·75 per cent. Grey-white

1·5 per cent. Cross-overs or Re-combination classes.

If the genes enter in the reverse combinations, the classes of cross-overs are different but *the percentages are the same.* For example, a grey-white female is mated to a yellow-red male. The offspring are grey-white males and grey-red females. A female is then mated to a double recessive yellow-white male. The FR_2 generation consists of four groups—

Grey-white	Yellow-red	Grey-red	Yellow-white
49·25 per cent.	49·25 per cent.	0·75 per cent.	0·75 per cent.

The double recessive male, yellow-white, has the constitution (ywX)(Y) and produces two kinds of sperms (ywX), and (Y). The results in the FR_2 generation can be explained on the assumption that in 1·5 per cent. of cases during the maturation of the ova there occurred an exchange of the genes, so that w became associated with y, instead of Y, and W with Y instead of y. The F_1 female then must produce four sorts of eggs in definite proportions—

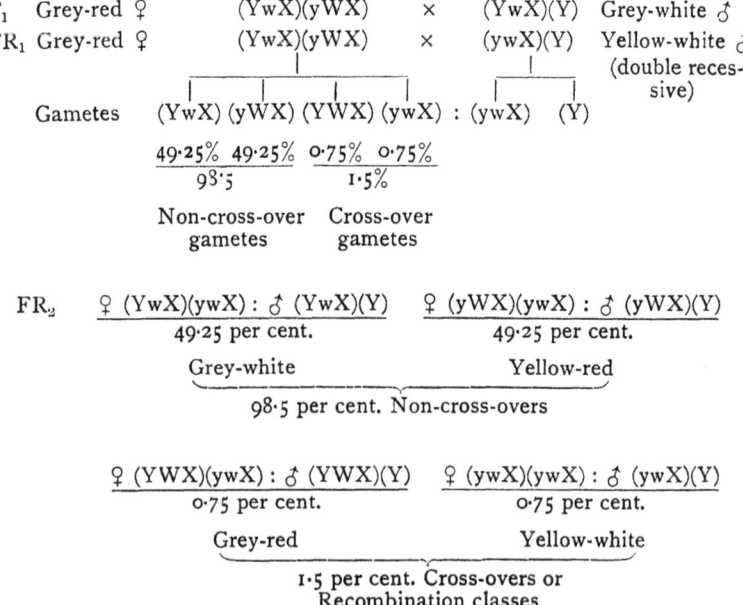

	Grey-white ♀	(YwX)(YwX)	×	(yWX)(Y)	Yellow-red ♂
F_1	Grey-red ♀	(YwX)(yWX)	×	(YwX)(Y)	Grey-white ♂
FR_1	Grey-red ♀	(YwX)(yWX)	×	(ywX)(Y)	Yellow-white ♂ (double recessive)

Gametes (YwX) (yWX) (YWX) (ywX) : (ywX) (Y)

49·25% 49·25% | 0·75% 0·75%
98·5 | 1·5%

Non-cross-over gametes | Cross-over gametes

FR_2 ♀ (YwX)(ywX) : ♂ (YwX)(Y) — 49·25 per cent. — Grey-white
♀ (yWX)(ywX) : ♂ (yWX)(Y) — 49·25 per cent. — Yellow-red

98·5 per cent. Non-cross-overs

♀ (YWX)(ywX) : ♂ (YWX)(Y) — 0·75 per cent. — Grey-red
♀ (ywX)(ywX) : ♂ (ywX)(Y) — 0·75 per cent. — Yellow-white

1·5 per cent. Cross-overs or Recombination classes

Genes borne by the same chromosome tend to hold together. They do not hold together because of any innate relation between them: they tend to preserve whatever combinations they have. Some 100 other characters of the first group have been studied in this way and for each pair there is found to be a characteristic mean cross-over value (C.O.V.) The C.O.V. between the same loci varies however. For example, in the case of the second chromosome Bridges and Morgan (1919) found that the percentage of crossing-over between purple and vestigial ranged from 7·8 and 17·8; that between purple and speck from 39·5 to 54·1; that between streak and curved from 36·2 to 49·4; that between black and purple from 4·9 to 10·0. In the case of the first chromosome, Detlefsen and Roberts (1918) found that in the offspring of 62 unselected pairs of Drosophila a range of from 10 to about 40 per cent. in C.O.V. between loci, the average for which had been defined as 32·8. Gowen (1919), testing for crossing-over in the third group, came to the conclusion that this phenomenon is one of the most variable.

Crossing-over may not take place at all; and in such cases linkage is said to be complete; or it may be less than 1 per cent. when linkage is strong. It may take place in about 50 per cent. of the individuals in an FR_2 and then the results would be indistinguishable from a case in which there is free assortment and in which the pairs of genes are borne by different chromosomes. But there is a characteristic percentage of crossing-over for each two genes resident upon one and the same chromosome under the same experimental conditions. The method used in such a case is to test the characters against others; if each is linked with a third then they are linked with each other; also if sufficiently large and accurate numbers are raised the actual situation will be recognised.

So far no mechanism by which this dissociation of linked characters and recombination in a certain percentage of cases could be effected has been discussed. As an explanation it is satisfactory as far as it goes, but since the phenomenon obviously demands an interchange of chromatin material by the members of a pair of homologous chromosomes it is necessary to inquire whether there is any cytological basis for this suggestion. It is a fact that, in certain cases, it has been actually demonstrated that in certain phases of cell-activity the members of each pair of homologous chromosomes approach each other and become intertwined —conjugate—and then separate again. The idea, that in synapsis homologous chromosomes twist about each other and in separating tend to break at places where they adhere and that in separating and recombining there occurs an exchange of chromatin material, was developed by Janssens (1909) and has been seized upon by Morgan and applied to the interpretation of the results of crossing-over. Actual

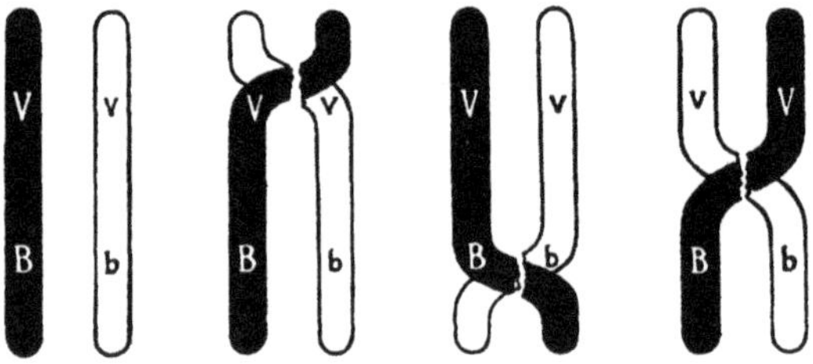

FIG. 31.—The Mechanism of Crossing-over. (*After* Muller.)

The relations of B and V, of b and v are only disturbed by crossing-over at points between them.

exchange of material has not been identified, but the conjugation of the chromosomes affords an opportunity for such interchange which would provide a suitable mechanism by which crossing-over could be effected.

For example, the case of crossing-over in black vestigial × grey long-winged experiment may be considered. One member of the second pair of chromosomes was received from the mother, the other from the father, and the constitution of an F_1 female with respect to the two characters concerned is (BV)(bv). The offspring of her mating with a double recessive (bv)(bv) male fall into four classes. Two of these correspond to the combinations received by the F_1 female from her parents; the two others are such as would be expected if interchange of chromatin material had taken place involving portions of the chromosome which bears one pair of the genes—vestigial and long-winged, or black and grey. The percentage (17 per cent.) indicates that the chances are about 5 : 1 that the combination that goes in together will remain linked.

As to why there is no crossing-over in the male Drosophila no explanation has as yet been found. It might be difficult for an X- and a Y-chromosome to intertwine and exchange chromatin material on account of their difference in shape. But the autosomes are alike in both sexes and there is no appreciable morphological bar to crossing-over in the male. Yet in the case of the male no crossing-over involving factors lying in the second and third groups has been encountered and it may be accepted as a working hypothesis that in Drosophila none occurs.

The reader should take care at this stage of the argument to see that he visualises clearly all that is involved in this conception of crossing-over. It is usual to speak of the cross-over percentage between black and vestigial, for example. But the process involves two chromosomes and four genes. On one member of the second pair of chromosomes are located, each in its own particular locus, the genes b and v; on the other member of the pair of chromosomes the genes B and V are located, B in a position exactly equivalent to that occupied by b in the other chromosome, V in a position exactly equivalent to that of v. Crossing-over involves the disruption of the relative positions of both pairs of genes, of the BV association and of the bv. A break in the continuity of the BV chromosome demands a break at an exactly corresponding point on the other chromosome of this homologous pair.

Sturtevant (1915) has identified definite genes on chromosomes II and III in Drosophila which alter the percentage of crossing-over in the different regions of the chromosome. A map of the chromosomes constructed from the results of crossing-over when these genes are present gives different distances between the genes but the order of the genes is unchanged. (See page 116.)

Muller (1916) found one such gene in chromosome III,

which when present in the simplex state decreased and in the duplex state increased the C.O.V. between loci in this chromosome. Moreover this gene exerted its maximum effects close to the locus in which it was situated, the effects diminishing with distance.

It has already been stated that the C.O.V. is very variable. Detlefsen and Roberts (1918) were able by selection through some ten to twenty generations of Drosophila to reduce the C.O.V. of the loci with which they were dealing from over 27·0 to 0·6 per cent. in one experiment, to about 6·0 per cent. in another, the stock breeding true to the new values. Whereas selection can reduce the C.O.V. to practically nothing, it cannot, in the other direction, raise it markedly owing to the complicating effect of double crossing-over.

Bridges (1915) has found that the percentage of crossing-over is increased with sub- and super-optimum temperature and diminished with age, and it is likely therefore that environmental circumstances may also affect the process. Plough (1921) has shown that only the middle portions of II and III chromosomes are affected in their crossing-over properties by temperature and age.

It should be recognised that the evidence as to crossing-over derived from an immense amount of data collected from breeding experiments with Drosophila is not as yet corroborated by any cytological demonstration of actual exchange of chromatin material between homologous chromosomes. But the experimental breeder awaits cytological confirmation with a quiet confidence.

The Mapping of the Chromosomes.—If the twisting of the members of the pairs of homologous chromosomes is taken as evidence of the phenomenon of crossing-over and if the genes are strung, as it were, like beads upon a string, each gene having its own proper locus upon a particular chromosome, then it follows that the percentage of crossing-over between any two loci may be taken as an indication of the distance between them. If the chromosomes are as likely to break, stick, and rejoin at one point as at any other along their length, then it follows that the further apart two genes lie in the chromosome the greater is the chance of crossing-over occurring, and conversely, the nearer together genes for different characters lie the smaller is the chance of crossing-over between them. Granting this, there lies here the possibility of constructing a diagrammatic map of the chromosomes showing the relative positions of the different genes borne by each chromosome. For example, if the genes A, B, and C form a linear series and if the gene B lies between A and C, then the crossing-over percentage between A and B should equal the sum of the crossing-over values for A and B and B and C. Using the crossing-over values as the basis for comparing the proximity of the genes *inter se*, it is possible to construct a map of the chromosomes from which predictable inferences can be drawn and verified The conception of the localisation of the genes in linear alignment is due to the peculiar differences between the percentage of crossing-over between genes of the same linkage group. The relation of three or more points to each other is a relation of linear order and cannot be represented in space in any other manner than by a series of points arranged in a line.

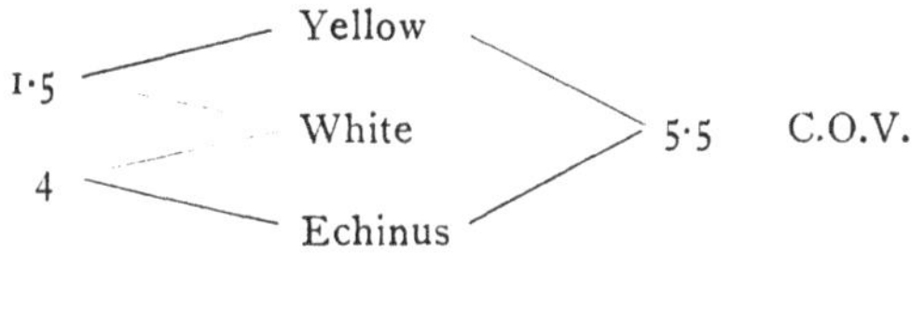

First, the linkage group of a character is determined and then cross-over experiments are carried out in order to place the gene in its own particular locus. For example, in the first linkage group, yellow body-colour and white eye-colour give a cross-over value of 1·5 per cent. Another eye character, echinus, gives 5·5 per cent. of crossing-over with yellow. The first chromosome can be represented by a straight line divided into units—cms., inches, or of whatever size is regarded as convenient.

Morgan has taken 1 per cent. crossing-over as the unit for expressing linkage relations. Expressed in such units —commonly known as morgans—the first chromosome has a length of 70, the second 107, the third 106, the fourth 1 respectively, and these figures correspond fairly well to the known relative sizes of the chromosomes when compared with each other in metaphase plates. In order to locate echinus in the first chromosome, a horizontal stroke is made cutting the line which represents the chromosome — this stroke marks the locus of yellow at 0·0 (zero); another horizontal mark, 1·5 units distant from the yellow, indicates the locus of white. The situation of echinus cannot be determined until the cross-over percentage with white is found, for otherwise it is not known whether echinus lies "North" or "South" of yellow. It is found that cross-over percentage with white is 4. Thus, echinus is 4 morgans distant from white and 5·5 units distant from yellow, *i.e.*, it lies on the same side of yellow as does white.

Another sex-linked character, ruby-eye colour, gives 7·5 per cent. of recombination classes with yellow. If it lies to the "North" or left of yellow then with white it should give 9·0 per cent. of cross-overs, if to the "South" or right then 6 per cent. Breeding experiments show the latter figure to be the true one and the gene for ruby can be marked on the map. Theoretically, echinus should give 2 per cent. of crossing-over with ruby and 4 per cent. with white—it is possible to predict these results. This relation of the genes one to another is as that of points in a line and so force is given to the conception that the chromosomes are to be regarded as linear arrangements of genes.

When the loci of a number of genes in a given group have been plotted accurately, with a new gene it is only necessary to determine the linkage relation with any two of the already plotted genes in order to determine its locus and to be able to predict its linkage value with any other members of the group.

In further explanation, the table on page 118 giving some of the characters in group III may be consulted.

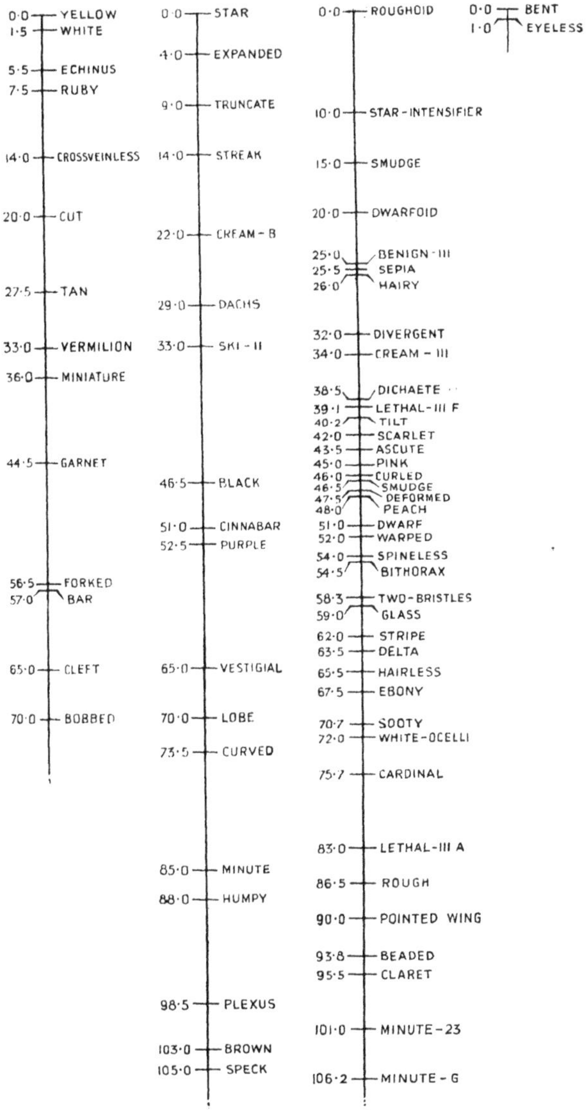

FIG. 32.—The Chromosome Map of *Drosophila melanogaster*. (*After* Morgan and Bridges.)

Character.	Symbol.	Locus.	Effects mainly
Roughoid . . .	ru	0·0	Eye-texture.
Star-intensifier . .	s-i	10·0	Star-eye.
Smudge . . .	sm	15·0	Eye-texture.
Benign III . .	be III	25·0	Tumour-growth.
Sepia . . .	se	26·0	Eye-colour.
Hairy . . .	h	26·0	Extra hairs.
Divergent . .	dv	32·0	Wing-posture.
Cream III . .	cr III	34·0	Eye-colour.
Dichaete . . .	D	38·5	Wing-bristles.
Lethal IIIf . .	l IIIf	39·1	Life.
Tilt	tt	40·2	Wing-posture.
Scarlet . . .	st	42·0	Eye-colour.
Ascute . . .	as	43·5	Scutellum.
Pink	p	45·0	Eye-colour.
Curled . . .	cu	46·0	Wing-curvature.
Smudge . . .	sm	46·5	Eye-texture.
Deformed . . .	Df	47·5	Eye-shape.
Peach . . .	p^p	48·0	Eye-colour.
Dwarf . . .	dw	51·0	Body-size.
Warped . . .	wp	52·0	Wing.
Spineless . . .	ss	54·0	Bristle-size.
Bithorax . . .	bx	54·5	Thorax segmentation.
Two-bristles . .	2b	58·3	Bristle-number.
Glass . . .	gl	59·0	Eye-colour and texture.
Stripe . .	sr	62·0	Thorax pattern.
Delta . . .	Δ	63·5	Venation.
Hairless . . .	H	65·5	Bristles.
Ebony . . .	e	67·5	Body-colour.
Sooty . . .	e^s	70·7	" "
White ocelli . .	wp	72·0	Ocellar-colour.
Cardinal . . .	cd	75·7	Eye-colour.
Lethal IIIa . .	l IIIa	83·0	Life.
Rough . . .	rp	86·5	Eye-texture.
Pointed wing . .	Pw	90·0	Venation.
Beaded . . .	Bd	93·8	Wing-margin.
Claret . . .	ca	95·5	Eye-colour.
Minute f . . .	Mf	105·0	Bristle-size.
Minute g . . .	Mg	106·2	" "

In describing a fly with more than one mutant character, if all these characters belong to one and the same group then they are mentioned in the order of their position in relation to the North end (0·0) of the chromosome—so, roughoid, hairy, bithorax; if the characters belong to different groups those of group I precede those of group II, and so on.

A mutant character may be based on more than one gene and in this case all the genes concerned are given the same name, but Roman numerals are employed to distinguish them—so, olive, olive (II), olive (III).

In the case of two distinct mutant characters which are indistinguishable (mimics) their genes are distinguished by the addition of letters — so, safranin (chromosome III); safranin b (chromosome II).

A glance at the map of the chromosomes of *Drosophila melanogaster* shows that some genes are located over 100 units of distance apart. The cross-over percentage between such has been obtained by the estimation of the cross-over percentage between each of these with several others lying between them. It is of importance to note that until each chromosome is more or less completely mapped, it is possible to get a number of linked characters in excess of the number of chromosome pairs.

For example, the characters corresponding to the genes A and B show linkage as do those corresponding to C and D, but until the genes E and F have been located A and B would appear to segregate independently of C and D, and not until the interrelation of A, B, E, F, C, D had been demonstrated would the fact that all these genes are resident upon one and the same chromosome, *i.e.*, that all the corresponding characters are included in one and the same linkage group, be recognised.

Fig. 33.

If sticking, tearing, and reunion is possible at one point, it can happen at two or more and a double cross-over at two levels in the same linked series at the same time, until recognised as such would seem to contradict the conclusion that the factors are arranged in a linear series. But by marking intermediate points between the extreme ones all double cross-overs can be recognised and the distance corrected for them.

The hypothesis of linear arrangement of the genes has received considerable support from what Morgan had called a three-point experiment, *i.e.*, one involving three different loci in one and the same chromosome. For example, white has its locus at 1·0, miniature (wing-form) at 36·0, and Bar (eye pattern) at 57·0 on chromosome I. Actual data show that white and miniature give 33·2 per cent. of cross-overs, and miniature and Bar 20·5 per cent.; 33·2 + 20·5 per cent. = 53·7 per cent., and, therefore, theoretically, the percentage of crossing-over between white and Bar should equal 53·7, whereas in reality it is 43·6 per cent., *i.e.*, 10·1 per cent. short of the calculated value.

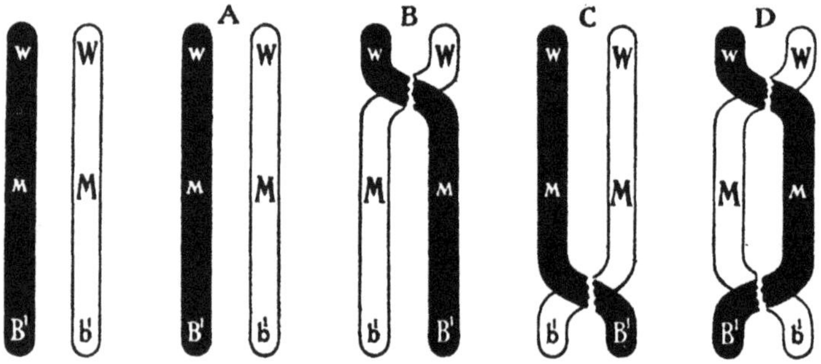

FIG. 34.—A Three-point Experiment. (*After* Morgan.)

A female heterozygous for these three characters has the constitution (wmBX)(WMbX) and lays eggs of the following sorts—

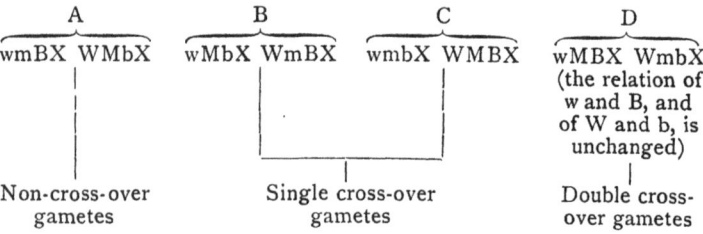

A	B	C	D
wmBX WMbX	wMbX WmBX	wmbX WMBX	wMBX WmbX (the relation of w and B, and of W and b, is unchanged)
Non-cross-over gametes	Single cross-over gametes		Double cross-over gametes

It is the double crossing-over that accounts for the low percentage of crossing-over between white and Bar as compared with the sum of the crossing-over values given by white and miniature, and miniature and Bar. Experimental results when analysed indicate that in the instance of white—miniature—Bar double crossing-over occurs in 10·1 per cent. of cases. Since double crossing-over of this type

(D) does not involve a rearrangement of the loci W and b, the actual crossing-over between white and Bar obtained by experiment will fall short of the calculated value 53·7 per cent. by 10·1 per cent. and will equal 43·6 per cent. In Drosophila it seems that the occurrence of multiple crossing-over prevents a C.O.V. of much more than 50.

Breeding experiments have demonstrated that though theoretically crossing-over might affect isolated genes here and there along the chromosome, actually it usually takes the form of exchange of large corresponding sections of the chromosomes. Muller (1916) made up a stock in which the females carried twelve sex-linked characters: from one parent they received the genes for yellow body-colour (y), white eye-colour (w), Abnormal abdomen (A), bifid wings (bi), vermilion eye-colour (v), miniature wings (m), sable body-colour (s), rudimentary wings (r), forked spines (f), and from the other parent the genes for the normal allelomorphs of all these characters (normal abdomen, a; not-bifid, Bi; not-miniature, M; not-sable, S, etc.) and also the factors for cherry eye-colour (w^c), club wings (cl), and Bar eye (B). Their constitution, therefore, was as follows:—

(ywAbiClvmsrfbX)(Yw^caBiclVMSRFBX).

Crossing-over in 712 individuals was found to be as follows:—

Non-cross-over		386
Single cross-over:—		
yellow and white	7	
white and Abnormal	8	
Abnormal and bifid	15	
bifid and club	44	
club and vermilion	97	
vermilion and miniature	16	
miniature and sable	37	
sable and rudimentary	66	
rudimentary and forked	5	
forked and Bar	1	
	—	296

Double cross-over:—

Y — W	Cl — V	1
Y — W	M — S	1
Y — W	S — R	2
Y — W	R — F	1
W — A	Cl — V	1
W — A	R — F	1
A — Bi	Cl — V	1
A — Bi	S — R	1
Bi — Cl	M — S	2
Bi — Cl	S — R	7
Cl — V	V — M	1
Cl — V	S — R	8
Cl — V	R — F	2
Cl — V	F — B	1
		30

There was no crossing-over in 54·4 per cent. of cases, single crossing-over in 41·7 per cent., and double crossing-over in 4·2 per cent. No example of triple crossing-over was observed. The values agree satisfactorily with those calculated from the three-point experiments involving the genes W, M, and B in this chromosome. The occurrence of double cross-overs supplies considerable evidence of the section as opposed to the single-factor exchange.

Interference is a consequence of the sectional mode of interchange of chromatic material between homologous chromosomes. The term is used to designate the observed fact that when crossing-over occurs at any given point along the chromosome, the regions on either side of the point are protected from coincident crossing-over, since there can be no close twisting or possibility of breaking near by the first point. The phenomenon of interference provides additional force to the conception of the linear arrangement of the genes. Interference decreases with increase of distance.

The theory that the chromosomes constitute the material basis of inheritance, has received strong support from the study of certain unusual genetical phenomena.

The chromosome mechanism is sufficient to explain the processes of segregation and recombination, but in order to demonstrate that there is a *specific* relation between chromosome and character it is necessary almost to extirpate a chromosome and obtain, as a consequence, an absence of the character, the gene for which is resident upon that chromosome. This operation has not yet been performed by an experimental biologist, but Drosophila with a single IV chromosome or containing three instead of two have been identified by Bridges (1921). A fly with but a single IV is a small pale individual which has a dark trident, small slender bristles and which hatches late. The wings are blunt and but slightly spread and the eyes are large and rounded. Such a strain is known as "Diminished Bristles." Such a female will produce two kinds of mature eggs; those with and those without the IV chromosome. The eggs with the single IV is normal, but the one without, if fertilised by a sperm carrying a gene for a recessive character on the IV results in an individual which will exhibit this recessive character of the father. A male with but one IV chromosome produces two kinds of sperm, one with a IV and one without. Mated to a normal ♀ the results will be equivalent to those above. A male and a female each possessing only one IV when mated might be expected to produce some offspring (25 per cent.) without a IV. None such appear, however, and ratios show that they die.

"Diminished" ♂ is mated to "Eyeless" ♀♀—the gene for eyeless is resident on the IV chromosome and the character is recessive. The male produces two kinds of sperm—those with a IV and those without. All the eggs contain a IV and upon it is resident the gene for the character eyeless. Two kinds of offspring result—"diminished" with but one IV chromosome, and since these received that from the eyeless mother, these flies will exhibit the recessive character; whilst the others will be normal-looking flies though heterozygous for the eyeless character. It is seen that when "diminished" is mated to a stock exhibiting a recessive character, the gene for which is resident upon the IV, the recessive character behaves as though it were a dominant.

Individuals with three IV chromosomes were also discovered by Bridges and are dark with a faint trident, long bristles, small smooth eyes and long narrow wings.

Such a triploid IV individual produces two sorts of gametes, those with two IV's and those with one, and when, for example, such a triplex individual is mated to an eyeless, half the offspring will be triploid IV's, and when two such are interbred to produce an F_2, the ratio will not be 3 : 1. As a matter of fact, it is something like 26 : 1 which is the expectation for such a chromosome situation. In back-crosses the F_1 flies give a 5 : 1 and not a 1 : 1 ratio.

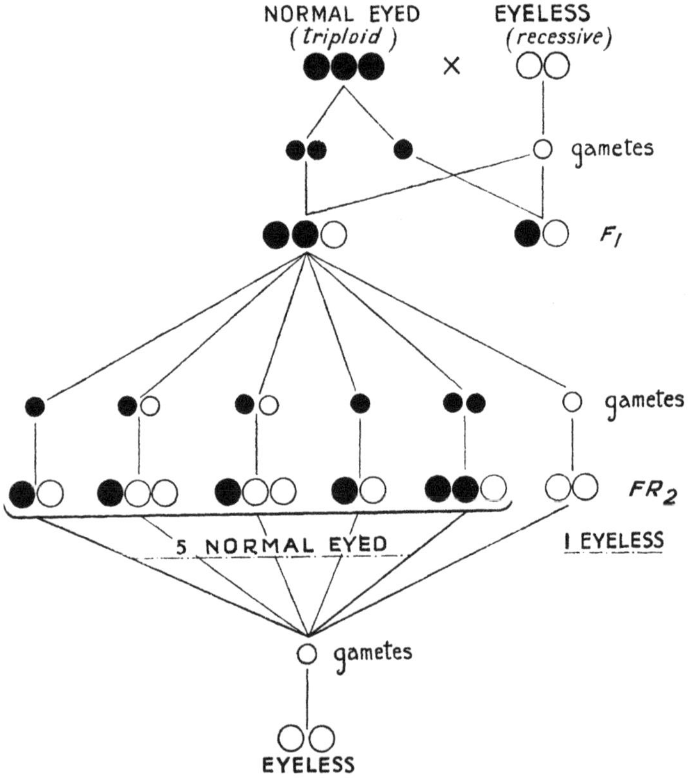

FIG. 35.—Back-cross of Triploid IV. (*After* Morgan.)

New phenotypes and genotypes in Drosophila can result from alterations involving a single locus in a chromosome; a whole chromosome, as is seen in chromosome elimination or duplication, or the whole chromosome group as is seen in cases of triploidy; and from a mutation that involves a section of a particular chromosome as is seen from the work of Bridges (1917) and of Mohr, in which it is shown that the loss or inactivation of an entire definite measurable section results in a definite modification in characterisation. The Y-chromosome of the male may be structurally perfect but physiologically inactive in Drosophila—an instance of inactivation deficiency. As a result of sectional inactivation of a chromosome, lethal effects, suppression of crossing-over and false dominance of included recessive genes are seen in breeding experiments.

Mohr (1923) has investigated the case of a new mutation, called Notch 8, in the X-chromosome which affects not a locus but a definite and measurable section of the chromosome near the left (North) end which includes the loci of white (recessive) facet (recessive) and Abnormal Abdomen (partially dominant). These loci are situated 1·5, 2·7 and ± 4·5 units of distance from yellow. He found that in the heterozygous female white and facet, in spite of the fact that they are recessives, were exhibited, and concluded that the section of the other X-chromosome from non-white to non-facet had, as a result of a mutation, become inactivated, and lost the normal action of the contained genetical materials. The loci in other parts of the X-chromosome were unaffected and only this length of about 4·7 units was involved. The framework of the chromosome is affected as well as the genes, for crossing-over is entirely suppressed within the abnormal section. Mohr made the interesting observation that the genes in that section of the other X-chromosome, which in its mate was physiologically inactive, are exaggerated in their effect.

In explanation of sectional deficiency two possibilities present themselves, (1) a simultaneous mutation involving a series of adjacent loci or (2) a physical loss or complete physiological inactivation of a section. The latter is regarded as being the more reasonable. These cases provide strong evidence for the correctness of the theory of the linear order of the genes and of the reality of the chromosome maps.

Evidence from a different source provides not only proof of the rôle of the chromosomes in inheritance but also demonstrates very clearly the continuity of the chromosomes through successive cell generations. Different genera of sea-urchin have been hybridised by Herbst (1909), Baltzer (1910), and others. When the eggs of Sphærechinus were fertilised with sperms of Strongylocentrotus, the free-swimming larvæ or plutei inherited both paternal and maternal characters; when the reciprocal cross was made the plutei displayed the characters almost exclusively of the mother. On cytological examination Baltzer found that in the latter case a curious anomaly occurs in the first few segmentation divisions for most of the chromosomes contributed by the sperm were thrown off the spindle and left behind when the daughter-nuclei reformed, so that the purely maternal type of inheritance as contrasted with the bi-parental type in the first cross is associated with the elimination of the chromosomes contributed by the father.

Federley (1913), working on the "chocolate tip" moth Pygæra, found that the chromosomes of certain species of this genus differ both in size and number, and that when crosses are made the hybrids display an abnormal number which can be identified as paternal or maternal in origin. The haploid number in *P. curtula* is 29, in *P. anachoreta* 30. The spermatogonia of the hybrid have 59, but in the spermatocytes very few chromosomes pair; they divide equationally in both divisions with the result that the mature gametes contain (about) 59. If the F_1 is back-crossed to the parental anachoreta, the spermatogonia of the offspring possess (nearly) 89 chromosomes. In its spermatocytes the two sets of anachoreta chromosomes pair so that on the spindle of the first spermatocytes there are about 30 (bivalent) anachoreta chromosomes and about 29 curtula. The mature gamete will therefore contain nearly 59 chromosomes as did those of the F_1.

Corresponding with these cytological facts Federley found that the F_1 individuals exhibited both curtula and anachoreta characters, and that in the back-crosses there was no character segregation, the individuals having the same characterisation as the F_1. Since all the gametes of the back-crosses contain both curtula and anachoreta chromosomes, it would be expected that no segregation of characters would occur if the factors for these characters are borne on the chromosomes. Analogous conclusions were derived by Doncaster and Harrison (1914) from their study of other moth hybrids.

CHAPTER V

THE NATURE OF THE GENE AND THE EXPRESSION OF GENETIC ACTION

As yet no one knows exactly what a "gene" is. The factor in the germ-plasm, the gene in the chromosome, is recognised by its effects during the development of the individual; the character is the end-product of a long chain of developmental stages involving interaction between the cells and their external environment, the outer world, and their internal environment, the products of activity of other cells, including the internal secretions or hormones, which recent work has shown to play so important a rôle in co-ordinating the sequence of ontogenetic events. The absence of an essential ingredient in the external environment will profoundly modify the character of the individual, hence genetic experiment must always be conducted under standardised external conditions, while the part played by the "internal environment" illustrates how the absence of one gene may profoundly affect the manifestation of another. Thus the Mexican Salamander, a geographical race of *Amblystoma tigrinum*, is characterised by a hereditary endocrine deficiency which prevents the adult characters from appearing, though the potency of thyroid extract to induce metamorphosis shows that the Axolotl actually possesses the hereditary antecedents of the anatomical figuration characteristic of the adults of related races of the same species. The expression of the action of a gene is influenced by the remainder of the genotype.

Lethal Effects.—In Drosophila there is a gene "eyeless" situated in the fourth linkage group, which produces a condition of rudimentary eyes or even their complete absence. However, a fly without eyes can live. But if there is a gene which in its expression produces a non-functional condition of a vital organ then such individuals cannot live.

Yellow mice produce smaller litters than mice of other colours and on the average in these litters there are 2 yellows to 1 grey. Yellow mice will not breed true but always throw a proportion of grey offspring. The ratio 2:1 suggests that there is another 1 missing —the homozygous yellow, and that the ratio actually is 1 homozygous yellow, 2 heterozygous yellows, 1 grey, though for some reason the homozygous yellow is never seen. If a pregnant yellow mouse is dissected, early degenerate embryos will be found in addition to those which are normally developing. It can be accepted that the degenerate zygotes are the homozygous yellow individuals, and that linked with each gene for yellow is a *lethal factor* which in its expression produces a non-viable embryo probably because some vital organ or tissue therein is either profoundly imperfect or absent. Death occurs at too early a stage of development for the condition to be identified.

F_1	(YL)G	×	(YL)G
F_2	(YL)(YL) (dies)	(YL)G (YL)G	GG
	Yellow	Yellow	Grey

The duplex condition of the lethal factor causes death during early development, a simplex condition does not. Greys are ordinary recessives, and on interbreeding give nothing but greys. Yellow × grey will give half yellows, half greys, and litters of the ordinary mouse size. There is weighty reason for suspecting that lethals somewhat similar in their action to this are a common cause of embryonic death in the domesticated animals. There would appear to be one in the white cat for this habitually produces smaller litters than coloured cats.

Dunn (1923) has demonstrated the action of a lethal factor in the fowl and has shown that this is either closely or completely linked with the factor which in its action determines the difference between coloured and recessive white plumage colour. He mated a Pit-Game cock of unknown origin with a White Wyandotte hen and got a coloured F_1. The F_2 consisted of 105 coloureds and 33 whites. The difference between the characters coloured and recessive white plumage is that of a single factor, Pit Game is CC : White Wyandotte cc. The F_1 males were mated with their mother and yielded 51 coloureds and 29 whites, although equal numbers of the two phenotypes were expected. The deficiency of whites in this generation was found to be due to abnormal ratios in the progeny of two of the F_1 cockerels. One of these actually gave 19 coloureds and 8 whites, a 2 : 1 ratio when mated with his mother, yet when mated with his sisters he gave a normal ratio of 17 coloureds : 5 whites. The next season he was used in the following matings and the results obtained were as under :—

Mate.	Phenotype.	Offspring.		Total.	Expected.	
		Coloured.	White.		Coloured.	White.
Daughter .	Cc	18	5	23	17·3	5·7
Half-sister .	Cc	29	5	34	25·5	8·5
Niece . .	cc	10	10	20	10·0	10·0
Mother . .	cc	19	8	27	13·5	13·5
Aunt . .	cc	17	8	25	12·5	12·5
„ . .	cc	2	1	3	1·5	1·5
Cousin . .	cc	9	5	14	7·0	7·0
„ . .	cc	1	2	3	1·5	1·5
„ . .	cc	10	8	18	9·0	9·0

In the last six matings there is a considerable departure from the expected ratios; in fact the ratios obtained resemble a 2 : 1 rather than a 1 : 1. The inference is that the individuals which are carrying some factor in the duplex state are missing, that a differential mortality is responsible for the absence of certain of the genotypes. The facts can be accommodated by the following scheme. The original mating was (CL)(CL) × (cL)(cl); the white Wyandotte carrying a recessive lethal gene l in the simplex condition. The F_1 individuals would then be (CL)(cL) or (CL)(cl). The mating of the F_1 males of the genotype (CL)(cl) with the mother (cL)(cl) would yield the following genotypes (CL)(cL), (CL)(cl), (cL)(cl) and (cl)(cl). Of these the last is non-viable, so that a ratio 2 coloureds : 1 white is produced.

From this work it emerges that if in a "pure" stock there is a high mortality of embryos early in incubation, if there is a low mortality when this stock is out-crossed, and if certain of the back-crosses of F_1 individuals, produced by such an out-cross to the parent stock which exhibited the high mortality, show a high mortality, then the presence of a lethal factor is to be suspected.

Little (1920) has found that in the case of the mouse there is a factor intimately associated with that for white coat colour, which when present in the duplex condition behaves as a lethal. Jones (1922) has recorded what seems to be a similar case in the cat. He had noted that the primary sex-ratio in cats was distinctly higher than the secondary, and had interpreted the difference as evidence of selective degeneration in a proportion of the fœtuses. He then noted that the number of degenerating fœtuses in the case of the white female was greater than that in the non-white, and suggests that in some white female cats a lethal action of some sort is operative when the factor for white is present even in the simplex condition.

In Drosophila, Morgan has identified a considerable number of lethal factors which in their action lead to more or less profound disturbance of the expected phenotypic ratios. Many of these lethals are resident in the X-chromosome. One, lethal III, is placed about the point 26·5, and since it is in the X-chromosome, the XY male cannot also possess the factor for its normal allelomorph. If a white-eyed female with this gene lethal III (l_3) in a simplex condition is crossed with a red-eyed male with the gene for the allelomorphic normal condition, all the daughters will be red-eyed, but only half will possess the normal L_3 in the duplex condition—

P_1	$(wl_3X)(wL_3X)$	×	$(WL_3)Y$	
F_1	$(WL_3X)(wl_3X)$ Red-eyed ♀ l_3 in simplex state	$(wl_3X)Y$ White-eyed ♂ with l_3	$(wL_3X)(WL_3X)$ Red-eyed ♀ L_3 in duplex state	$(wL_3X)Y$ White-eyed ♂ with L_3

The female duplex for L_3 when mated to their brothers with L_3 produce an F_2 consisting of the following classes: 1 red ♀, 1 red ♂, 1 white ♀, 1 white ♂, or 1 female to 1 male, which is unremarkable. The female simplex for l_3 mated to her brother with L_3 produces an F_2 including 4 red ♀ ♀, 3 red ♂ ♂, 4 white ♀ ♀, 1 white ♂, *i.e.*, 7 reds to 5 whites in every 12, or 2 females to 1 male in every 3. The absence of 1 male in this ratio gives the clue to the lethal factor involved. A male with l_3 (the lethal) perishes not only in F_2 but also in F_1. There were thus no $(wl_3X)Y$ males in F_1, all the males had the constitution $(wL_3X)Y$. Lethal III (l_3) is distant 25 units from W, so that 25 per cent. of cross-over gametes can be expected. Any crossing-over in the female duplex for L_3 will not affect the result, for every male will receive from his mother the X-chromosome carrying L_3, but the females of F_1 with the constitution $(wl_3X)(WL_3X)$ will produce four sorts of gametes in the following proportions—

(wl_3X)	(WL_3X)	(wL_3X)	(Wl_3X)
3	3	1	1

The zygotes in the F_2 will then be as follow:—

	♀ ♀		♂ ♂		
3	$(wl_3X)(wL_3X)$	White	$(wl_3X)Y$	White (die)	3
3	$(WL_3X)(wL_3X)$	Red	$(WL_3X)Y$	Red	3
1	$(wL_3X)(wL_3X)$	White	$(wL_3X)Y$	White	1
1	$(Wl_3X)(wL_3X)$	Red	$(Wl_3X)Y$	Red (dies)	1

4 white ♀ ♀, 1 white ♂, 4 red ♀ ♀, 3 red ♂ ♂ (7 reds : 5 whites)
and 8 ♀ ♀ : 4 ♂ ♂
2 : 1

Here, then, is one cause of a profoundly disturbed sex-ratio and of an unusually small litter.

The lethals in the X-chromosome are numbered l_1, l_2, l_3 and so on, in the order of their discovery; lethals on the autosomes are referred to as l IIa, l IIb, l IIc, l IIIa, l IIIb and so on, the Roman numerals indicating the particular chromosome concerned, and the small letter the order of their discovery.

Similar Effects produced by Different Genes.—Sable, black, and ebony body colour in Drosophila are indistinguishable to the inexperienced eye. Yet breeding experiments show that they belong to different linkage groups and are situated on Chromosomes I, II, and III respectively. Black × sable produces the wild type grey body colour in F_1. So do the matings black and ebony or ebony and sable. "Bow" wings (I) and "arc" (II) both yield a wing character in which the wings are curved downwards over the abdomen. Fringed (II) and Spread (III) both give thin textured wings held out nearly at right angles to the body.

The Manifold Effects of a Single Gene.—It is not to be imagined for a moment that the action of a gene determines the exhibition of its corresponding character and that alone. A gene, judged by its effects, often visibly affects several widely different structures of the body. For example, the gene for "rudimentary" wings is identified by its effect upon the characterisation of the wings but further inspection of such a stock will elicit the fact that it produces other constant effects—the hind limbs are shorter than those of the wild-type fly, the females are almost completely sterile and the viability of the stock is comparatively low. Since the females are sterile, the culture has to be maintained by using heterozygous individuals. If this is true in the case of the visible characters there is every reason to hold that it is true also of the physiological characters. Fecundity and wing-pattern are both affected by the action of one and the same gene. There is no such thing as a "unit" character *sensu stricto*, but it is convenient to refer to a gene in terms of its most obvious effect. This matter bears upon the group characters of the systematist. Such characters in themselves are often insignificant and seem insufficient to separate group from group. But regarded from the Mendelian point of view, it is possible that the group characters are really only the most obvious effects of the various genes possessed by the different groups and that the group differences which really matter are the others, probably physiological rather than morphological in nature, the effects of which are not seen and have not yet been measured.

Variation.—Biologists up till recently have used the term "variation" to include all phenotypic differences distinguishing the generations, and since no two generations are absolutely alike it seemed to them that heredity and variation were but two aspects of a single process, co-extensive one with the other. It is now known that heredity and variation are two fundamentally distinct problems. It is also recognised that the differences between parent and offspring are not necessarily genetic variations, for the characters of an individual are the end-products of a long series of reactions into which environmental forces enter at every stage. Variation is of two kinds: (1) genetic, and (2) that which is due to the conditioning of genetic action by environmental forces.

Genetic Variation.—In addition to the variation which follows from the presence in the genotype of modifying and multiple factors there is also genetic difference based on the duplex and the simplex states of a gene. When a pair of alternative characters is concerned complete dominance is often the rule. In Drosophila it is usual for the normal allelomorph to show dominance over the mutant character and as will be remembered every character of the culinary pea investigated by Mendel fell readily into the dominant or recessive class. But though even on fairly close examination it would appear that dominance is complete, there are reasons for believing that in most, if not in all, cases the completeness of dominance is more apparent than real, that in most cases there is a difference in the expression of a character in an individual which carries the gene for the dominant character in the duplex state and one with that gene in the simplex state. In Drosophila the long-winged condition is dominant to miniature wings, but Lutz (1913) has demonstrated that if accurate measurements are made it is possible to distinguish between homozygous and heterozygous long-winged individuals.

In many cases the F_1 individuals exhibit a condition which has every appearance of being exactly intermediate between the characters of the parental forms, as in the case of the Blue Andalusian. Bateson and Saunders (1902) first suggested that the blue was probably a heterozygote of black and splashed-white and in 1905-6 Bateson and Punnett tested this suggestion by extensive breeding experiments, finally concluding that the suggestion was a correct one. The case was further investigated by Goldschmidt, the Hagedoorns, and more recently by Lippincott, and these investigators were led to the conclusion that it was not one of simple homozygosis and heterozygosis, but that the blue was a dihybrid.

Lippincott (1918) points out that the 1 : 2 : 1 ratio in the F_2 of a black × splashed-white mating can be regarded as compounded of two 3 : 1 ratios involving linkage. The blue is like the black in that both are self-coloured birds, and resembles the splashed-white, in that the pigment is restricted to certain parts of the feather and takes the form of rounded granules as opposed to the rod-shaped granules of the black variety.

	Pigment NOT RESTRICTED in Barbule-cells : EXTENDED through Plumage.	Pigment RESTRICTED in Barbule-cells : EXTENDED through Plumage.	Pigment RESTRICTED in Barbule-cells : NOT EXTENDED through Plumage.
Phenotype	Black	Blue	Blue-splashed White
Ratio for Restriction	1	:	3
Ratio for Extension	3	:	1

He postulates two linked factors, R, which arranges and restricts the pigment in the feather structure so that it gives a bluish-grey appearance, and E, which extends the pigment present to all the feathers of the body, both of these acting in the presence of P, the factor producing black pigment.

The black has the constitution PP(rE)(rE), the splashed-white PP(Re)(Re) and the blue will therefore be PP(Re)(rE). Blue mated to blue will give the 1 : 2 : 1 ratio, so, 1 PP(rE)(rE) : 2 pp(rE)(Re) : 1 PP(Re)(Re).

On the assumption that the recessive white varieties of fowls are homozygous for the factors E and p, p being the recessive allelomorph of P, the factor necessary for the production of black pigment in the feathers, Lippincott explains the results of the mating of the Andalusian with such genotypes as the following :—

			Per cent.	Per cent.
Blue-splashed Andalusian ♂ PP(Re)(Re)	×	White Wyandotte or White Plymouth Rock ♀♀ pp(rE)(rE)	100 Blues Pp(Re)(rE)	0 Blacks
White Wyandotte or White Plymouth Rock ♂ pp(rE)(rE)	×	Blue-splashed Andalusian ♀♀ PP(Re)(Re)	100 "	0 "
Blue Andalusian ♂ PP(Re)(rE)	×	White Wyandotte or White Plymouth Rock ♀♀ pp(rE)(rE)	50 " Pp(Re)(rE)	50 " Pp(rE)(rE)
White Wyandotte or White Plymouth Rock ♂	×	Blue Andalusian ♀♀	50 "	50 "
Black Andalusian ♂ PP(rE)(rE)	×	White Wyandotte or White Plymouth Rock ♀♀	0 "	100 " Pp(rE)(rE)
White Wyandotte or White Plymouth Rock ♂	×	Black Andalusian ♀♀	0 "	100 "

Reciprocal crosses of White Wyandottes and White Plymouth Rocks give only whites, and it is reasonable therefore to hold that the recessive white of both breeds is due to the same factor p in a duplex condition, since there is no evidence of recombination. It was found that the recessive White Rocks carried pattern-factors as cryptomeres, hidden because in the absence of P they had nothing on which to act. They possessed the sex-linked pattern factor for barring, and all pigmented offspring by a White Plymouth Rock cock and Blue Andalusian hens exhibit at hatching the occipital spot which indicates the presence of the barring factor. The progeny of a White Wyandotte cross frequently show Wyandotte lacing, evidence of the derivation of the White from the Silver-laced Wyandotte, and the presence of the factors for lacing in the P-lacking white.

Further experimentation showed that as far as the factors under discussion were concerned, the Black Langshan was identical with the Black Andalusian, being PP(rE)(rE) and that the Blue Orpington was identical with the Blue Andalusian, being Pp(Re)(rE).

Occasionally Blue Leghorns appear in flocks of pure-bred Whites. Lippincott investigated the breeding behaviour of two such and the writer has recently confirmed his results in the case of three others.

The white of the White Leghorn is a dominant white, and the White Leghorn is a pigment-possessing bird, but owing to the action of an inhibiting factor, called I by Hadley (1915), this pigment does not become expressed. The constitution of the White Leghorn as far as plumage colour is concerned is IIPP(rE)(rE), the formula for the black of the Black Andalusian plus this inhibiting factor.

					Blue-splashed White.	White.
			Black.	Blue.	Blue-splashed White.	White.
White Leghorn ♂ IIPP(rE)(rE)	×	Blue Leghorn ♀ iiPP(Re)(rE)	...	...	...	100 per cent.
Blue Andalusian ♂ iiPP(Re)(rE)	×	" "	25 per cent.	50 per cent.	25 per cent.	...
White Plymouth Rock ♂ iipp(rE)(rE) or White Wyandotte	×	" "	50 per cent.	50 per cent.	...	...
Black Andalusian ♂ iiPP(rE)(rE)	×	" "	50 per cent.	50 per cent.	...	...

The mutual relations of the factors R and E are such that they are never found together in the same gamete. R and E are therefore either allelomorphic, occupying identical loci on homologous chromosomes, or each is linked so closely to the recessive allelomorph of the other (Re) and (rE), that crossing-over rarely, if ever, occurs. No evidence of crossing-over has presented itself, but the case is very similar to that of Castle's (1919) black rats which, on being interbred, invariably yielded whites, blacks, and red-eyed yellows in the ratio of 1 : 2 : 1. Evidence of crossing-over would be supplied by the appearance of a true-breeding blue in the case of the fowl, of a true-breeding black in the case of the rat. It should be noted that breeders claim to have produced a true-breeding blue fowl. Ibsen and Dunn collaborated with Castle in his work, and Dunn (1920) reported the occurrence of between 1 and 2 per cent. of cross-overs. In the case of the fowl if as a result of crossing-over between Re and rE, gametes with the constitution RE were produced there would be great possibilities of producing a true-breeding Blue Andalusian. But it may be that in the fowl there are genes like those discovered by Sturtevant on the II Chromosome of Drosophila which almost completely inhibit crossing-over in the regions adjacent to their own loci.

It is impossible to speak with any certainty as to the origin of the Blue Leghorns which occasionally appear in a pure-bred white flock. It seems possible that two White Leghorns, each with the factor I in the simplex condition and one possessing the factor R are mated by chance, and out of this mating, IiPP(rE)(rE) × IiPP(Re)(rE), iiPP(Re)(rE) birds could result. This is mere conjecture, but the breeding results indicate that this is the constitution of these Blue Leghorns.

In other instances the F_1 characterisation is intermediate, but the degree of expression of the character is very variable, ranging from nearly the condition present in one parent to that in the other. Bar eye is a typical example of this. The F_1 of a normal × bar-eyed mating consist entirely of individuals with bar eyes. The males are as bar-eyed as the P_1 bar-eyed, the females vary from very nearly round eye to typical bar—

P_1	(BX)(BX)	×	(bX)Y
F_1	(BX)(bX)	:	(BX)(Y)

The male of F_1, with respect to the genes concerned, has the same genetic constitution as a male of a pure bar-eyed race, whereas the F_1 female is different from homozygous bar-eyed females. The eye character of such will be the end result of the competitive interaction of the genes B and b within a particular environment—the fly (a certain genotype during development)—and so the expression of this character is variable. A "black" (bb) fly is much darker than the wild type grey-bodied fly (BB), but the F_1 grey (Bb) is a shade

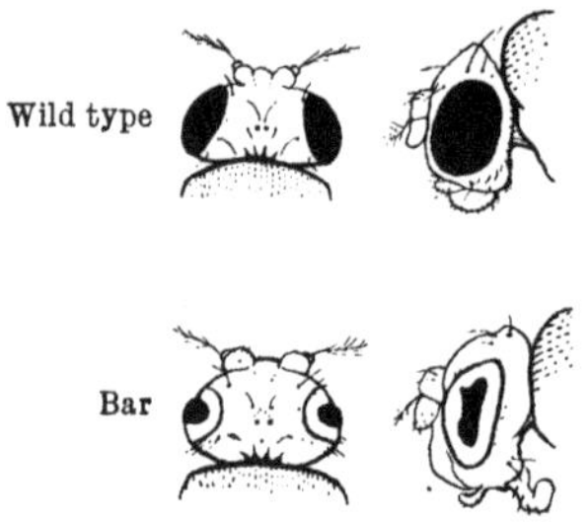

FIG. 36.—Bar. (*After* Morgan.)

darker than the BB. An ebony fly (ee) is again much darker than the wild fly (EE) and the heterozygous individual (Ee) is a shade darker than the EE. When a black fly is mated to an ebony, the F_1 individuals are slightly darker than the parental forms, and in F_2 there is a series ranging from individuals darker than either the black or ebony forms to the wild grey, so—

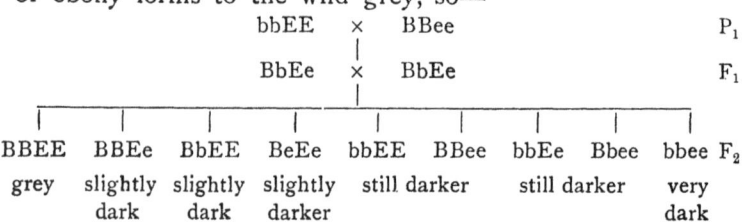

bbEE × BBee P_1

BbEe × BbEe F_1

BBEE	BBEe	BbEE	BeEe	bbEE	BBee	bbEe	Bbee	bbee	F_2
grey	slightly dark	slightly dark	slightly darker	still darker		still darker		very dark	

Dominance is not complete and every group, each with its own mode, overlaps its neighbours. The body colour further varies with the age of the individual.

In addition to these two genes b and e there are many others which produce a dark body-colour so that if in a breeding experiment each of these had not been investigated and identified previously, the results would not be interpretable and would seem to fall outside the Mendelian scheme.

A small variability in F_1 and a greater variability in F_2 indicate the presence and action of many genes producing similar or apparently similar effects. This, as has been seen, applies particularly to quantitative characters such as size and length, but it must not be forgotten that in the case of qualitative characters there may be differences which cannot be appreciated by the eye. Delicate shades of colour differences may not be identified, for the eye is not so accurate a gauge as the calipers or the balance.

Genetical Action and External Environment.—The degree of expression of genetical action may be conditioned by external environmental circumstances. It is a matter of common observation that locality has an important influence on animals with regard to the expression of their genotypes. The fleece, the size, the flavour of a sheep of one and the same breed differ markedly according to the climatic conditions, and with different food and soil and exercise. It is no uncommon thing for a litter of pigs to be born completely hairless. The pigs are of normal weight and size, they are carried the full gestation period and are born alive only to die within a short time. The condition is the result of hypofunctioning of the maternal thyroid gland and is prevented and cured by the administration of iodine and green food. The thyroid of the fœtal pigs is likewise in a state of hypofunctioning and in consequence the hair is not developed—the character is not expressed until the thyroid deficiency is made good. This deficiency is not genetic in origin, it is the result of faulty feeding of penned-up animals that cannot choose their food for themselves.

The expression of the gene for abnormal abdomen in Drosophila depends upon the amount of moisture in the food. When the food is moist the abnormal abdomen is exhibited and under these conditions abnormal abdomen × normal gives the expected ratio. With dry food the abnormal abdomen character is not expressed; with moist food flies carrying this factor produce offspring with abnormal abdomen; those without it do not. Reduplication of legs or parts of legs is another instance of environmental conditioning of factorial expression, as has been shown by

Hoge (1915). Stocks carrying the factor for this crossed with normal flies produce, when kept at a temperature below 10° C., offspring obeying the Mendelian scheme, but at ordinary temperature the condition is not expressed and its mode of inheritance is obscured. In hot climates there would be no evidence that the factor for this recessive character was being transmitted regularly.

Age can influence the degree of expression of a character. For example, in Drosophila a young pink-eyed fly can readily be distinguished from a purple-eyed, but as the individuals age the eye-colour of both becomes a dark purple shade and the two can no longer be distinguished. Newly-hatched black-bodied flies are indistinguishable from the normal grey wild-type since the body pigmentation is not developed at this time.

In certain cases although two principal genes, affecting one and the same structure and not being resident in one and the same locus, are present, the character based upon one of these only is exhibited. For example, a fly with the genes for both white and pink, or with the genes for both white and purple, has white eyes. The character white is *epistatic*, to pink and to purple, which are *hypostatic* in relation to white.

It is important to recognise the distinction between dominance and epistasis; between hypostasis and recessivity. Dominance and recessivity are terms applied to the behaviour of alternative characters based upon genes which occupy one and the same locus on a particular chromosome. For example, in Drosophila not-white is the dominant and white is the recessive of one particular pair of allelomorphic characters and this fact is recorded by the use of the symbols W and w in the representation of their genes. The characters white and purple on the other hand do not constitute an allelomorphic pair; each is a member of a different pair, not-white and white, not-purple and purple, and the relationship of white and purple is very different from that of the members of the not-white and white or of not-purple and purple pairs. The action of the gene w prevents the manifestation of the action of the gene p when both are present in the same genotype and to express this fact the term epistatic is applied to the behaviour of the gene w, hypostatic to that of the gene p. The difference between dominance and epistasis is made clear in the F_2. If in the P_1 a white-eyed male is mated to a wild-type, in the F_2 there will be 3 wild-type to 1 white-eye in every 4 on the average, or if a wild-type is mated with a purple-eyed fly, in F_2 there will be 3 wild-type to each purple-eyed. But if a white-eyed male is mated to a purple-eyed female the F_1 males will have the constitution Pp(WX)Y and the females Pp(WX)(wX) and all will have the wild-type eye-colour, and if these are interbred in the F_2 there will be in every 16 on the average, 9 wild-type, 4 white-eyed and 3 purple, so—

PP(WX)(WX)	Wild-type	PP(WX)(wX)	Wild-type
PP(WX)Y	"	PP(wX)Y	White
Pp(WX)(WX)	"	Pp(WX)(wX)	Wild-type
Pp(WX)Y	"	Pp(wX)Y	White
Pp(WX)(WX)	"	Pp(WX)(wX)	Wild-type
Pp(WX)Y	"	Pp(wX)Y	White
pp(WX)(WX)	Purple	pp(WX)(wX)	Purple
pp(WX)Y	"	pp(wX)Y	White

This is really a 9 : 3 : 3 : 1 ratio, save that in the case of the double recessive the white is epistatic in relation to purple and so the individual will have white eyes.

The effect of the synchronous presence of epistatic and hypostatic characters in other sorts of matings can be indicated as follows:—

(1) Two dominants—A is the factor for a dominant character of one allelomorphic pair, B that for the dominant of another. The character based on B is epistatic in relation to that based on A.

P_1		AAbb × aaBB		
F_1		AaBb (exhibit the epistatic character)		
F_2	1 AABB 2 AABb 3 AaBB 4 AaBb	1 aaBB 2 aaBb	1 AAbb 2 Aabb	aabb
	12 Exhibit epistatic character		3 Exhibit hypostatic character	1 Exhibits neither character

(2) One character is the dominant of a pair, the other the recessive of another pair. The character based on B is epistatic to that based on a.

P_1 aabb × AABB

F_1 AaBb

(exhibit the epistatic character)

F_2	AABB	aaBB	AAbb	aabb
	AABb	aaBb	Aabb	
	Aabb			
	AaBb			
	12 Exhibit epistatic character		3 Exhibit neither character	1 Exhibits hypostatic character

(3) Each of the two characters is the recessive of a different pair. The character based on b is epistatic to that based on a.

P_1 aaBB × AAbb

F_1 AaBb

(exhibit neither character)

F_2	AABB	AAbb	aabb	aaBB
	AABb	Aabb		aaBb
	AaBB			
	AaBb			
	9 Exhibit neither	4 Exhibit epistatic character		3 Exhibit hypostatic character

It is seen that the F_1 characterisation is not a true indication of the exact relation of the characters concerned. The character which is expressed may be either the dominant member of an allelomorphic pair or it may be epistatic to another which further breeding will show to be not its corresponding recessive. To raise an F_1 is not sufficient in character analysis.

Multiple Allelomorphs.—It has been suggested that the difference between allelomorphic characters is an outward expression of a difference in a particular chromosome at a particular locus and that this difference is possibly chemical in nature. A certain sort of change in the chromatin at a particular point of the X-chromosome of Drosophila results in the production of white-eye instead of the red-eye.

White-eye is associated with a change in the chromatin at a point 1·5 units of distance from yellow. A white-eyed male mated to a red-eyed female produces a red-eyed F_1, and in the F_2 there are 3 red-eyed and 1 white-eyed individuals in every 4. Red is dominant to white; white is a recessive mutant character. Later, in a culture of white-eyed flies an individual with eosin coloured eyes appeared. An eosin-eyed male mated to a red-eyed female gives a red-eyed F_1, and in the F_2 3 reds to 1 eosin; eosin is a recessive mutant character allelomorphic to red, as was also white. Later, there appeared flies with eye-colours cherry, tinged, blood, buff, coral, ivory, apricot, écru, and in each case their eye-colours were allelomorphic to red.

If a white-eyed male is mated with an eosin-eyed female, in F_2 there are 3 eosins to every 1 white. Eosin and white are allelomorphs, just as are white and red and eosin and red.

The linkage value of white and yellow is 1·5, *i.e.*, crossing-over between white and yellow occurs about once in a hundred times. Eosin gives the same linkage value with yellow and so do also cherry, tinged, blood, buff, apricot ivory, écru, and coral. White-eye gives 44 per cent. of crossing-over with bar; so do all the others. The genes for white (w), eosin (w^e), cherry (w^c), écru ($w^{é}$), tinged (w^t) blood (w^b), buff (w^{bu}), apricot (w^a), ivory (w^i), and coral (w^{co}) must therefore either occupy one and the same locus or else lie so extremely close together that they show complete linkage about this point. If they occupy one and the same locus then one and only one of them can be present in the same chromosome at the same time. White-eye occurred in a red-eyed culture; so did cherry, and if the genes for white and for cherry occupy different loci a cherry-eyed individual possesses the normal allelomorph of the white-eye and the white-eye that of the cherry. A cherry-eyed individual would then have the constitution $(Ww^cX)(Ww^cX)$ or $(Ww^cX)(Y)$, whereas a white-eyed individual would be $(wW^cX)(wW^cX)$ or $(wW^cX)(Y)$. Consequently, on crossing they should provide a combination of genes the action of which would result in the production of red-eye $(Ww^cX)(wW^cX)$.

But if the gene for cherry-eye occupies the same locus as that for white—and this is equivalent to saying that the mutation which produced cherry and the mutation which produced white occurred in the same locus—then cherry mated with white should not produce a red-eyed F_1. As a matter of fact, such a mating produces an F_1 in which the females have an eye-colour intermediate between cherry and white, and the males have cherry eyes, so—

P_1	Cherry ♀	$(w^cX)(w^cX)$	×	$(wX)(Y)$	White ♂
F_1	Cherry-white ♀♀	$(w^cX)(wX)$	:	$(w^cX)(Y)$	Cherry ♂♂

Similarly in the case of eosin and white—

P_1	Eosin ♀	$(w^eX)(w^eX)$	×	$(wX)(Y)$	White ♂
F_1	Eosin-white ♀♀	$(w^eX)(wX)$	:	$(w^eX)(Y)$	Eosin ♂♂

The eye-colours eosin, ivory, apricot, and cherry supply a reasonable explanation of certain forms of sexual dimorphism. In the case of animals it is not uncommon for the sexes to be strikingly distinct. The theory of sexual selection endeavours to explain the origin and perpetuation of the distinctive characters of the two sexes by suggesting that individuals of the one sex preferentially mated with individuals of the other which exhibited certain characters to a marked degree and so *through time* the sexes diverged. But as is seen in the case of cherry and eosin eye-colours, a striking difference may become established as a result of a single mutation. Many of the distinguishing sex characters may be explained in this way —homozygosis and heterozygosis resulting from the XX and XY constitutions.

White-eye appeared in a red-eyed culture, eosin appeared in a white-eyed culture. Eosin, therefore, might be looked upon as the result of two consecutive mutations affecting neighbouring and completely linked loci. If it is held that cherry and white are completely linked, then they must each differ from red by the same gene, but they are not alike, so that, according to this view, one of them must differ from red by still another gene, and since each arose from red it follows that one of them has arisen by a simultaneous mutation in two loci completely linked and affecting the same chromosome.

An interpretation alternative to that of complete linkage, and far more reasonable, is that of *Multiple Allelomorphs*. A certain change in the organisation of the chromatin at 1·5 units of distance from zero on Chromosome I resulted in the production of the character white eye-colour. The condition in this locus is now represented as w as opposed to that in the wild-type fly W. Another sort of change in this localised area of chromatin resulted in the production of eosin eye-colour; another in cherry, another in tinged, another in blood, another in buff; others in ivory, apricot, and écru respectively, and yet another in coral. Red (W), white (w), cherry (w^c), eosin (w^e), tinged (w^t), blood (w^b), buff (w^{bu}), écru ($w^{\acute{e}}$), apricot (w^a), ivory (w^i), and coral (w^{co}), constitute a multiple system of 10 allelomorphs all due to different states of the same area of chromatin, and so all affecting the same character. If so many changes are possible, there is no reason why *return* or *reverse* mutation should not occur. Eosin arose from white; white in turn should arise from eosin; it has done so on several occasions. Morgan has suggested that perhaps the chromosomes may be regarded as a chain of chemically complex substances (proteins), and that any rearrangement of what may be compared to the atoms in the molecule might well produce a modification in the character which stands in relation to that particular area of the chromosome in which this change has occurred. It is of interest to note that it has been observed in Drosophila that certain loci undergo mutation more than others and that this is shown not only by the recurrence of the same mutant character but also in the occurrence of multiple allelomorphs.

A quadruple system of allelomorphs has been identified in the mouse—the grey, the white-bellied, the yellow, and the black; in the rabbit there is a triple system consisting of the Himalayan, the albino and the self-coloured.

The wild fly has a red eye-colour and the genetical requirement for this consists in the "normal" state of the chromatin at more than one locus on more than one chromosome. A change in the state of the chromatin in one of these many loci will result in an alteration of the eye-colour. The white-buff series is at point 1·5, vermilion is at point 33·0 on Chromosome I; on Chromosome II at point 40·0 is the locus for purple; at point 25·0 on Chromosome III is the locus for pink, and so on. In fact, Morgan states that at least 25 genes are known to be concerned with eye-colour in *Drosophila melanogaster.* The wild-type eye-colour is to be represented by a formula which symbolises not-white, not-vermilion, not-purple, not-pink, etc., which thus indicates that in none of the loci concerned with eye-colour has a change from the normal occurred. A change in one locus throws the whole eye-colour system out of gear; a mutant character will appear. A purple-eyed fly is one in which a change in the chromatin has occurred at one situation; a pink-eyed is one in which the change occurred at another, and so on. A normal-eyed fly might thus be represented by the following chromosome map—

	I	II	III	IV
W = Not-white-buff . . .	W	...	...	...
V = Not-vermilion . . .	V	...	Pk	...
P = Not-purple . . .	...	P	...	...
Pk = Not-pink, and so on.				

Or by the formulæ—

♀ (WVX)(WVX) PP PkPk.
♂ (WVX)Y PP PkPk.

A purple-eyed is similar save that P is replaced by p; a pink-eyed fly has Pk replaced by pk, so—

W	...	...		W	...	...
V	...	Pk		V	...	pk
...	p	...		...	P	...
(WVX)(WVX)pp PkPk				(WVX)(WVX)PP pkpk		

The mating of purple with pink can be shown thus—

	W	...	...		W	...	...
	V	...	Pk	×	V	...	pk
	...	p	...		...	P	...
i.e.		pp PkPk		×		PP pkpk	

Not-purple and purple. Pp Pkpk = Wild-type.
Not-pink and pink.

The F_1 individuals are heterozygous for both characters and, as a result of the competitive balancing action of the genes P and p, Pk and pk, the flies show red eye-colour. The wild-type eye-colour is exhibited by the F_1 of a mating in which the parents differ one from the other in this way —where two different loci on the same or on different chromosomes are concerned. But when the mating is between individuals showing mutant characters depending on differences in the same locus (multiple allelomorphs), the red eye-colour is not produced in F_1 but a colour intermediate between those of the parents.

Mutation in a certain locus implies nothing more than a change in the state of the chromatin in this particular situation. As to the exact nature of such a change it is idle as yet to speculate. Mutation is rare; the gene "wild-type" and "mutant" is exceedingly stable. It is of interest to note that certain loci are more prone to mutation than others and that mutation is not restricted to any particular phase of the individual's life history. It is also to be noted that mutation yielding a comparatively slight alteration in characterisation is more common than that which leads to profound change therein. It is probable that the most common mutations of all are those which yield end-results so insignificant that they are not observed; unsuspected "lethals" are possibly the commonest of all mutations.

When mutation occurs it is usually restricted to one locus. Muller has shown, however, that a mutation in one and the same locus does not always lead to the same result. In Drosophila a mutation in a certain locus may result in a shortened wing, an eruption on the thorax, in a lethal effect or in any combination of these. But the effect of the mutation is preferential, it occurs more often in some directions than in others, though this tendency itself may become changed as a result of another mutation. A mutant character is usually recessive and in Drosophila is commonly deleterious in its action, being "retrogressive" rather than progressive. In Drosophila also it is found that any combination of recessive characters (morphological) is almost invariably associated with a disadvantageous physiological characterisation.

A mutation may be *gametic*, *i.e.*, it may occur previous to the maturation of the gamete, when, unless the chromosome concerned passes into the polar body in the case of the ovum, its effects may be profound and patent upon the entire development of the individual. If the mutation is gametic, then obviously it must enter the zygote from one parent only, and if it is a recessive mutation the corresponding character will not appear until some subsequent generation when two individuals simplex in respect of it chance to mate.

A mutation may be *zygotic*, *i.e.*, it may occur immediately after fertilisation and, in these circumstances, its effects will be exhibited by the developing individual.

A mutation may be *somatic*, *i.e.*, it may occur in a cell in the body of an organism. The germ-cells are not affected, but one individual somatic cell and the tissues having their origin in this particular cell will exhibit the mutant character. It is in this fashion that bud variations, chimeras and the like arise.

A study of the circumstances in which a mutant form appears will indicate the origin and the time of the actual mutation. If but one mutant appears in a culture then it can be assumed that the mutation occurred in the late stages of oogenesis, for otherwise there must have been more than one mutant. If a mutation results in the production of a gene which in its reactions conditions a recessive character, which is linked to a lethal, the character may not be exhibited for a long time after the occurrence of the mutation, for not until crossing-over has occurred and has separated the genes for the recessive and lethal characters will the recessive be seen, since all individuals homozygous for the linked lethal will perish and in the heterozygous condition it will not be observed.

Parallel mutations — mutations occurring in different germ-plasms but yielding the same character—are fairly common. Many such have already been examined in the different species of Drosophila. In the case of the domesticated animals, the polled condition has been recorded in horned races of cattle, sheep, and deer; short-leggedness in the horse, cattle, sheep, dogs, and the fowl; taillessness in the horse, sheep, pig, dog, cat, and fowl; syndactylism in cattle and swine; polydactylism in the horse, cattle, sheep, deer, pig, dog, cat, guinea-pig, and fowl; Angora hair in cattle, sheep, goat, cat, rabbit, and mouse; both rabbits and guinea-pigs present the same series of coat-colour varieties.

The critics of the gene maintain that the overwhelming majority of Mendelian mutations have arisen under the unhealthy circumstances of domestication and are pathological in nature. They refute the suggestion that the gene is "a vital unit which controls energy, material, and pattern and out of which definite form develops," and regard it as the measure of the amount of pathological damage which the hereditary substance has undergone. It is true that our present-day knowledge of hereditary transmission in the case of Drosophila is founded on the behaviour of characters, very many of which may be regarded as distinctly pathological, but actually it is the hereditary transmission of *normal* characters which has been studied by contrasting normal with "pathological," and in any case the prominence of the abnormal is due to the fact that the unusual is more readily observed. "The geneticist knows that opposed to each defect-producing element in the germ-plasm there is a normal partner of that element which we call its allelomorph. We cannot study the inheritance of one member of such a pair of genes without at the same time studying the other. Hence, whatever we learn about those hereditary elements that stand for defects, we learn just as much about the normal partners of those elements. In a word, heredity is not confined to a study of the shuffling of those genes that produce abnormal forms, but is equally concerned with what is going on when normal genes are redistributed. This method of pitting one gene against the other furnishes the only kind of information relating to heredity about which we have precise knowledge." Each mutant gene implies a normal allelomorph and the latter exerts the same type of action as the former as is shown by the multiple allelomorphic series. There are great numbers of Mendelian characters which cannot be regarded as pathological; and, after all, the normal is but the characterisation of the average, and pathology includes both the harmful and the unusual. The unusual is abnormal though it is not necessarily deleterious.

The Bearing of Genetic Theory upon the Species Problem.—Among the mutations met with in Drosophila there are several so profound that the new forms exhibit characters sufficient to remove their exhibitors from the species in which Drosophila is placed by the systematist. Since the mutations in Drosophila produce characters in some cases as striking as those which mark off species from species, it is inevitable that the possible bearing of the Drosophila work upon the problem of evolution should be discussed discretely. "Wingless," "eyeless," "reduplicated-legs" are instances of such recessive characters; "Bar" an instance of a dominant. "Tan" (body-colour) flies differ from the wild-type in that they are negatively heliotropic. "Tan" is a sex-linked character, and if a "tan" female is mated to a wild-type male all the sons are tan and all the daughters grey. But if such an F_1 culture is disturbed, all the females fly to the light and all the males do not. (Here, incidentally, is a method of picking up a physiological character by means of a visible morphological one.) These characters may not constitute the sort of variations upon which the advance of a race may have been made, but at least they do illustrate the extent of variation.

The evolution theory is a hypothesis which seeks to interpret the facts of the progressive differentiation of living types as they have spread over the earth during the ages in terms of the ordinary phenomena of reproduction. This being so, the theory must stand or fall according to the adequacy or otherwise of the reproductive mechanism to account for the genetic discontinuity that exists among living organisms. Present-day knowledge of the Mendelian inheritance can explain the persistence and accumulation of structural differences of accepted evolutionary significance without any appeal to such agencies as geographical isolation or even to natural selection. It is known that new types do arise, and having arisen, persist in virtue of the integrity and segregation of hereditary factors, unless they are incapable of surviving. There is a considerable amount of evidence also which justifies the view that the characters which distinguish the breeding-units—the species in the Linnæan sense—are also inherited in a manner compatible with the chromosome hypothesis, as will be seen when the question of the sex-ratio and of fecundity are discussed. The final justification of the evolutionary hypothesis will be found when under experimental conditions intersterile mutant forms appear in a stock and when the nature of mutations has been laid bare.

Natural selection is the appraiser of new characters and the eliminator of the possessors of the undesirable, but in itself it does not produce anything new. The evolution of a race depends upon the appearance of new characters and the modification of the old, and for advance or for regression new characters must appear and must be transmitted to succeeding generations.

Bateson (1914) pointed out that it was desirable to consider the trend of genetical thought in that there were suggestions which went to show that evolution had occurred through the loss of inhibiting factors—that the living organism in the beginning had been equipped with the factors for all characters that can ever become exhibited by any of the descendant species and that characters became expressed as the steady loss of inhibiting factors proceeded. It is not so difficult to accept the view of evolution through factorial loss as to accept that which demands the acquisition of factors during phylogeny—evolution through factorial gain. But neither view is so satisfactory as that suggested by the work of Morgan and his school, for it is not difficult to accept the idea of a plastic organisation within a highly complex biochemical unit.

An apparently insignificant variation in the matter of external and morphological characters can be associated with a variation in the physiological characters sufficient to constitute a real "life and death" difference 'twixt the mutant form and the ancestral stock. Evolution need not have been a "war to the knife" with the survival of the fittest and the extirpation of the weak, but it may have been a gentle process during which mutations modified the old through incorporation into the race. Evolution need not have been a gradual process of morphological transformation of the old into the new in response to the impress of exercise or environment; it can have been a process by which a new characterisation has arisen through independent germinal alterations.

The feather of the bird is not necessarily the modified scale of a reptile but may be a distinctly different characterisation based upon an entirely different genotype. A certain genotype results in a certain characterisation—scales; mutation — alteration — in this genotype results in a new genotype and thus leads to another characterisation. The old genotype is transformed into the new but the old characterisation is not transformed, it disappears and is replaced. Scales and feathers are not homologous structures — homology attempts to establish a similarity in origin and nature of structures seemingly different and is based on the assumption that during the course of evolution structures have undergone transformation yet remain fundamentally the same. In fact this conception of homologous structures cannot be accommodated by the chromosome hypothesis until it can be experimentally demonstrated that the genes themselves can pass through a process of gradual modification.

It is a far cry from Drosophila to the mammal, but such characters of wild animals as have been examined by the methods of the geneticist conform in their behaviour in inheritance to those so well understood in the case of the fruit-fly. Frances Pitt (1921), for example, found that in the case of the polecat × ferret cross the F_1 individuals exhibited the general appearance and temperament of the polecat while the characters of the skull were as those of the ferret. M'Arthur (1923) states that the mating pure silver fox × red fox gives an F_1 of an intermediate coat-colour (patchy) and that the F_2 consist of 1 red, 2 patchy and 1 silver in every 4 on the average. Silver × patchy gives 50 per cent. silver and 50 per cent. patchy. In the case of the silver there are several factors concerned and it is known that pale silver is incompletely dominant to dark silver. The coat-colours of the skunk obey the Mendelian scheme in their mode of inheritance. Black, seal-brown, striped, white and albino coat-colours are known. Genetics has its applications in the new industry of fur-farming. If in the wild a mutation occurs, a new character can appear. There is no bar to the appearance of new characters which are useless to the individual. The origin of mutations which obey the Mendelian scheme of inheritance has no relation to the question of the evolutionary value of characters already in existence even though these also are inherited in a typically Mendelian fashion. If the Drosophila type of mutation is pathological, the Mendelian type of inheritance certainly is not, for characters of accepted evolutionary significance are known to be inherited in exactly the same manner as the classical "tall" and "dwarf" in Mendel's own work. If a character is neither advantageous or disadvantageous, the chance that it will become established in the race is extremely small. If it is disadvantageous to the extent of handicapping the individual and rendering it incapable of continued existence, it has no chance of becoming established; if the character confers advantage upon its possessor, then there is every chance for it to become incorporated in the race, and with such an increase in the number of individuals exhibiting the new character there is an increased chance for further advance through a second mutation of the same sort.

A species as recognised by the systematist is an association of individuals all of which exhibit a common morphological character-complex; such species are generally defined without any first-hand knowledge as to their behaviour as breeding-units. It is perhaps due to this fact that most workers of the Mendelian school, with the notable exception of Bateson, have turned their attention from the historic problem of the origin of species to the more immediate question as to the origin of characters.

Nevertheless, as Bateson has rightly pointed out, the fundamental discontinuity of species in the Linnæan sense as breeding units has still to be interpreted in terms of the factorial hypothesis which though it has shed much light on the discontinuity of animal structure has not greatly illuminated the problem of the discontinuity of the breeding-unit. Until further light has been shed on this issue the validity of the assumption upon which the evolution theory rests will not have found a satisfactory basis in experimental inquiry.

The species may be a gene-complex, as suggested by Morgan, and the morphological characters may be linked with physiological characters which really separate unit from unit. Mutation affecting a purely morphological character may result in the origin of a distinct breeding-unit. For example, a tailless cock (a dominant mutant form of the ordinary domestic fowl) cannot fertilise a hackleless hen (another dominant mutant form), for the simple reason that he cannot balance himself during the sexual act. Each bird is perfectly fertile when mated with normal fowls, and the reciprocal mating is productive. In cases in which reciprocal matings are made impossible for mechanical reasons two discrete breeding-units may arise.

A mutant lethal factor may be such that in the simplex state its action is balanced by its normal allelomorph, but in the duplex state the combined action of the two results in the production of anatomical anomaly and physiological derangement of a kind that render the further development of the zygote impossible or profoundly abnormal. Such is the case of the homozygous yellow mouse. Or else, a mutant factor may be of such a nature that alone, either in the simplex or in the duplex condition, it produces no evident effects; but combined with a complementary factor of the same nature it results in a non-viable condition and the mating of two individuals which carry such complementary lethal factors is rendered abortive.

A mutant appears in a stock; a lethal factor is present in the simplex state, and in the course of time there will make their appearance also individuals with this factor in the duplex state. The nature of the factor is such that alone it results in no appreciable effect. Synchronously, or at a different time and in a different race of the same stock another mutation occurs and a factor appears whose action is complementary to that of the one referred to above, and in time individuals with this factor in the duplex state will be produced. Two distinct breeding-units may thus arise within a common stock; each can successfully mate within its own group and with the parent stock, but the mating between the groups is rendered abortive. The expression of the action of such complementary lethal factors may take the form of incompatibility in the form of the copulatory apparatus or in the physiological relationship between the male and female or between the ovum and the sperm; of anatomical anomaly or of physiological derangement leading to an abnormal development of the zygote and its death, of hydramnios or of dystocia, or of sterility of the F_1 heterogametic sex. The two groups, however, have had their origin in a common germ-plasm and so, in the light of return and regional mutations, it is to be expected that parallel mutations will occur. Members of the two groups will exhibit characters which were borne by the common stock from which the groups arose, and characters which have resulted through mutation since the groups became distinct, some of these being the result of parallel mutation and some of mutation which has occurred in one group only. Such mutant morphological characters as are linked with the respective complementary lethals cannot be brought into genetic association and will become the distinguishing characters of the group.

CHAPTER VI

THE MECHANISM OF SEX-DETERMINATION

SEX is the term applied to the differentiation of individuals for the production of dissimilar gametes. A female is an individual organised for the production of ova; a male, one that is equipped for the production of spermatozoa, the function of which is to reach the ova and to unite with them in the process of fertilisation to form the zygote in which a new individual has its origin. In the great majority of animals every individual is either a male or a female; in each species there is a fairly constant average ratio between the numbers of males and females born and this ratio is usually not far from equality, although it varies considerably from species to species. In most animals the difference between the sexes is not restricted to the sex-glands but involves also the structures of the accessory sexual apparatus which is concerned with the conveyance of the products of the gonads to the site of fertilisation and in the viviparous female with the transit of the fœtus during parturition, the external organs of generation concerned with the act of sexual congress, and the secondary sexual characters which are not concerned directly with sexual union but which in certain instances play their part in courtship, combat, concealment, and, in the case of the female, in the care and nourishment of the young.

Mendelian heredity is a manifestation of sexual reproduction and a possible reason for the success of sexual over asexual reproduction is the opportunity bisexuality affords for the mingling of different genotypes and the consequent creation of different genotypic recombinations to form plentiful raw material upon which the selective agencies may work. For example, if N mutations occur in the germ-plasm of an asexually reproducing organism only N types of individuals can arise, whereas if N mutations occur in the germ-plasm of a sexually reproducing organism 2 N types can be formed. Ten mutations mean 10 possible types in the first case, 1024 in the second. Sex is the basis of evolutionary plasticity since through sex, mutations which have occurred independently in time and remotely in space can meet to reinforce each other. Circumstantial evidence from the study of comparative morphology suggests the view that one of the great steps in organic evolution was the establishment of sexual fusion and of cross-fertilisation. Parthenogenesis, the origin of a new individual in the development of the unfertilised egg, is the rule for some groups of animals such as the Rotifers; Autogamy—self-fertilisation—has sufficed for others such as the liver-fluke; but the general rule is that those organisms which practised some form of cross-fertilisation, at least occasionally, hold considerable advantage over those which have continued through one line of descent, judging at least from the fact that their descendants have persisted in greater numbers. Even in the case of the hermaphrodite animals, mechanisms were developed which enabled them to exercise one of the most important functions of bisexuality—cross-fertilisation—without giving up the probable energy conservation which the production of both ova and sperm by one and the same individual entails. In some the individual functions first as a female and later as a male, the state of protogynous hermaphroditism found in the Turbellarians and Tunicates; in others, as in the tape-worm, protandrous hermaphroditism holds, the individual functioning first as a male and then as a female. In certain genera of Thoracica (e.g. *Scalpellum*) and Rhizocephala (e.g. *Sacculina*) the great majority of individuals are hermaphrodites, but in addition to these there are a few tiny complemental males which supply the means of occasional cross-fertilisation. In other cases, continual autogamy is prevented by the physiological condition of self-sterility, as in *Ciona intestinalis.* Among the animals with a relatively complex organisation and high motor activity such as the Cephalopoda, Arachnoida, most Insects and Vertebrates, bisexuality is almost invariably found to exist, the groups are gonochoristic.

At the beginning of this century, it was generally believed that at the time of fertilisation the egg was completely ambivalent as regards the future sex of the resulting zygote; it was customary to refer the sex of an organism to the conditions incident to development. But certain facts of general biology are now known which are not susceptible to interpretation of this kind. They point to the view that sex in the higher animals is usually predetermined at the time of fertilisation. Identical twins, *i.e.*, twin zygotes derived from a single fertilised ovum, are always of the same sex. Such polyembryony is rare in the human, but in the Texas nine-banded Armadillo it is the rule for four young to be produced at a time, all of the same sex and remarkably alike. Newman (1923) was able to show that in the case of the Armadillo a single fertilised ovum after development to a certain stage budded off four embryos. On the other hand, in those cases in which the different embryos arise from separate ova it is known that the individuals are not invariably of the same sex. There is no appreciable reason why, if purely environmental factors are at work in determining the sex of the offspring, litters produced from one egg should be of the same sex, while litters produced from separate eggs should include both males and females. From such observations as these it would appear that the sex of the individual is determined by the constitution of the fertilised ovum at the time of fertilisation. Parthenogenesis in the Hymenoptera and other organisms supplies further evidence in support of this con-

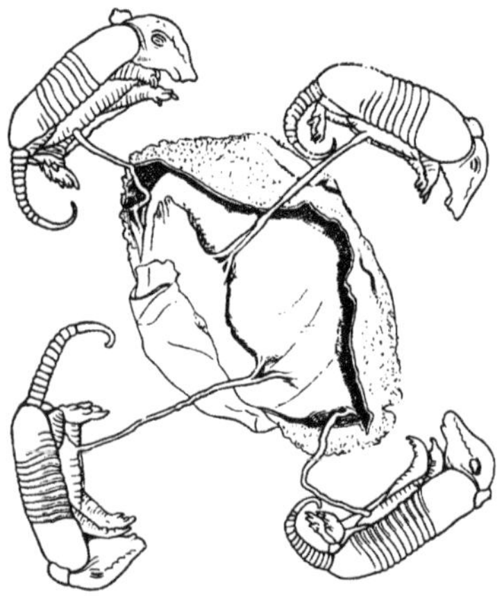

FIG. 37.—Polyembryony in the nine-banded Texas Armadillo. (*After* Newman.)

tention. The eggs of bees will develop without fertilisation, but should they do so the resulting individuals are invariably males. Fertilised eggs, on the other hand, usually become females (queens and workers). The sex of the individual depends on whether fertilisation occurs or not, and thus is established before the inception of embryonic existence.

Sex-Linkage in Abraxas.—The results of the experimental breeding work involving sex-linked characters (*i.e.*, characters which in their transmission from generation to generation

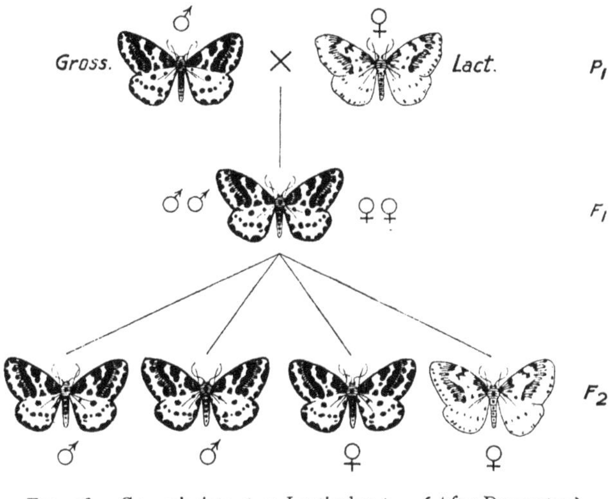

FIG. 38.—Grossulariata ♂ × Lacticolor ♀. (*After* Doncaster.)

are associated with the sex-determining mechanism) bear directly upon this question. Sex-linked inheritance was first studied by Doncaster (1908) in the currant moth, *Abraxas*, two varieties of which, var. *grossulariata* and var. *lacticolor*, are distinguished by the colour-pattern of the wings. When a lacticolor female was mated to a grossulariata male, all the F_1 individuals were grossulariata; the grossulariata pattern is therefore dominant to the lacticolor. In the F_2 both types were found in the proportion of 3 grossulariata to 1 lacticolor, but all the lacticolors were females. When the F_1 heterozygous grossulariata male was back-crossed with lacticolor females, the result was the expected one, *e.g.*, equal numbers of both sexes of grossulariata and lacticolor forms. When one of these lacticolor males was mated to an F_1 heterozygous grossulariata female, equal numbers of grossulariata and lacticolor forms resulted, but all the former were males and all the latter females.

When a lacticolor male was mated to a grossulariata female, the males in F_1 were all grossulariata, the females all lacticolor. Reciprocal crosses thus gave different results.

This can only be interpreted on the assumption that

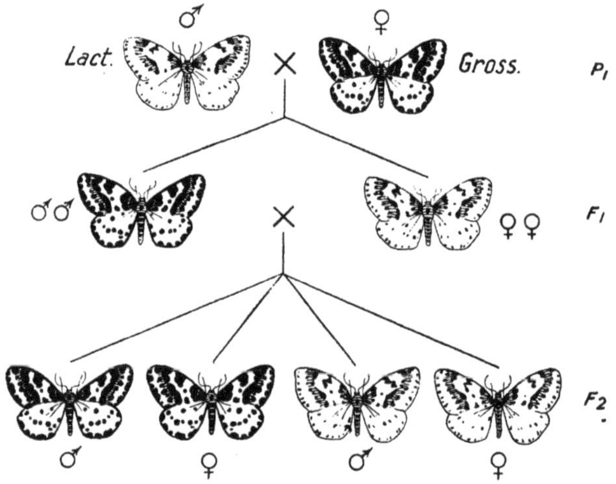

FIG. 39.—Lacticolor ♂ × Grossulariata ♀. (*After* Doncaster.)

homozygous *grossulariata* males transmit the *grossulariata* character to the offspring of both sexes, while a *grossulariata* female transmits it only to her sons. Hence it would seem that the female produces two sorts of gametes—those which bear the factor for the grossulariata character and are destined, if fertilised, to become males; and those which do not carry this factor and are destined to become females. The female then is constitutionally heterozygous for the character grossulariata, and the factor for this character is most intimately associated with another which, if present in the duplex state, determines maleness. The results of further breeding completely confirm this hypothesis.

The argument can be made clearer by the use of the conventional symbols of the geneticist. Let X represent the hypothetical factor which, when present in duplicate, leads to the establishment of maleness, and when present in the simplex state, to femaleness. The male sex-constitution can then be symbolised as XX and the female conveniently as XY. Let G and g respectively represent the factors for the dominant grossulariata and the recessive lacticolor characters. Let (GX) and (gX), in brackets, indicate that the grossulariata and lacticolor factors are intimately associated with the X.

P_1 A male (XX) Homozygous for the grossulariata character	(GX)(GX) × (gX)Y	P_1 A female (XY) Lacticolor. Constitutionally heterozygous for this character
P_1 gametes	(GX) (gX) : Y	
F_1 A male (XX) Grossulariata (G is dominant): heterozygous	(GX)(gX) × (GX)Y	A female (XY) Grossulariata. Constitutionally heterozygous
F_1 gametes	(GX) : (gX) (GX) : Y	

F_2	(GX)(GX) ♂♂ homozygous	(GX)Y ♀♀ (GX)(gX) ♂♂ heterozygous	(gX)Y ♀♀ constitutionally heterozygous
	grossulariata		lacticolor

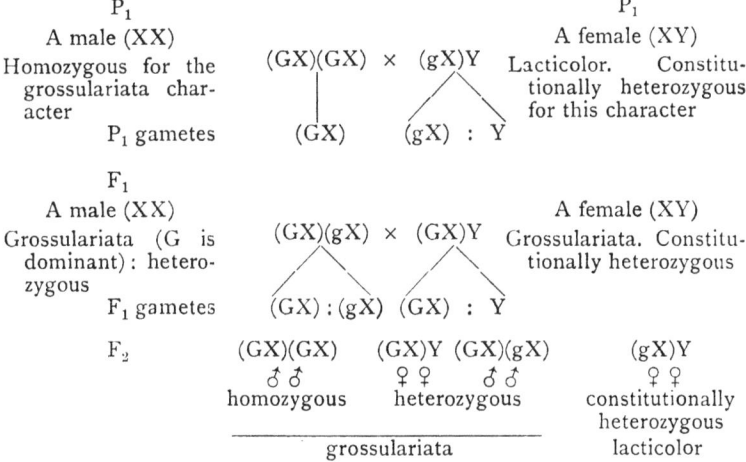

All the lacticolor in F_2 are females. The recessive character of the grandmother has been transmitted to one half of the grand-daughters and to none of the grandsons.

Reciprocal cross—

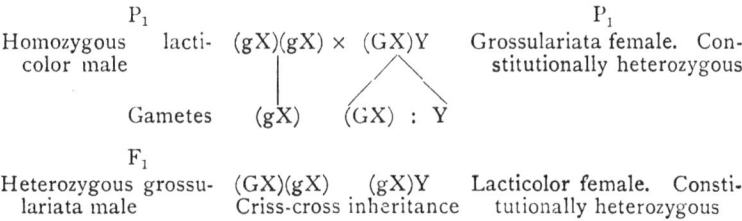

P_1 Homozygous lacticolor male	(gX)(gX) × (GX)Y	P_1 Grossulariata female. Constitutionally heterozygous
Gametes	(gX) (GX) : Y	
F_1 Heterozygous grossulariata male	(GX)(gX) (gX)Y Criss-cross inheritance	Lacticolor female. Constitutionally heterozygous

This interpretation can be shown diagrammatically as follows, assuming that there is an XY or sex-chromosome mechanism and that the factors for the sex-linked characters are resident in the X, as appeared to be the case in Drosophila.

The son receives one X-chromosome from his father and one from his mother. In the reciprocal cross (Fig. 41), as the latter X carries the factor for grossulariata, he will exhibit the grossulariata character. The daughter has but a single X-chromosome and this she receives from her lacticolor father, who must be homozygous for this character, since grossulariata is dominant and would be exhibited even

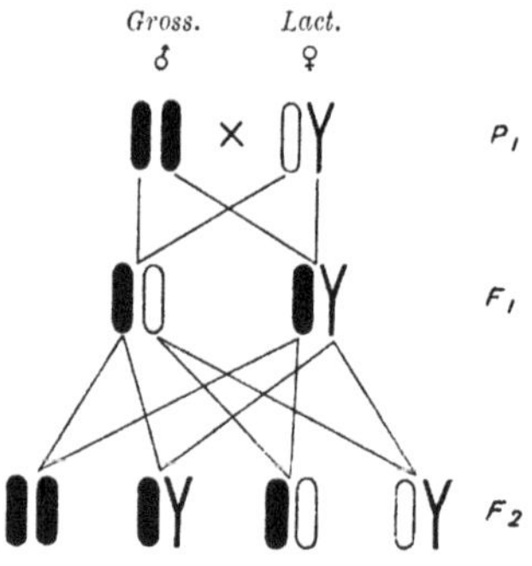

FIG. 40.

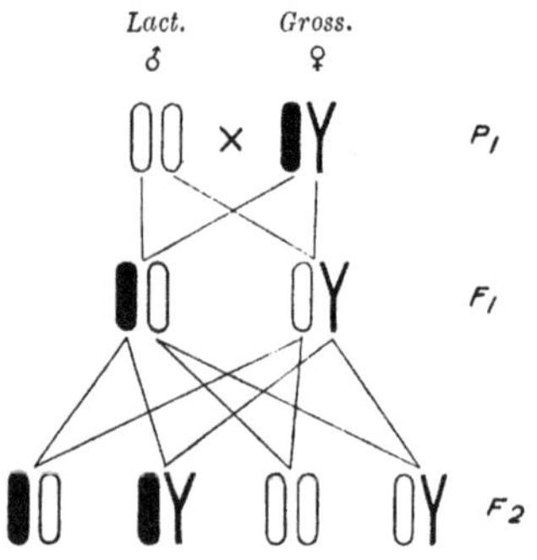

FIG. 41.

if the factor for this character were present only in the simplex state. All the daughters therefore will be lacticolor.

From the study of the transmission of these sex-linked characters the conclusion emerges that the sex of Abraxas is decided by the simplex or duplex condition of some component which, when present in duplicate, leads to the establishment of maleness. The evidence suggests that there is a sex-determining mechanism, an XY-mechanism, that the sex-chromosome constitution of the male is XX, that of the female XY, and that the factors for the sex-linked characters are borne upon the X-chromosome as are also those which when present in duplicate lead to the production of males.

Doncaster examined Abraxas cytologically and found that both male and female had 56 chromosomes and that in the female no obviously unequal pair could be distinguished. It is thus seen that the evidence for an XY-mechanism may be derived solely from breeding experiments involving sex-linked characters, and that the X- and the Y-chromosomes may not be different in shape and size. However, Doncaster found that in one line of his Abraxas many of the females gave none but female offspring. Theoretically this would be expected if these females possessed no X-chromosome. On examination it was found that these females had 55 instead of 56 chromosomes and so during the maturation divisions of the ova 28 chromosomes foregathered at one pole, 27 at the other, so that the mature ovum contains either 27 or 28 (27 + the Y). The sex-chromosome content of these eggs is either O or Y, and these are fertilised by an X-bearing sperm to yield XO and XY zygotes, all females. The Y-chromosome in Abraxas is as functionless as it is in the case of Drosophila as far as sex-determination is concerned. By tracing the distribution of visible characters it is thus possible to follow the transmission from generation to generation of "sex-determining" factors the fate of which is linked with that of those corresponding to the grossulariata and lacticolor characters. In Abraxas the female is the heterogametic sex, elaborating, as far as the sex-determining mechanism is concerned, two sorts of gametes, and the male is homogametic.

Sex-Linkage in the Fowl.—A precisely similar mode of inheritance of sex-linked characters is found in birds, and this fact, enunciated so ably by Punnett, has been taken advantage of by poultry keepers, since it enables them to tell the sex of chickens at hatching.

Barred (dominant) and non-barred (recessive) are the members of a sex-linked pair of characters. A black (non-barred) cock mated with barred hens will throw barred sons and black (non-barred) daughters, and since the chicken which is to become a barred adult is black but with a characteristic whitish spot on the top of the head in addition to the white under-parts, whereas the day-old chick that is to become a black (non-barred) bird has not the white head-spot, it is possible to distinguish the sex of any bird in the F_1 of this mating at the time of hatching. The size and distinctness of the head-spot are very variable; it may

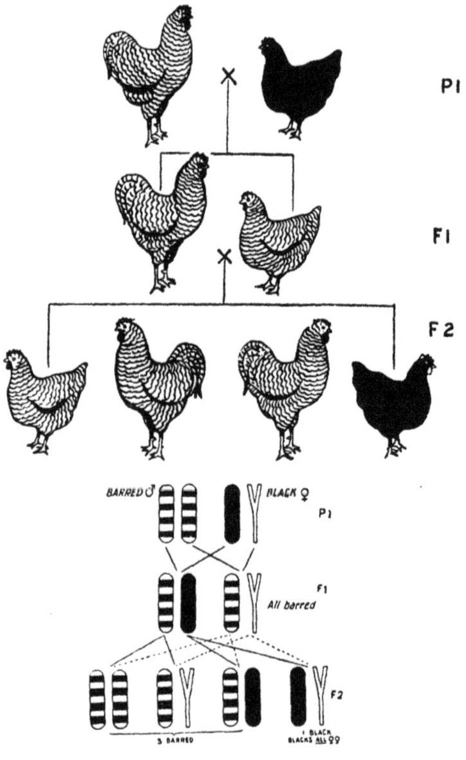

FIG. 42.—Barred ♂ × Black ♀.

involve but a few down-feathers, or it may be quite large but this is of no importance; if there is a yellowish-grey spot on the top of the head of a chicken in this mating, that chicken will be a male and will be barred. The following breeds can be used and will give precise results. (It should be noted that the plan of giving the cock first is not the usual one. For example, Barred Rock × Langshan signifies that the Rock is the hen and the sign × is interpreted as meaning "fertilised by.")

Black Cocks.	*Barred Hens.*
Orpington	Barred Rock
Langshan	Scots Grey
Australorp	Cuckoo Leghorn
Rock	Crele Game
Minorca	Barred Dominique
Leghorn	
(Also the Black-Reds, such as Brown Leghorn, and similarly coloured cocks).	

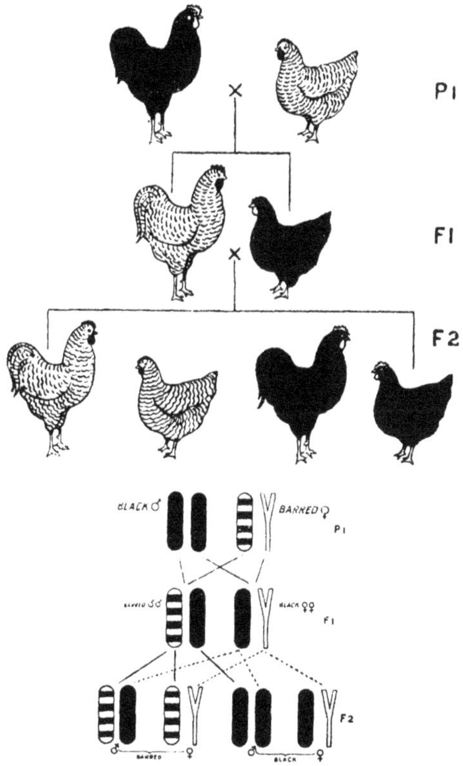

FIG. 43.—Black ♂ × Barred ♀.

(It is to be noted that the barring in these cases is that of the Plymouth Rock and of the Scots Grey breeds and not that of the Campine or the Hamburgh. The first type of barring takes the form of alternative bands of lighter and darker shades of the fundamental colour and is the result of the action of a dominant sex-linked gene acting upon a black or brown basis. The second type takes the form of alternate bars of black and white in the Silver Campine, of black and gold in the Gold variety, of white and gold in the Chamois.)

Slate-coloured shank and light-coloured shank are another pair of such sex-linked characters. When a slaty-legged (black-eyed) cock is mated with hens with light coloured legs (and also eyes), the male chicks have light-coloured legs (and eyes) whereas the females have slaty—

Dark-shanked Cocks.	*Light-shanked Hens.*
Hamburgh	Leghorn
Langshan	Scots Grey
Black Rock	Barred Rock
La Bresse (black and white)	Light Sussex
Campine	
Willow-legged Game	
Buttercup	
Australorp	

It should be stated however, that the exact shade of the leg colour in the day-old chick is often very indistinct and it should not be relied upon for sex-identification commercially.

Gold and silver plumage-colours constitute a third pair of sex-linked characters in the fowl. When a gold cock is mated with silver hens, the daughters are gold, the sons silver. Since the down colour of a gold is a rich buff and that of a silver a silvery white, the sex of the day-old chick can be recognised. (See table opposite.)

A gold may be a gold and black, self-gold, or self-black; a silver may be a silver and black, self-silver, or self-black; and there are two parallel series—a gold-black and a silver-black. In the all-blacks the gold and silver are hidden by the epistatic black and in the case of the chicks of breeds occupying the middle parts of the series there is a brown-black pigmented pattern in the down which reduces the area of the gold or silver ground. For this reason the clearest demonstrations of the sex-linked mode of inheritance of these plumage characters, gold and silver, are seen when the crosses are made with breeds towards the gold and silver ends of the series, though those made with birds from the opposite ends of the two series are fairly satisfactory.

Gold Cocks.	*Silver Hens.*
Minorca	Black Rock
Spanish	Houdan
Barnevelder	Exchequer Leghorn
Brown-breasted Red	Berchen
Marsh Daisy	Salmon Faverolle
Redcap	Silver Spangled Hamburgh
Golden Spangled Hamburgh	,, ,, Polish
,, ,, Polish	Dark Dorking
Malay	Dark Brahma
Indian Game	Silver Dorking
Brown Leghorn	Aseel
Partridge Cochin	Columbian Wyandotte
Partridge Wyandotte	Duckwing Game and Leghorn
Black-red Game	Silver Campine
Sicilian Buttercup	Silver Wyandotte
Orloff	Light Sussex
Golden Wyandotte	Light Brahma
Gold Pencilled Hamburgh	White Wyandotte
Golden Campine	
Red Sussex	
Rhode Island Red	
Buff Leghorn	
Buff Rock	
Buff Orpington	
Buff Wyandotte	
Buff Cochin	

It should be noted that in addition to the silver there is a white indistinguishable on inspection. There is also a red that cannot be distinguished from gold save by breeding. Silver and gold are sex-linked characters while white and red are not. The white of the White Leghorn is not a silver and the White Leghorn cannot be used in a sex-linked mating. The white of the White Wyandotte, on the other hand, is a silver usually, but in many cases Wyandotte has been crossed with Leghorn and so rendered unsuitable for a sex-linked mating. The white of the Silkie is a white and not a silver; the red on the saddle of a white bird is red and not a gold.

It is commonly held that the sex of the future chick can be identified by the position of the "speck" in the egg, by the shape and by the size of the egg. But actual experiment has provided an uncompromising refutation of these speculations. Eggs selected by breeders and incubated in a research institution have never failed so far to contradict the prophecy of the breeder—males and females in normal proportions were always hatched (94 males to 100 females according to Pearl (1917), who studied some 22,000 chickens of known sex). The trap-nest has shown that some hens lay only pointed eggs, others only rounded ones, and that large eggs yield both males and females as do also small ones. In the case of the dove and the pigeon, Riddle finds that those eggs which yield females are larger and contain more food material for the embryo than those which become males. The size difference is small, however, and the "large" eggs and the "small" eggs vary in size; there is overlapping of the curves when the size is plotted in a graph and for this reason it is impossible to predict from the size of the egg alone the sex of the future bird.

The problem of the differential production of the two sexes is not yet solved, and for the time being the commercial egg-farmer must consider the advisability of eliminating the males among his day-old chicks. This he can do if it should be shown by experience that the sex-linked cross is a business proposition. It would seem that to-day this system of breeding is best employed within a breed which contains a gold and a silver variety—the Sussex for example. If good dual-purpose Red and Light Sussex are used there should be no waste, for the cockerels could be segregated, caponised, and fattened.

There is another aspect of sex-linked inheritance in poultry. There are reasons for suspecting that "high-fecundity" is a sex-linked character. If this is so and if the factor for this character is possessed by a strain of silver and barred fowls, it would be expected that the linkage relations of these three characters would be such that any barred silver bird would also possess the much desired high-fecundity character. Here lies the great promise which the phenomenon of sex-linkage holds out to the breeder. By its aid he may be able to "pick up" a physiological character by following the inheritance of superficial characters that he can readily appreciate. If high-fecundity is a sex-linked character found widely in the different breeds and if linkage holds, the breeder may be able to dispense to some extent with the trap-nest.

Haldane (1921) tested for linkage between two sex-linked genes; B, the gene for barring, and S, the gene inhibiting yellow pigmentation which converts "gold" hackle feathers into "silver."

P_1	(bsX)(bsX) Brown Leghorn	×	(BSX)Y Barred Plymouth Rock
FR_1	(BSX)(bsX) F_1 male	×	(bsX)Y Brown Leghorn
FR_2	(BSX)(bsX) : (BSX)Y Barred silver 30		(bsX)(bsX) : (bsX)Y Unbarred gold 21
	(bSX)(bsX) : (bSX)Y Unbarred silver 17		(BsX)(bsX) : (BsX)Y Barred gold 10

This corresponds to the following series of spermatozoa: 30 BS, 21 bs, 17 bS, 10 Bs. Crossing-over occurs in 27 cases out of 78, *i.e.*, 34·6 per cent., with a probable error of 3·6 per cent., that is to say, there is undoubtedly linkage. The numbers of barred and unbarred are practically equal, but there is 50 per cent. excess of silver over gold, due perhaps to selective mortality. If the locus for the high-fecundity factor is situated between those of B and S it will be possible to transfer this gene to breeds of low fecundity.

Agar (1924) using Rhode Island Reds (gold non-barred) and Barred Rocks (silver and barred) and Golden-laced Wyandottes obtained results which agree very closely with the above.

Serebrovsky (1922) deals with the same two genes B and S and introduces a third sex-linked gene K which results in a slowly-developing thick and luxuriant plumage; k = quickly developing plumage. The gene M for melanin pigment is not sex-linked.

P_1	mm(kbsX)(kbsX) Orloff	×	MM(KBSX)Y Plymouth Rock
F_1	Mm(kbsX)(KBSX) Barred	×	Mm(kbsX)Y Black

The numbers in F_2 are not yet sufficiently large to enable one to speak of percentages, but it is noticed that crossing-over is very frequent. It mostly results in the production of individuals coloured like the Plymouth Rock but with quickly-developing plumage, *i.e.*, having the constitution (kSBX)(ksbX) or (kSBX)Y or of individuals of the (KsbX)(ksbX) type ("unbarred golds" of Haldane but black in the presence of M). In one case there appeared a chick with slow development of feathers and silver but without barring, having the constitution (KSbX)(ksbX). Judging by proportions, the break of the chromosomes occurs more often between K and the other two genes, and the relative positions of these three genes upon the chromosome must be somewhat as follows—

K............................ S .... B

(Note that no crossing-over occurs in the heterogametic sex. This fact is of use in deciding which sex is the heterogametic one in those cases where the XY-mechanism has not been disclosed cytologically.)

The Case of the Tortoiseshell Cat.—The other type of sex-linked inheritance is the Drosophila type, which has already been considered and in which the male is the heterogametic sex. The nature of this mode of inheritance, first recognised in man and in the cat, was not completely appreciated until the work with Drosophila had been carried out. As an example the case of the tortoiseshell cat may be considered.

It is accepted that the mating black ♂ × yellow ♀ gives tortoiseshell ♀♀, yellow ♂♂; that yellow ♂ × black ♀ gives tortoiseshell ♀♀, black ♂♂, and an occasional black ♀; that black ♂ × tortoiseshell ♀ gives tortoiseshell ♀♀, black ♀♀, and yellow ♂♂, and black ♂♂; and that yellow ♂ × tortoiseshell ♀ gives yellow ♀ ♀, tortoiseshell ♀ ♀, yellow ♂ ♂, black ♂ ♂, and an occasional black ♀.

This being so, it follows, as Little (1918) has pointed out, that black and yellow in the cat are sex-linked characters and that together they constitute the tortoiseshell character. The facts can be explained if the following assumptions are made. The allelomorphic factors B (black) and b (yellow) are resident in the X-chromosomes, and the Y-chromosome of the male does not carry these factors. The female, possessing two X-chromosomes can have one bearing the factor for black, another bearing the factor for yellow; she can be tortoiseshell. The male can have either the factor for black or for yellow in his single X-chromosome. He cannot be tortoiseshell. It will be noted that this interpretation demands that in the cat the male shall have the XY sex-chromosome constitutions, not the XO.

1.	Black ♂		Yellow ♀
P_1	(BX)Y	×	(bX)(bX)
F_1	(BX)(bX)		(bX)Y
	Tortoise ♀		Yellow ♂
2.	Yellow ♂		Black ♀
P_1	(bX)Y	×	(BX)(BX)
F_1	(BX)(bX)		(BX)Y
	Tortoise ♀		Black ♂
3.	Black ♂		Tortoise ♀
P_1	(BX)Y	×	(BX)(bX)
F_1	(BX)(BX)		(BX)Y
	Black ♀		Black ♂
	(BX)(bX)		(bX)Y
	Tortoise ♀		Yellow ♂
4.	Yellow ♂		Tortoise ♀
P_1	(bX)Y	×	(BX)(bX)
F_1	(BX)(bX)		(ByX)Y
	Tortoise ♀		Black ♂
	(bX)(bX)		(bX)Y
	Yellow ♀		Yellow ♂

BB = black
Bb = tortoise
bb = yellow

This scheme has not accounted for the exceptional black female that appears in the F_1 of matings 2 and 4, nor for the fact that a sterile tortoiseshell male very exceptionally makes its appearance. The occasional black female is possibly due to the occasional complete expression of black in the simplex state, and the tortoiseshell male the result of crossing-over between the X and the Y in a yellow male and between the Xs in females. The above is a typical example of intermediate sex-linked inheritance.

Sperm-Dimorphism.—The conclusion that a difference in the gametes of the two sexes is correlated with the sex of the future individual is supported by the results of cytological research. As early as 1902, McClung was able to demonstrate that in various Orthoptera (the crickets, cockroaches and grasshoppers) there is in the male an unpaired chromosome instead of the equal pair in the case of the female. The constitution of the female is XX, of the male XO, so that while all the female gametes must contain an X element, only half of the spermatozoa will do so. An egg fertilised by an X-bearing sperm must give rise to an XX type of individual, a female. An egg fertilised by a sperm which lacks the X will give rise to an XO type of individual, a male. In the cockroach Hogben (1921) found 34 chromosomes in the female, Morse (1909) found 33 in the male, so that all eggs receive 17 chromosomes, while of the spermatozoa half receive 17, half 16. $17+17=34=$ ♀ ; $17+16=33=$ ♂. Later it was found by Wilson (1906) and others that the number of chromosomes was identical in both sexes in many instances, but that while in one sex the X was equally paired, in the other it was paired with an unequal mate; the female is XX, the male XY in some groups, in others the female is XY and the male XX. Goodrich (1916), Zeleny and Faust (1915), Parkes (1923), and Wodsedalek (1913) have not only shown that there are in certain cases demonstrable shape differences distinguishing the two sorts of gametes elaborated by the heterogametic sex, but by measuring the length of the sperm-head have shown that there are two intergrading size-classes. It is suggested that in the mammal the larger sperm is the X-bearing—the female-determining.

Non-Disjunction.—Thorough investigation of the phenomenon of *non-disjunction* finally placed the correlation between sex-determination and the distribution of the X- and Y-chromosomes on an unshakable foundation. The work of Bridges (1916) in a most spectacular way demonstrated the precision with which the distribution of the chromosomes and sex-linked characters coincide. In his

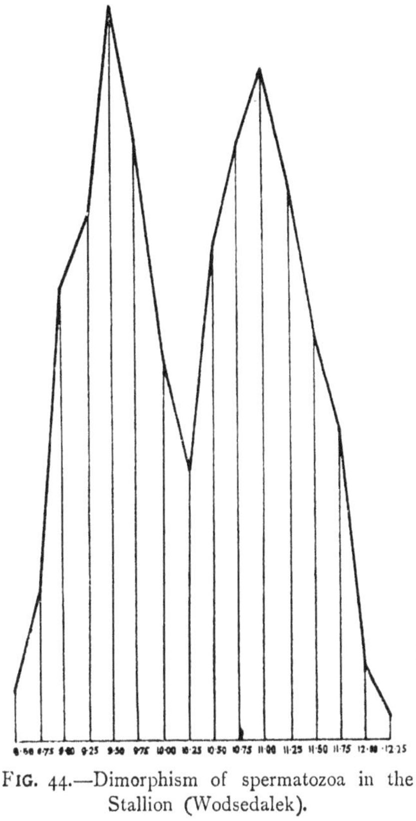

FIG. 44.—Dimorphism of spermatozoa in the Stallion (Wodsedalek).

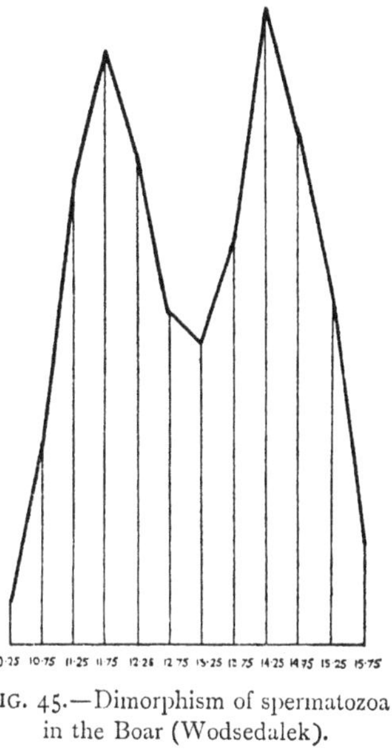

FIG. 45.—Dimorphism of spermatozoa in the Boar (Wodsedalek).

non-disjunctional work Bridges actually dealt with the mutant eye-colour character "vermilion," but "white" eye-colour may be used as an example. It will be remembered that in the mating red-eyed ♂ and white-eyed ♀ of Drosophila produces white-eyed ♂ ♂ and red-eyed ♀ ♀, so—

P_1	(WX)Y	×	(wX)(wX)
F_1	(WX)(wX)	:	(wX)Y

During the course of certain experiments there appeared in F_1, in addition to the usual two classes of offspring, certain exceptional white-eyed females and red-eyed males; when such a white-eyed female was mated to a red-eyed male, again all four classes appeared in the resulting FD_2: white-eyed females, which when bred behaved in a similar abnormal fashion; red-eyed females, of which half gave normal and half exceptional results in further breeding; red-eyed males behaving normally, and white-eyed males, of which some produced the usual sorts of offspring and some produced exceptional daughters. On cytological examination of such exceptional white-eyed females, Bridges found that the dividing nuclei of their cells displayed a Y element in addition to the normal pair of Xs. The condition was that of *secondary non-disjunction* and can be interpreted on the assumption that at reduction of the egg in which this individual had its origin, the XX pair in exceptional cases failed to *disjoin* so that the mature ovum contained either two XX or none. An egg which possesses two Xs instead of one may be fertilised by an X-bearing or a Y-bearing sperm and so the resulting zygotes may come to have three X elements or two Xs and a Y. An XXX individual is a female, an XXY individual is also a female although it possesses a Y-chromosome in addition to its two Xs. An egg which possesses no X element at all can be fertilised by an X-bearing or by a Y-bearing sperm to form an XO or an OY individual, and of these an XO individual is a male, quite normal in appearance but sterile; an OY does not develop. The type of non-disjunction consequent upon the failure of the two X-chromosomes to disjoin is known as *primary non-disjunction* of Chromosome I. The type of non-disjunction consequent upon the presence of an extra sex-chromosome is known as *secondary non-disjunction* of the sex-chromosomes. Save for an unusual sex-ratio the presence of such (cytologically) exceptional males and females would not be suspected in one and the same strain; but should such a non-disjunctional female be employed in a sex-linked experiment the appearance of exceptional phenotypes would indicate what was happening. For example, the mating of a red-eyed male and a white-eyed primary non-disjunctional female would give the following results:—

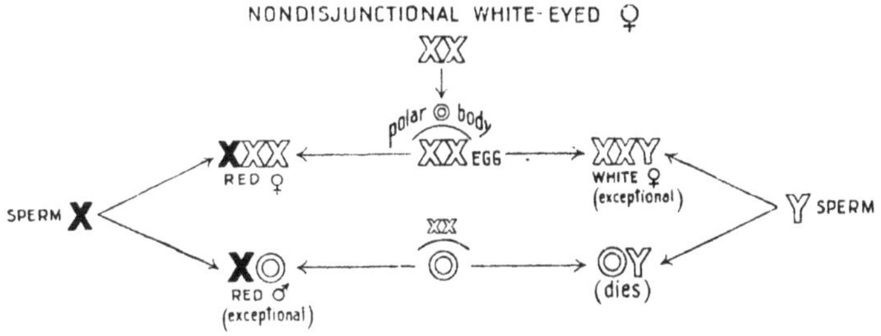

FIG. 46.—Primary non-disjunction.

In the case of the XXY white-eyed female encountered by Bridges it is assumed that when homologous chromosomes pair in synapsis, two types of reduction division are possible. If the Xs conjugate, then in reduction they disjoin and pass to opposite poles and the Y-chromosome will pass to one or the other pole. Thus X and XY ova will be produced in equal numbers. If, on the other hand, an X conjugates with the Y, then X and Y pass to opposite poles where one of them will be joined by the other X. Thus, X, XX, XY, and Y ova will be produced. From experimental evidence it has been determined that in non-disjunctional females, *homo-synapsis* (the pairing of the two X-chromosomes) occurs in 84 per cent. of cases and *hetero-synapsis* (the pairing of an X with the Y) in 16 per cent.:—

				XXY			
Homo-synapsis 84%	XX	Y		XY		X	*Hetero-synapsis* 16%
Reduction	X	XY	X	Y	XX	XY	Reduction
	42%	42%	4%	4%	4%	4%	
Ova	$(X)^{XY}$	$(XY)^{X}$		$(XX)^{Y}$		$(Y)^{XX}$	Ova
	46%	46%		4%		4%	

The ova of an XXY white-eyed non-disjunctional female may then be of four sorts associated with four sorts of polar bodies. If this female is white-eyed there can be no gene for the red-eyed condition in her genetic constitution and the genes for white-eye are borne upon the X-chromosomes. If her ova are fertilised by the sperm of a red-eyed male (the gene for red eye being carried on the single X-chromosome) the history of her chromosomes which bear the gene for white-eye can be followed.

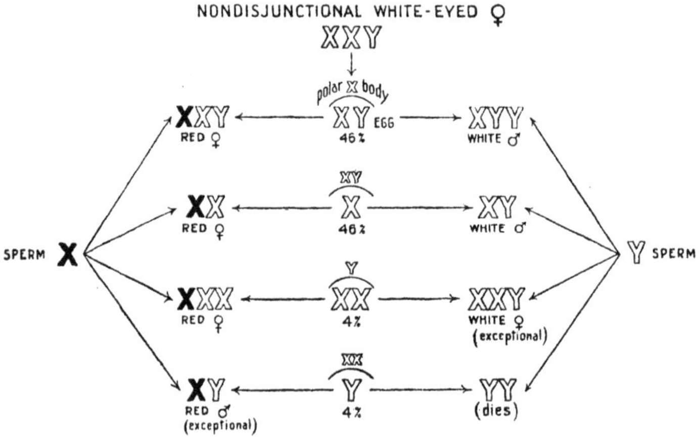

FIG. 47.—Secondary non-disjunction. (*After* Bridges.)

The exceptional white-eyed daughters of the non-disjunctional XXY female and the red-eyed XY male are white-eyed because they do not get one of their X-chromosomes from their father; the exceptional red-eyed males are red-eyed because they get their Y-chromosome from their mother, and their X from their father.

Thus, the non-disjunction of the X-chromosomes can explain the entire series of the exceptional genetic phenomena which occur in these strains. When once a non-disjunctional female is present in a stock unusual results must accumulate in increasing proportions. The experimental breeding results, backed by the cytological evidence, turned what seemed to be in direct contradistinction to the scheme of sex-linked inheritance based on the chromosome theory of heredity into a most spectacular confirmation of this theory. A consideration of the results of non-disjunction will indicate how chromosome aberration can lead to dissimilarity in the characterisation of closely related individuals. The irregularities in the behaviour of the chromosomes may be of various kinds and occur in all probability during the maturation division of the gametes. The migration of the chromosomes to the poles of the dividing cell may be irregular, so that the two daughter-cells would come to possess an abnormal number. The essential feature in chromosome aberration is the quantitative abnormality in the chromosome content as opposed to the qualitative abnormality in the case of mutation.

The Y-chromosome in Drosophila, a partner to the X-chromosome during gametogenesis, is not concerned in the determination of sex. One X, or one dose of some sex-determining gene or genes upon the X, normally results in the production of a male, two doses producing a female. Sex-linked characters are associated with the sex-determining mechanism because their genes are located in the sex-chromosomes and these characters do not necessarily have anything to do with the sexual organisation of the individual; they are sex-linked, not sex-limited characters, and are mainly concerned in the general development of the body as are most of the characters the genes of which are placed upon the other chromosomes. The facts of sex-linked inheritance point to the conclusion that sex is determined at the time of fertilisation and that the XY-chromosome mechanism provides in each generation equal proportions of males and females.

Since there is such aberration of the sex-chromosome behaviour, it is justifiable to think that if it were possible to control the behaviour of the X-chromosome (the female being XX) at the reduction division which occurs during polar-body formation, causing it to remain in the egg or to be cast out into the polar body, a profound disturbance of the relative proportions of the sexes in the following generation would result.

Gynandromorphism.—Further support for the connection of the chromosomes and sex is found in the study of gynandromorphism. A gynandromorph is an individual of a bisexual species which is a mosaic of the male and the female characters; it is a sex-mosaic in space. In insects gynandromorphs are relatively common. In a bilateral gynandromorph one half of the body is entirely male in its characters, the other half entirely female. If such a bilateral gynandromorph happens to be heterozygous for certain sex-linked characters the sex-linked characterisation may be different on the two sides of the body, but in the case of the non-sex-linked characters they are never different on the male and the female side. The male and female parts differ in the X-chromosome constitution. From such facts as those observed in Drosophila it can be concluded that the cause of gynandromorphism in this animal at least is a lagging behind of one of the X-chromosomes after one of the early cleavage divisions of a female zygote, XX in constitution, and its consequent failure to become incorporated in the resulting nucleus which will possess one X-chromosome instead of two. The daughter half-chromosome is lost in the midplate or in the cell wall.

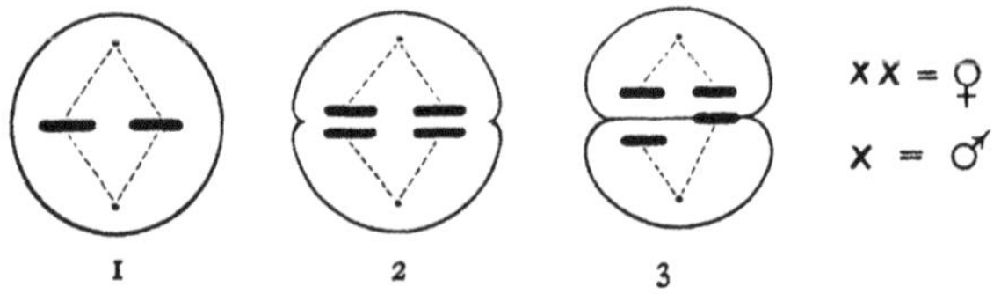

FIG. 48.—The Cytological basis of Gynandromorphism.

1. The zygote (one X from the father and one from the mother). 2. Longitudinal splitting of the chromosomes. 3. Division of cell-body: XX = ♀ ; X = ♂. (*After* Morgan and Bridges.)

Bilateral gynandromorphs can be produced only if the chromosome aberration occurs at the first division of the zygote; if it occurs at the second, one-quarter of the body will be male, and so forth. Gynandromorphs in Drosophila are females in which, as a result of abnormal chromosome behaviour, certain definite areas of the body become male in their characterisation. Such gynandromorphs are sex-mosaics in space and constitute another piece of evidence supporting the chromosome theory. A critical case confirming this hypothesis is that in which a yellow-white (sex-linked) male was mated to a female homozygous for the recessive non-sex-linked characters peach eye-colour, spineless body, kidney eye-shape, sooty body-colour and rough eye. A gynandromorph resulted, male on one side (with short wing, sex-comb on the fore leg, shorter bristles), and female on the other. On both sides of the body were exhibited all the dominant characters the genes of which were carried by the spermatozoon. The gynandromorph started as an XX female, one X carrying the genes for yellow and for white, the other carrying the genes for grey and for red, the normal allelomorphs. A yellow-white bearing daughter-X was eliminated and lost. Both male and female sides of the body received the autosomes bearing the genes for the non-sex-linked dominant characters.

Y-borne Genes in the Fish: Crossing-over between X and Y.—The results of countless breeding experiments involving sex-linkage all point to the conclusion that in Drosophila the Y-chromosome is empty or physiologically inert, that upon it either no genes are borne, or they are inactive, unless it be granted in the light of the non-disjunction experiments, that there is a gene for fertility on the Y, as an XO male is sterile, while an XY is fertile. But the impossibility of testing this gene for fertility against a mutated state producing relative or absolute infertility, makes it impossible yet awhile to regard the suggestion seriously. The statement that no genes are resident upon the Y-chromosome in Drosophila implies nothing more than that, as no mutant characters have occurred which have their genes placed, as the result of routine linkage and crossing-over experiments, upon this chromosome, it is assumed that there are no genes resident in the Y. There has been no mutation in the Y of Drosophila, and therefore no means of exploring the unmutated state. Arguing from this, it has been generally accepted that in cases other than Drosophila, the Y-chromosome is the dummy mate of the single X. But the recent work of Schmidt and of Winge (1922) on the millions fish, *Lebistes recticulatus*, and of Aida (1921) on *Aplocheilus latipes*, the small ornamental fish of Japan, has made this generalisation impossible. Schmidt and Winge have found that the ♂ and ♀ of Lebistes differ markedly in appearance, the female being larger than the male and of a plain grey-green colour, while the male, according to the race to which it belongs, is adorned with red or yellow spots on the side, with vertical stripes, with a rounded or an elongated caudal fin, or with a black spot on the dorsal fin. The males of different races are easily distinguished but the females of all races look alike. A male of any race mated with a female of the same or of any other race produces plain grey-green daughters and sons ornamented like himself. In the F_2 generation again all the males are coloured like the P_1 males, there is no segregation. An F_1 male mated to a female of any race produces sons like himself; an F_1 female mated to any male will produce sons coloured like their father. The mother in no way influences the colouring of her sons which persistently reproduce their father's colour. Certain characters in Lebistes are limited to the male. Such a mode of inheritance can readily be understood if the characters concerned are sex-linked and if their genes are resident upon the Y-chromosome in a case in which the male is heterogametic, and if the characters are epistatic to those affecting the same parts the genes for which are borne upon the autosomes that the zygote receives from the maternal parent.

Winge has shown that there are 46 chromosomes in the male and the female and that it is not possible to identify the different pairs. The Y-chromosome always bears genes for some colour or other and is transmitted only from father to son. Even if the X-chromosome also bears genes for colour the female remains uncoloured, but in the male the colour is a compromise between the usual sex-linked and the sex-limited characterisations and the two kinds of sex-associated characters can be identified. As a result of his breeding experiments Winge was able to distinguish the following sorts of X- and Y-chromosomes according to the different genes borne thereupon:—

X_0 Which does not involve any colour pattern of the male.

X_s *Sulphureus*, bearing genes producing a sulphur yellow colour in the dorsal fin, in the tail and the caudal fin, and red colour in the lower edge of the caudal fin.

Y_r *Ruber*, bearing genes producing red colour in upper edge of caudal fin, a large oblong red spot below and behind the dorsal fin, and a dark side dot on the tail.

Y_i *Iridescens*, producing a mother-of-pearl body sheen, 2 to 3 red side spots and black side dots on tail and body.

Y_m *Maculatus*, producing a large black dot on dorsal fin, a large red side spot and a black dot at the gat.

Y_f *Ferrugineus*, producing black rust-coloured part in caudal fin and a black side dot on the tail.

In one experiment in which an X_0X_0 female was crossed with an X_sY_r male, 44 males with the constitution X_0Y_r were produced, all exhibiting the characters of their male parent, red colour proximally in the upper edge of the caudal fin, a long red side spot placed below and behind the dorsal fin, a dark side spot on the tail near the caudal fin, and a colourless dorsal fin, characters the genes for which are resident in the Y-chromosome. But in addition there was a male which had a dorsal fin yellow in colour and yellow pigment in the lower side of the tail, characters the genes for which are resident in the X-chromosome, while it lacked completely the red and yellow colours on the caudal fin which was quite unpigmented. This case is interpreted by Winge as an instance of crossing-over between the X_s and Y_r chromosomes during the spermatogenesis of the X_sY_r parent; he points out that apparently there is no more difficulty in crossing-over between the X and Y in Lebistes than in the case of the autosomes; all are morphologically alike.

These colour genes were not resident in the X_0 derived from the mother: all the characters based upon the Y-borne genes derived from the father were exhibited; in addition there were characters the genes for which are borne upon the X of an X_s race. This kind of X was in association with the Y_r chromosome in the X_sY_r parent (the father). It follows therefore that the Y_r chromosome was not completely a Y-chromosome but was an association of part of an X_s and of a Y_r; such an association could be established by a crossing-over with the result that four sorts of sperm would be produced: X_s and Y_r, part X_s and part Y_r, part Y_r and part X_s.

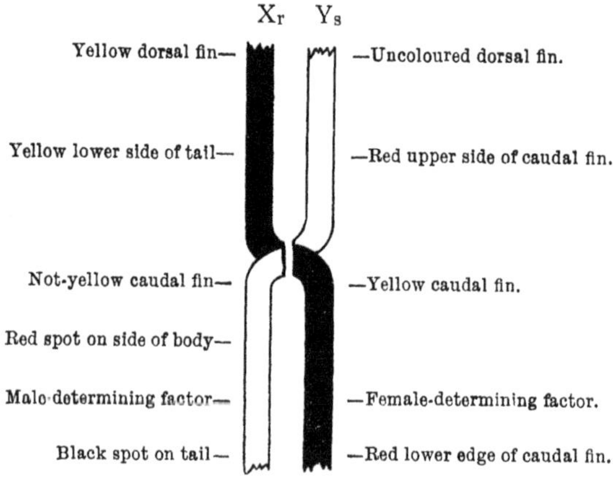

FIG. 49.—Crossing-over between X and Y in *Lebistes reticulatus.*

Winge has shown more recently that the X-chromosome may carry another gene, *elongatus* (e), responsible for an elongated caudal fin, and that this gene may cross over so as to be borne upon the Y so that a X-linked character may, as a result of such crossing-over, become sex-limited in the transmission. The following diagram shows Winge's interpretation of the case. The male used ought to have had the factor (m) in the Y-chromosome and the factor (e) in the X, but the individuals A, B, and C, for example, could only have been obtained as a result of crossing-over of the X and the Y of the male parent. From his results Winge also concluded that the chromosomes X and Y respectively contain a recessive female sex-determining factor and a dominant male sex-determining factor, that maleness and femaleness in the fish constitute a simple Mendelian pair of allelomorphic characters.

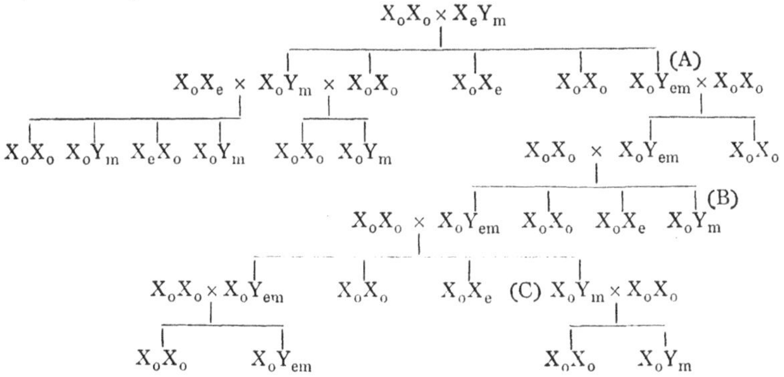

Winge termed this peculiar type of inheritance "one-sided masculine inheritance"—a clumsy term at best. It would seem better to reserve the term "sex-linked" for those characters the genes for which are resident in the sex-chromosomes, the X and the Y, and further to distinguish between them by using the terms X-linked to define the mode of inheritance met with in Drosophila, and Y-linked to define the sex-limited inheritance of characters the genes for which are resident in the Y-chromosome. Such sex-limited characters, in the absence of crossing-over, will only appear in the heterogametic sex.

Aida's work on Aplocheilus supports Winge's hypothesis and affords weighty evidence that in the fish crossing-over between X- and Y-chromosomes can and does occur. Aplocheilus as found in nature is brownish in colour, but four coloured varieties are known to the fancier—red, variegated red, white, and variegated white, and of these all the whites without exception are females. White is recessive to any other colour and breeds true; brown is dominant to red giving a 3 : 1 ratio in the F_2. Brown and white gives in F_2 brown, blue (a new colour variety), red and white in the ratio 9 : 3 : 3 : 1. Blue × red give all browns. Variegated red × red give all variegated; variegated red × white give in the F_1 all variegated, and in F_2 variegated reds, variegated whites, reds and whites in the proportions of 9 : 3 : 3 : 1. From the above it follows that in the characterisation of the skin three genes are involved :—

B	able to produce	black pigment (melanophore)	uniformly.
R	„ „	red (yellow) (xanthophore)	„
B′	„ „	black pigment partially, resulting in variegated.	

The gametic constitution of the different varieties will then be as follows :—

Brown	BBRR	White	bbrr
Blue	BBrr	Variegated white	B′B′rr
Red	bbRR	Variegated red	B′B′RR

Aida found that when a white female was mated to a brown, red, or variegated red male (*i.e.* any male duplex for R), all the white individuals in F_2 were females (with a few exceptions). On the other hand, having bred white males and mated them to females duplex for R, *e.g.*, BBRR, bbRR, B′B′RR, he found that in the F_2 all the whites, blues, and variegated whites were males (again with a few exceptions). These extraordinary results Aida interpreted as follows: (1) This fish belongs to the XY type of sex organisation. (2) The gene for Red is located in the chromosomes X and Y. A homozygous red male will have the constitution bb(RX)(RY), a female duplex for R will be bb(RX)(RX). In no other manner can the production of red males (red being dominant) from the cross red male × white female be explained.

Red ♂ — White ♀

bb(RX)(RY) × bb(rX)(rX)

b(RX) b(RY) = b(rX) Gametes

bb(RX)(rX) Red ♀♀ — bb(rX)(RY) Red ♂♂ × bb(rX)(rX) White ♀♀

b(rX) b(RY) — b(rX) Gametes

bb(rX)(rX) White ♀♀ — bb(rX)(RY) Red ♂♂

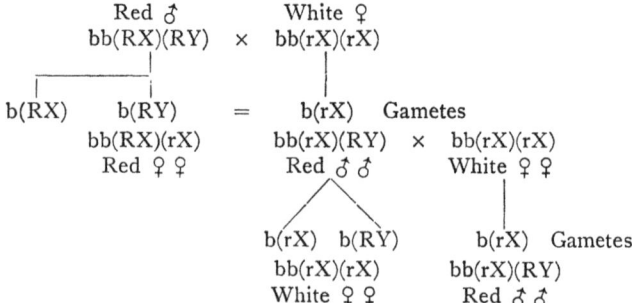

The Y-chromosome is restricted to the male line, so that all males in the progeny of any mating in which either a brown BB(RX)(RY) or a red bb(RX)(RY) male is used must be red, variegated red, or brown, whereas all individuals lacking this Y-borne dominant gene R—whites, variegated whites, and blues—must be females. For example:—

Brown ♂ BB(RX)(RY) × bb(rX)(rX) White ♀

Gametes B(RX) B(RY) b(rX)

Brown ♀ Bb(RX)(rX) × Bb(rX)(RY) Brown ♂

Gametes B(RX) B(rX) b(RX) b(rX) : B(rX) b(rX) B(RY) b(RY)

	BrX	brX	BRY	bRY
BRX	BB RX rX Brown ♀	Bb RX rX Brown ♀	BB RX RY Brown ♂	Bb RX RY Brown ♂
BrX	BB rX rX Blue ♀	Bb rX rX Blue ♀	BB rX RY Brown ♂	Bb rX RY Brown ♂
bRX	Bb RX rX Brown ♀	bb RX rX Red ♀	Bb RX RY Brown ♂	bb RX RY Red ♂
brX	Bb rX rX Blue ♀	bb rX rX White ♀	Bb rX RY Brown ♂	bb rX RY Red ♂

All the males are brown or red, while all the blues and whites are females.

Aida found further that evidence of crossing-over between the X- and Y-chromosomes was not rare in Aplocheilus: for example, in the heterozygous red male × white female experiment in which the females produced were white and the males red, exceptional red females appeared having the constitution bb(RX)(rX), and exceptional white males, bb(rX)(rY), were also occasionally encountered. Aida satisfied himself by further breeding that these were not instances of the results of non-disjunction in which case the exceptional red females would have the constitution bb(rX)(rX)(RY) and the exceptional white males, bb(rX)O. To test this question as to which of the two respective constitutions the exceptional male individuals had, the following experiment was carried out:—

bb(RX)(rX)	×	bb(RX)(rY)	or	bb(RX)O
Heterozygous		Heterozygous		Non-disjunctional
Red ♀		exceptional		Red ♂
		Red ♂		

The offspring of the mating were as follows:—

Red : White = 3 : 1	Reds	146 ♀♀ : 57 ♂♂
	Whites	2 ♀♀ : 80 ♂♂

The fact that two white females were produced shows conclusively that the gametic constitution of the red male could not be bb(RX)O, since the white female must be bb(rX)(rX) and in the mating bb(RX)(rX) × bb(RX)O there is but one single gene r, thus:—

bb(RX)(rX)		×	bb(RX)O
b(RX)	b(rX)	b(RX)	bO
bb(RX)(RX)	bb(RX)O	bb(RX)(rX)	bb(rX)O
Red ♀	Red ♂	Red ♀	White ♂

and no white females.

Whereas, if the male had the other constitution bb(RX)(rY) and if a crossing-over occurred between the chromosomes RX and rY of the male, so that (rX) and (RY) resulted, the production of bb(rX)(rX) females may be explained clearly—

bb(RX)(rX)		×	bb(RX)(rY)		
b(RX)	b(rX)	b(RX)	b(rY)	b(rX)	b(RY)
				(Cross-over gametes)	

bb(RX)(RX)	bb(RX)(rY)	bb(RX)(rX)	bb(rX)(rY)
Red ♀	Red ♂	Red ♀	White ♂
bb(RX(rX)	bb(RX)(RY)	bb(rX)(rX)	bb(rX)(RY)
Red ♀	Red ♂	White ♀	Red ♂
		Exceptional	

A review of the above facts leads to the following conclusions: the regular production in each generation of more or less equal numbers of male and female offspring suggests that some sex-determining mechanism is involved; the evidence of sex-linked inheritance suggests that as the result of the action of this mechanism one sex is heterogametic, the other homogametic; the facts of cytology suggest that this mechanism is the sex-chromosome mechanism. Sex is determined at the time of fertilisation by the nature of the sex-determining genes brought into the zygote by the conjugating gametes.

CHAPTER VII

THE PHYSIOLOGY OF SEX-DIFFERENTIATION

A "determined" male has the genetic constitution represented by the formula XY in the Drosophila type, XX in the Abraxas group; a "determined" female, XX, or XY respectively. The individual at this time is the zygote (the fertilised egg) and much must happen before it can become a functional male or female. The complicated processes of sex-differentiation, during which the sex-organisation of the individual assumes one or other type, male or female, must be pursued before the one sex can be distinguished from the other by differences in anatomical structure, in physiological functioning and in psychological characterisation; before the genotypic male becomes the phenotypic male, the genotypic female the phenotypic female.

That the sex-determining XY-mechanism is not the only agency involved in the production of a sexually functional individual is shown perfectly clearly in the case of the marine worm Bonellia, in which it is known that environmental stimuli control the ultimate sexual destiny of the individual. Bonellia displays the most extreme form of sex-dimorphism in the animal kingdom. The female has a bulky bean-shaped body, about 2 inches long, and an enormously prolonged proboscis bifurcating at its distal extremity. The male is a minute organism whose internal organs, save those connected with reproduction, are entirely degenerate and which lives as a parasite in the uterus of the female. Baltzer (1914) found that in Bonellia the question whether an individual shall function as a male or as a female is mainly determined by an accident of situation. The eggs hatch out as free swimming larvæ; if a larva settles down upon the sea-bottom it becomes, after a short period of sexual indifference, a female; but if by chance, or perhaps by attraction, a larva settles down upon the proboscis of a mature female, it develops into a male. Any larva can become either a phenotypic male or a female and as to which it is to be is decided by position. Baltzer took larvæ at various periods after they had settled upon a female proboscis but before they had become completely male, and forced them to lead an independent life. As a result he obtained intersexual forms, the degree of intersexuality depending upon the length of time the larvæ had been allowed to remain on the proboscis of the female.

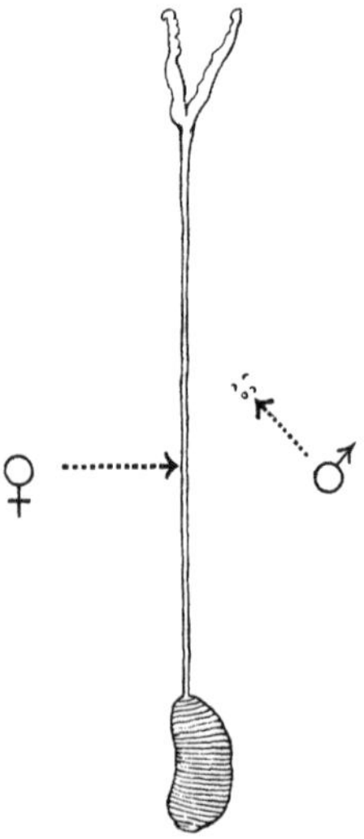

FIG. 50.
Bonellia viridis.

The case of Bonellia, if this animal has a sex-chromosome sex-determining mechanism, at once demands a revision of the definition of male and female, since it shows quite clearly that the "genetic" female can become a functional female or a functional male; a "genetic" male, a functional male or a functional female; and that the sex-chromosome sex-determining mechanism can be over-ridden. A genetic male is an individual with the appropriate genotypic constitution; a functional male is an individual which is anatomically, physiologically and psychologically equipped to function as a male, elaborating functional sperm and fertilising the ova of the female—in short, a phenotypic male.

The efficacy of purely external stimuli to influence sex-differentiation is also seen in the case of the slipper limpet, Crepidula, which, introduced to this country from America, became such a plague to oyster-fisheries. Crepidula lives gregariously in chains; the free-swimming young settle on older individuals and grow where they settle. Each individual, after attaching itself, passes through a phase of sexual indifference, then through a male phase, producing spermatozoa, then through a hermaphrodite phase, producing both spermatozoa and ova, and finally ends its days as a female producing ova only. Gould (1917) found that in *Crepidula plana* the male phase occurs only if the individual settles in propinquity to a larger individual, larger and older and therefore a female; but that if the individual is isolated and so prevented from settling

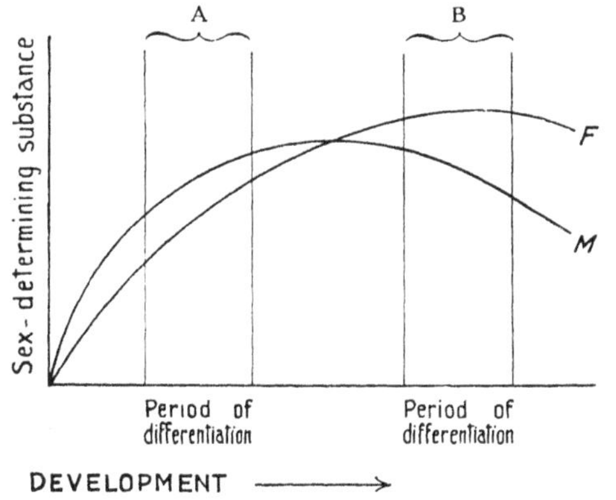

FIG. 51.

A is the phase of sex-differentiation pursued at a time during development when the male-differentiating substances are effectively in excess; the result is a male type of sex-organisation. B is the same phase pursued under conditions when the female-differentiating substances are effectively in excess; the result is a female type of sex-organisation.

upon a female, it passes directly from the neutral to the female phase.

An ingenious hypothesis has been advanced to cover the observed facts concerning Bonellia, and in this matter the case of Crepidula is very similar. It is suggested that the sex-determining genes produce sex-differentiating substances under the direction of which the differentiation of the sex-organisation is pursued. Goldschmidt (1923) supposes that in all the individuals there is at first an excess of male-differentiating substance, but that the production of the female-differentiating substance after a time overtakes this.

Further, he supposes that the secretion of the proboscis of the female of Bonellia has the effect of accelerating the process of differentiation as opposed to the process of growth, of antedating, as it were, the period during development when sexual differentiation occurs. When differentiation is rapid, the sex-organisation matures under the influence of the male-differentiating substance; when it is not accelerated, under that of the female-differentiating substance. The mode of sex-differentiation is determined by a varying physiological state in connection with varying environment and secretions from other individuals.

The cases of Bonellia and Crepidula, suggestive as they are, lose much force because in them a sex-determining chromosome mechanism has not been disclosed. However, there is abundant evidence derived from other and satisfactory sources which shows quite clearly that the explanation outlined above can be extended very generally indeed.

Balanced Genetic Intersexuality in Drosophila.

Since the difference in the sex-chromosomes is the only apparent difference in the genetic constitution of the sexes it follows that the X or something lodged in it is female-determining while male-determination is an affair of the rest of the chromosomes (exclusive of the Y which, as was seen in the results of non-disjunction, plays no part in the process of sex-determination). In Drosophila the female is duplex for the X, the male simplex. If the female-determining factor is designated F and the sum of the male-determining factors in one set of autosomes M, then whilst both sexes possess 2M, the female possesses 2X, the male 1X. Thus 2F must be $>$ 2M and 1F must be $<$ 2M.

In consequence of certain experimental results obtained by Bridges (1921) a clearer understanding of the genetical basis of sex-determination has become available, and the above conception has to be modified. A "brown" mutant of Drosophila was back-crossed to a parent stock and produced individuals which were of two sorts: females, and individuals which displayed intermediate sex-characters. These intersexes could be divided into two groups, those predominantly male, and those only tending towards the male condition. The results of breeding experiments led Bridges to the conclusion that, for one group of genes at least, the females were triploid, having inherited a double instead of a single component from their fathers. Cytological examination confirmed this opinion, for he found that chromosomes II and III were present in triplicate, while the IV chromosomes was in some cases diploid, in others triploid. *The X-chromosome was triple in the females, double in the intersexes.*

From this it could be argued that a ratio 1X : 1A (where A = one complete set of autosomes) will give females

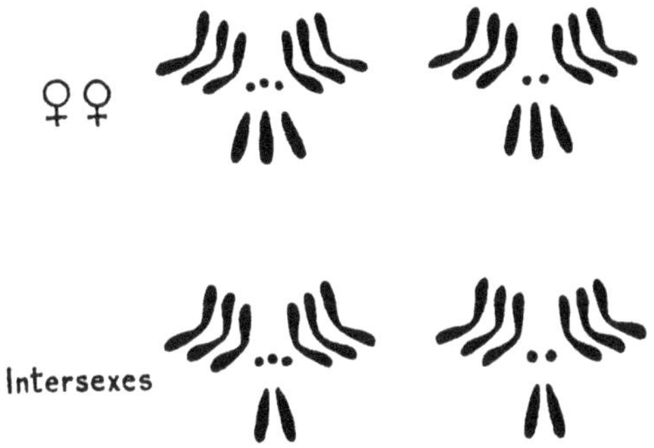

FIG. 52. (*After* Bridges.)

(3X : 3A, or 2X : 2A); a ratio of 1X : 2A, or more than 2A, will give males (1X : 2A, or 1X : 3A), while 1X : 1·5A will give intersexes (2X : 3A); and that an accurate balance of male and female-differentiating substances leads to a condition of *balanced* intersexuality. Bridges concluded that in Drosophila sex was determined by the correct quantitative balance between the male- and female-determining factors resident in the chromosomes, by the ratio between the X-chromosomes and the sets of autosomes and that the effective relation is the ratio of the number of X-chromosomes and the number of autosomes. In Drosophila a haploid (1X : 1A) has not yet been encountered, but according to the above hypothesis it would be a female. Now in some groups, *e.g.*, Rotifera, Thysanoptera, Aleyrodidæ,

Hymenoptera, and Acaridæ, the females are diploid, the males haploid, and it is commonly accepted that this condition is but a modification of the ordinary type of sex-determination. But it would seem that this cannot be so, if Bridges' conclusions stand. Schrader and Sturtevant (1923), however, have shown how by a modification of Bridges' hypothesis the haploid male can be brought into line. These authors suggest that the effective relation in the matter of sex-determination is not the ratio of the number of X-chromosomes and of autosomes, but the algebraic sum of X + A. They assign a numerical value of − 6 to the X-chromosomes and of + 2 to one set of autosomes. Then—

A super-male will be	X + 3A	Algebraic sum	0
A male "	X + 2A		− 2
A haploid male "	X + A		− 4
An intersex "	2X + 3A		− 6
A diploid female "	2X + 2A		− 8
A triploid " "	3X + 3A		− 12
A super- " "	3X + 2A		− 14

So that if the threshold for maleness is at − 5 and that for femaleness at − 7 the result is consistent with the view that the haploid Drosophila will be male. This suggestion provides a satisfactory explanation of Nachtsheim's (1913) and Doncaster's (1915) work on the cytological basis for the production of males by parthenogenesis throughout the Hymenoptera. Nachtsheim suggests that the male is X + A, the female 2X + 2A, the ratio X : A being the same in both. The parthenogenetically-produced male of the bee and of the gall-wasp is a haploid male and could be interpreted on the above hypothesis by assigning arbitrary numerical values of opposite signs to X and A with a defined threshold of the algebraic sum for the ♀ condition—

For example X = − 2 : A = + 1
♀ = 2X + 2A = − 4 + 2 = − 2
♂ = X + A = − 2 + 1 = − 1

Some individuals of this triploid strain had two instead of three IV chromosomes. These were intersexuals but considerably more female in type than those with the IV in triploid. From this it may be inferred that chromosome

IV carries a disproportionately large share of the male-determining factors.

Sturtevant (1920) has described another type of intersex in Drosophila and has shown that the condition is due to the action of a single mutant gene resident in one of the autosomes. It is remarkable that a single mutation can affect the sexual differentiation of the individual so profoundly.

Sex-differentiation in Insects and Mammals Contrasted.

Reference to the condition of intersexuality makes it necessary straightway to discuss the relation of the sex-glands to the rest of the organism. The differentiation of the sex-equipment of the individual usually results in the establishment of an efficiently equipped female or of a male capable of sexual functioning. In the case of one large group of the animal kingdom there are cogent reasons, which will be given later, for holding that this differentiation from a common type of architecture is pursued under the specific control of the sex-glands. To this group belong birds, mammals, and certain invertebrates. In the remainder the functioning of the sex-glands exerts no effect upon such differentiation. In this second group are placed the insects.

In the case of the insect, the mode of sex-differentiation is decided with the event of fertilisation; a genotypic female invariably becomes possessed of a female sex-equipment. In *Lymantria dispar*, the Gipsy moth, the female is larger than the male and her wings are banded white, whereas those of the male are brown. If the sex-glands of the caterpillar are destroyed, these external characters of the moth which develops from that caterpillar are precisely as they would have been had no operation been performed. Meisenheimer (1909) removed the ovaries of female caterpillars and replaced them by testes from male caterpillars and *vice versa*. The implanted organs of the opposite sex flourished in their new surroundings but nevertheless the external characters, when they came to be exhibited, were found to be quite unaffected by this operative interference. Male moths with all the male characters might have their bodies full of ripe eggs. Hegner (1914) destroyed the sex-glands in their earlier embryonic stages and found that even then the operation did not affect the assumption of the appropriate characters, so making it certain that Meisenheimer's results were not due to the operation of gonadectomy (extirpation of the sex-gland) having been performed after the gonad had exerted its influence upon the tissues concerned in the characterisation. Meisenheimer removed the gonads, replaced them by others from the opposite sex, and amputated the wings. The implanted gonads thrived and the wings were regenerated, but the characters were still those appropriate to the sex of the individual upon which the operation was performed.

More recently Finkler (1923) has carried out some experimental work with certain insects (such as Dytiscus) and claims to have attained some most startling results. He has shown that it is possible to replace the amputated head of a male by that of a female and *vice versa.* The bodily sexual characters, following this operation, undergo a complete change and become as those of the sex of the individual to which the transplanted head originally belonged. Blunck and Speyer (1924), repeating this work, have completely failed to confirm Finkler's findings. It is sufficient, however, for present purposes to recognise that in the insects the activity of the gonad does not play any part in the process of the differentiation of the sex-organisation.

In the case of the birds, mammals, and of certain invertebrates, on the other hand, the rôle of the functioning gonad in the processes of sex-differentiation is clearly demonstrable. It will be noted that in comparison with the insect, the mammal and the bird are infinitely longer lived. The higher forms grow to a large size before becoming sexually mature. In the sexually mature mammal, the male is to be distinguished from the female by differences in the situation and histological structure of the gonads (testes in the male, ovaries in the female); in the accessory sexual apparatus—a system of ducts (and associated glands) which convey the products of the gonads to the site of fertilisation and in the female harbour the developing fœtus (vasa deferentia and associated glands in the male, oviducts and uterus and vagina in the female); and in the external reproductive organs (penis and scrotum in the male, clitoris and vulva in the female).

At the beginning of this process of sex-differentiation the sex-organisation is represented by paired gonads (neither ovarian nor spermatic in structure), a rudimentary accessory sexual apparatus consisting of two pairs of ducts, the Wolffian and the Müllerian, and external genital organs which take the form of a phallus and a uro-genital sinus. As differentiation proceeds, it is seen that either the gonads become ovaries, the Müllerian ducts become the accessory sexual apparatus, whilst the Wolffian ducts atrophy, the phallus and uro-genital sinus become clitoris and vulva; or else the gonads assume the structure of testes, the Müllerian ducts atrophy whilst the Wolffian ducts become the vasa deferentia, and the embryonic external genitalia become penis and scrotum. One or the other type of sex-organisation is developed from embryonic structures commonly possessed by all individuals, genotypic male and genotypic female alike. (Figs. 53*a* and *b*.)

At about the time when the individual becomes sexually mature certain other characters distinguishing the sexes are exhibited. These include differences in the pitch of the voice, in the regional distribution of the hair, in the size of the mammary glands, in the size of horns and such like, and in sexual behaviour.

Wentworth (1916) points out that in the Ayrshire, black (deep mahogany) piebald is the simple allelomorph of red piebald and that the heterozygous males have black piebald coats, whereas the heterozygous females are red piebald. It is possible that the black is an intense red, that a BB individual is black be it male or female, while a Bb male is black and a Bb female red, the difference being associated with the difference in internal environment. Other instances of similar sex-dimorphism are the Ankoli cattle of Africa, in which the males are white and the cows red (Lydekker 1912), and the Tarentaise cattle of France in which the male is wheaten, the female fawn (George).

The Effects of Gonadectomy and Implantation in Mammals.

The results of castration and implantation experiments on birds and mammals make it perfectly clear that for the

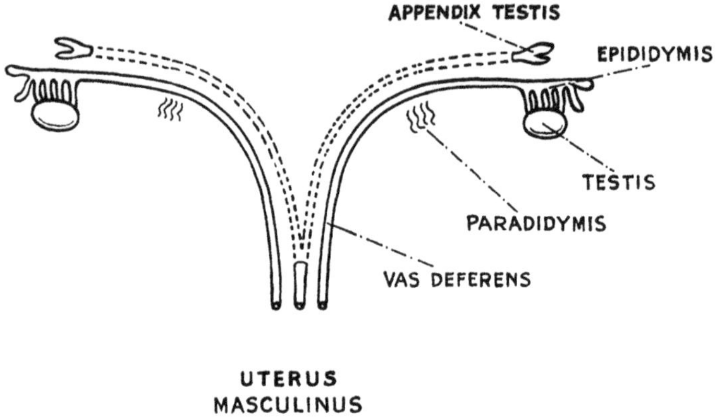

Sex-differentiation in the Male.

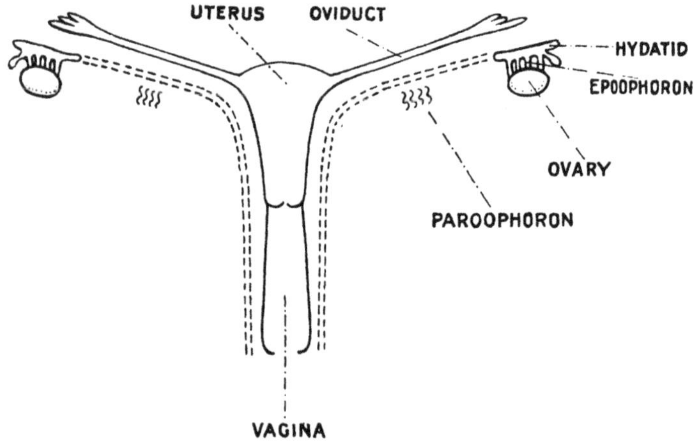

Sex-differentiation in the Female.

FIG. 53*a*.—Differentiation of Gonads and Internal Genitalia. (*After* Broman.)

development of the appropriate type of sexual characterisation the presence of a functioning gonad is essential, and histological studies have shown that the gonad of the mammal is built up of two sorts of tissue—the gametogenic, concerned with the elaboration of the gametes, sperm or ova, and that known as interstitial tissue. It has been recognised from the earliest times that castration in man and in domesticated mammals, besides causing suppression of sexual desire was followed by profound changes in the sexual characterisation, particularly if the operation was performed before

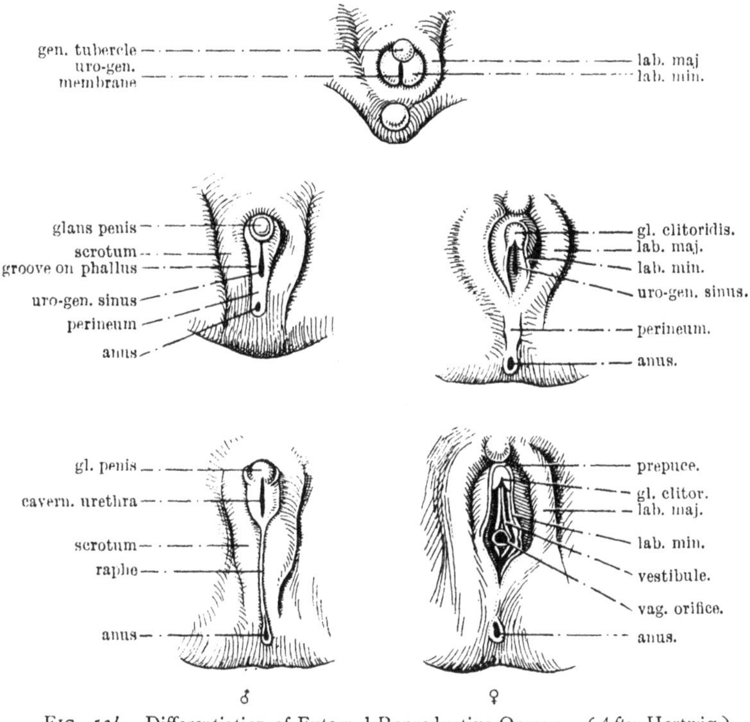

FIG. 53*b*.—Differentiation of External Reproductive Organs. (*After* Hertwig.)

puberty, but only during recent years have these effects been studied critically. Since for the development of these characters the presence of a functional gonad is necessary they will be referred to as secondary gonadic characters.

Steinach (1916) removed the reproductive glands from young guinea-pigs and grafted gonads from individuals of the opposite sex into some of the castrated animals. The animals which were merely castrated failed to develop the secondary gonadic characters which they would presumably have shown otherwise. Testes implanted into castrated males survived; they never developed spermatozoa, but the interstitial tissue multiplied very considerably and these males assumed the distinctive male characters to an exaggerated degree. Castrated males into which ovaries were successfully implanted became feminised and grew into animals with the appearance and habits of females, attractive to males and able to suckle the young of others. Ovariotomised females into which testes were successfully grafted became masculinised, looking and behaving like males.

In considering the brilliant work of Steinach, Lipschutz, Sand and others on the experimental feminisation of the phenotypic male and the masculinisation of the phenotypic female, doubts arise as to whether when recording the psycho-sexual changes following the operation, these authorities have remembered that it is impossible to isolate even a small group of individuals of the same sex without one or more quickly assuming the sexual habits appropriate to the opposite sex. Almost every utility poultry breeder possesses a laying hen that behaves as a male; it is impossible to pen a dozen cocks together without one or more being forced to play the rôle of a female; it is not uncommon for a young male dog to allow puppies or even kittens to suckle. Behaviour of this sort is extremely common among individuals in which reproductive activity is at a high level quite apart from any experimental interference, and allowance must be made for this fact.

Bouin and Ancel (1904, 1906) showed that in the horse and other animals, if the vasa differentia were ligatured, the spermatogenic tissue of the testis ceased to be functional and gradually underwent degeneration, whereas the interstitial tissue remained unaffected. They concluded that the origin of a specific "internal secretion" lay in the interstitial cells (cells of Leydig) and not in the spermatogenic tissue. They showed further that the effects of castration could be prevented by injection of the extract prepared from the interstitial tissue into castrated guinea-pigs. Bouin, Ancel, and others hold that a fœtal interstitial gland is present in the testis of the developing horse. It was Berthold (1849) who first based the idea on experimental evidence by castrating cocks and implanting the testes into new situations in the body, when he noted that the cock thus treated did not become a capon. Berthold concluded from these experiments that the testes elaborated substances which caused and preserved the cock's characters, and that these substances were elaborated by the testes, whether these are in the normal or abnormal position.

Tandler and Grosz (1913) subjected the testes of the roe buck to X-rays and thereby destroyed the spermatogenic tissue, leaving the interstitial tissue unimpaired. Knud Sand (1919) describes hypertrophy of the clitoris in a masculinised rat into which a testis was implanted after ovariotomy. Shattock and Seligmann (1904) occluded the vasa deferentia in Herdwick rams and found that this operation did not affect the development of the secondary gonadic characters. Marshall (1912) has shown that castration of a ram lamb of a breed in which only the males are horned is followed by the non-appearance of horns, and that if such castration is performed after the horns have begun to grow, they cease growing from that time onwards. A castrated ram lamb of a breed in which both sexes are horned grows horns like those of a female rather than like those of a male. Whitehead (1908) and others have found that there is an intimate association between the interstitial tissue and sexual instincts. The abdominal testis in the horse is aspermatic but the interstitial tissue is abundant, and such a "rig" exhibits exaggerated sexual behaviour. Crew (1921) has shown that the aspermatic condition of the undescended testis is due to the fact that for the final stages of spermatogenesis the temperature within the abdominal cavity is too high, being some 5° C. higher than that within the scrotum. This explanation has been confirmed and extended by Moore (1922, 1924) and by Moore and Quick (1924).

Rörig (1900) records three cases in which female deer

possessed horns as in the male; on examination it was found that the ovaries were diseased. Pearl and Surface (1915) record the case of a cow with ovarian cystic disease which assumed the general appearance of a bull. The effects of ovariotomy in the cow have been investigated by Tandler and Grosz. They found that the operation was followed by the assumption of characters intermediate between those of the male and the female, a neutral form. Knauer (1900) removed the ovaries of rabbits and dogs from the normal position and found that when implanted on peritoneum and muscle such ovaries survived and prevented the premature menopause which follows ovariotomy.

Hormonic Rejuvenation.

Brown Séquard in 1889 was the first to suggest that in addition to its effect upon the secondary gonadic characters and sexual instinct, the testis exerts a rejuvenating influence upon the organism as a whole. He injected subcutaneously testicular extract from dogs and guinea-pigs into animals and also into himself, and he was convinced that in both cases beneficial results followed and persisted for a time. In spite of these claims the practice was not continued and nothing further was done until 1913 when Lespinasse recorded a case of testicular transplantation in man. Lichtenstern (1916) of Vienna successfully operated on a soldier who had lost both testicles as the result of a gun-shot wound. The patient was rapidly developing the typical signs of complete castration when Lichtenstern implanted the undescended testis removed from another individual. The patient resumed all the characters of a normal male and soon married. Lichtenstern has also performed the operation for eunuchoidism and homosexuality as well as for impotence and general debility, and claims success. In 1918 Stanley and Kelker (1920) performed testicular transplantation using animal testes (goat, ram, deer, boar) instead of human. Necrosis was the usual fate of the implant, and in later experiments (over 1000 in 1922) men were injected with partially macerated testis in order to avoid this. The injected material could be felt beneath the skin for some time following the injection, but ultimately it became absorbed. From these experiments Stanley concluded that the injection of animal testis into the human was followed by transient benefit— increased sexual activity, bodily well-being, and power of vision.

Voronoff (1922) began his work in 1917. He reports the results of 120 testicular grafts performed upon animals and man. Numerous testicular grafts were made upon previously castrated male sheep and goats, in order to ascertain whether the implanted testicles could play their part in animals deprived of their own and replace these in their functions as endocrine glands. In those cases in which the grafts did not slough or were not too quickly absorbed, the ingrafted testicles dominated the secondary gonadic characters, sexual instinct, and virile capacity. Two senile rams were operated upon with the result that two months later a change in their bearing was observed and their broken-down air and dull look gave place to vivacity of movement and a bellicose disposition. Their vigour increased considerably from month to month and each became the sire of lambs. In one of these cases the graft was removed at the end of fourteen months and following this the condition of the animal declined once more and its vivacity disappeared. A new graft was then made, and some months later there remained no trace of its senile condition. Following this Voronoff undertook the operation on the human and claims equal success.

In Voronoff's work two points are emphasised: (1) the implanting of the prepared pieces of testes on the tunica vaginalis, *i.e.*, putting the graft in the natural position of the testis in the scrotum; and (2) the donor and the recipient must be as near akin as possible, *e.g.*, for the human Voronoff uses chimpanzee's testis. Thorek (1922), in America, has recently confirmed Voronoff in regard to the persistence of the chimpanzee graft in man.

Voronoff concludes from his results that senility is due in part to the diminution or disappearance of the internal secretion of the sex-gland, so that by supplying the testicular hormone (hormone = a chemical messenger) by means of a graft in the peritoneal cavity or in the tunica vaginalis, where it is not absorbed and does not necrose, the body can become rejuvenated. He holds the view that the epithelial cells are the agents of the cellular secretion, both internal and external, and that the seminal cell is at once exocrine (elaborating a product that is carried away by a duct) and endocrine (elaborating a product that is carried away by the blood-stream). He suggests that when these cells are deprived of their excretory canal they cease to elaborate the spermatozoa and act only in the endocrine sense and that the interstitial cells possess only a nutritive function. Whichever interpretation of the origin of the sex-hormone be the true one, it is enough to recognise that the gonad as a whole is the seat of hormone production, and it would seem that the operation might prove of great usefulness to breeders of stock if by it the service life of a really desirable sire could be extended. But the histological structure of undescended testes and of the testes after ligation of the vas deferens does not seem to support the contention that the interstitial cells are merely nutritive in function. If the testicles of a rat, for example, are removed and then transplanted into the subcutaneous tissues of the abdominal wall, the rat grows to the size of a full-grown male and behaves as such. On section the transplanted testes will show degenerate seminiferous tubules and hyperplastic interstitial tissue. If the rat is merely castrated, senility soon ensues. If, on the other hand, an old rat no longer sexually potent is operated upon and has one of its vasa deferentia ligatured, it becomes again vigorous and sexually potent. Ligation of the vas results in backward pressure in the seminiferous tubules and upon the interstitial tissue. The latter responds at once by an increase in the output of secretion and a sudden rejuvenescence results. The germinal tissue gradually degenerates and the interstitial tissue increases in amount, thus producing a greater amount of the internal secretion which results in a definite rejuvenescence of the tissues of the body generally; this at least is one explanation, though not the only one. Such an operation is known as Steinach's; it could quite easily be applied in the case of farm stock.

Sand in his record of the results of vasectomy in a dog confirms the conclusions of Steinach. The dog, which showed all the signs of advanced age, became rejuvenated after the operation of double vasectomy. Zondek (1921) has examined the results of ligation of the vas by using the definite scientific test of metabolism measurements, and finds that the Steinach operation produces a definite rise in the rate of metabolism, but that this passes off after a month or so.

Oslund (1924) maintains that following the operation of vasectomy the constituent tissues of the testes are unaltered, and that the degeneration of the seminiferous tubules and hypertrophy of the interstitial tissue is the result of the cryptorchism which follows the operation in certain cases. He maintains that vasectomy without artificial cryptorchism is useless.

The testicular graft operation promises good results in the case of a young male which at the time of normal sexual maturity shows signs of eunuchoidism. The grafts, though ultimately becoming absorbed, will function sufficiently to jockey the growing male through a period of physiological disturbance. Similarly a graft into a male with atrophied testicles stimulates these to renewed activity. (Morris 1916, and Walker 1924.)

Hormonic rejuvenation in the case of the female has been secured, according to several workers, as the result of treatment of the ovaries with X-rays. It is claimed that as a result of such treatment the oogenetic tissue is destroyed but that the interstitial tissue survives and flourishes to produce an increased effect upon the general economy. But since such treatment results in sterility it has no application in practical animal breeding. Ovarian grafting, however, is possible.

There are still other characters that distinguish the sexes, such as difference in size, shape of the skeleton, and in basal metabolism. Such differences in the pelvis of the human can be distinguished at about the third to fourth month of pregnancy. The relation between such characters and gonadic functioning is not yet defined. It is probable that they are secondary genotypic characters — based directly upon the genotype—and not secondary gonadic.

The Effects of Gonadectomy and Gonad Implantation in the Bird.

In the case of the fowl, castration of the cock produces the typical capon with small comb and spurs, and indifferent sex-instinct, while the plumage remains (or in the case of the hen-feathered cock, becomes) cocky, though less bright and more luxuriant than that of the functional male. Castration of the male guinea-fowl, which is feathered exactly like its mate, does not affect the plumage-characters at all.

Castrated henny-feathered ♂   Normal henny-feathered ♂

FIG. 54. Sebright Bantam.

Pézard (1919) claims to have induced in the fowl a condition exactly equivalent to that of surgical castration by keeping the birds on a strictly carnivorous diet, as a result of which a slow intoxication occurred and the sex-glands either atrophied or did not develop. Foges (1903) freed the testes of cocks and transplanted them into various positions in the body of the same fowl. In such cases in which the transplantation was successful the characters of the capon did not appear. The same result follows incomplete castration. Lœwy (1903) claims that injections of testicular extract into young capons restores the characters of the cock. Goodale (1916) found that after castration of the cock the feathers changed but little, though their growth was more luxuriant, and that the comb remained infantile. The spurs and moults were unaffected but the behaviour changed. The capon can and will on occasion crow and will tread a squatting hen. Pézard's (1918) observations are similar. He found that caponisation inhibited the growth of the head furnishings and removed all bellicosity. Injections of testicular extracts (interstitial) prepared by aqueous maceration of this tissue from the pig, caused the head furnishings to grow completely, as did also implantation of testicular tissue. Implantation of testicular tissue into an ovariotomised hen resulted in a growth of the comb.

Ovariotomy in the hen is followed by much more profound changes. The spurs grow and the plumage becomes cocky. Goodale found that the castrated drake retained the typical drake plumage but did not assume the peculiar summer plumage which somewhat resembles the usual plumage of the female. Ovariotomy in the female was followed in some cases, though not in all, by the assumption of the male type of plumage. In one case the duck retained the nuptial plumage of the drake and did not assume the eclipse plumage. Another one first assumed the nuptial plumage, then the eclipse, and later again the nuptial plumage. Morgan (1919) suggests that in this case some ovarian tissue was left in the body. Poll (1909) found that castrated ducks moulted normally. In the case of the ostrich, Duerden (1919) states that the red skin-coloration in the male of the North and South African variety and also the dark blue colour of the Southern are dependent upon the presence of the testes, but that the castrated cock attains the normal black plumage which distinguished him from the hen. Spaying of the hen ostrich is followed by the retention of the ordinary body colour but the normally grey feathers assume the blackness of the cock.

Ovariotomy in the fowl and duck is difficult owing to the diffuse condition of the ovary. It is wellnigh impossible in the pullet but can be done fairly easily in a few days old chick, as shown by Finlay (1923). Goodale performed the operation on Brown Leghorn pullets, a breed in which the coloration of cock and hen is markedly different. In the successful experiments the hen assumed the full plumage of the male with red saddle, black breast, and cocky hackles and spurs. The birds did not crow and the growth of the comb was irregular. Pézard's results are somewhat different and he concluded that ovariotomy has no influence on the development of the comb. Moreover, in Pézard's ovariotomised hens the tail sickles and the characteristically male feathers did not appear. Both Goodale and Pézard were able to "feminise" castrated males by the implantation of ovarian tissue. Finlay, operating on the three days' old Brown Leghorn chick, carried out the following scheme:—

Males.

(1) Normal male castrated.
(2) " " and testis implanted.
(3) " " and ovary "
(4) " in which one testis was extirpated and ovary implanted (*e.g.* testis and ovary in one and the same male).

Females.

(5) Normal female ovariotomised.
(6) " " and ovary implanted.
(7) " " and testis "
(8) " in which testis was implanted (*e.g.* ovary and testis in one and the same female).

So far as the external characters are concerned, it was noted that the following results were obtained:—

Group.	Size, shape, thickness of bones.	Comb.	Plumage.
1	♂	Infantile	Cocky, but capon-like (loose, luxuriant)
2	♂	♂	♂
3	♂	♀	♀
4	♂	♂	♀
5	♀	Infantile	Cocky, but capon-like
6	♀	♀	♀
7	♀	♂	♂
8	♀	♂	♀

The operation in these cases was performed at the earliest possible opportunity after hatching, so that the gonad was exerting its influence upon the body generally for the shortest (in 1 and 5) or for the longest possible time. It is to be noticed that certain of the characters which distinguish the sexes, size, shape, carriage were unaffected in every case; these sex-limited differences would appear to be secondary genotypic. It is possible that size is a sex-linked character and a duplex state of the factor may produce a greater end-result than a simplex (the cock being XX, the hen XY).

Certain of Finlay's classes can be found among developmentally abnormal fowls. Crew (1923) has described the developmental capon and the developmental poularde which fall into Finlay's groups 1 and 5 respectively. In these cases it was found that though testis and ovary had become differentiated, they had never functioned. The capon could be distinguished from the poularde in every case, however, by the size, shape, and carriage characters. A laying hen with cocky plumage is not uncommon. Examination of a series of these cases has shown that the explanation is that during a moult the ovary of the hen completely ceased to function, but that later it resumed its full activities.

In the mammal it is generally accepted that the reproductive glands function as ductless glands providing internal secretions which direct the development of the remaining structures of the sex equipment. In them the sex-determining gene mechanism results in the production of the sex-differentiating substances, possibly enzyme-like in constitution, and these direct the differentiation of the embryonic gonad into testis or into ovary. The gonad becomes differentiated and in it is developed the gametogenic tissue which provides the gametes, and interstitial tissue which provides the male or the female sex-hormone, specifically different, that directs the development of the appropriate accessory sexual apparatus and secondary gonadic characters. Every individual, XX and XY alike, at the beginning of the development of its sexual organisation possesses paired undifferentiated gonads, paired Müllerian and Wolffian ducts, and structures which are concerned in the later development of the secondary gonadic characters of both sexes. The first stage in sex-differentiation is the formation of ovaries or of testes from undifferentiated gonads. Next, under the direction of the hormone produced by testis or ovary, either the Müllerian or the Wolffian ducts continue their development to become the functional accessory sexual apparatus, and later, about the time of sexual maturity, under the influence of the sex-hormone the appropriate secondary gonadic characters are displayed. If, as appears probable, the sex-hormone is chemically identical throughout the life history of the individual, then the assumption of the different sexual characters at different stages of the life-cycle must imply that more than the sex-hormone is involved, or that interaction between gonad and the other endocrine glands such as pituitary and adrenal may be necessary, or that the different tissues respond only at a certain stage of growth which is not attained synchronously in all. The genotypic female, in the absence of disturbing agencies, develops ovaries: she develops these because she is a genotypic female and is not a genotypic female because she has ovaries. The phenotypic female, on the other hand, is a phenotypic female because she has developed ovaries.

The situation in birds is in the main in agreement with that in mammals, though the results of ovariotomy point to the conclusion that the physiological influence of this organ is such as *prevents* the assumption of the secondary gonadic characters of the male. Castration of the henny-feathered cock suggests that in the testis of such a male there is something which in its action is equivalent to some component of the ovary, since it too prevents the assumption in a male of the male secondary gonadic characterisation as far as plumage is concerned. This question will be considered further.

The sex-organisation can be classified for descriptive purposes as follows:—

SEXUAL CHARACTERS.

1. *The Genotypic.*

(The sex-determining factor-complex symbolised as XX or XY.)

2. *The Phenotypic.*

In the Insect.	In the Mammal.
A. The secondary genotypic characters (the expression of the genotype.)	*A.* The secondary genotypic characters. Among these the primary gonadic characters (ovary or testis).
	B. The secondary gonadic characters, depending for their expression upon the activity of the functional gonad.

Genetic Intersexuality in the Gipsy Moth.

In insects, the gonad exerts no influence upon the processes of sex-differentiation. The tissues of an individual are either XX or XY, are physiologically male or female, and those concerned in the development of the sex equipment pursue that development in the male or in the female direction. No abnormality in the differentiation of the sex-gland can affect the differentiation of the rest of the sexual characters, for this is predetermined by the genotype. Any unusual differentiation is but the outward visible sign of an unusual genotype.

It has long been known to entomologists that local races of closely allied species of moths, when crossed, yield offspring that show characteristics of both sexes. For example, if European specimens of the notorious forest pest, the Gipsy moth, *Lymantria dispar*, are bred among themselves the offspring are unremarkable. The same is true in the case of the Japanese variety (*L. japonica*). But if crosses are made between these two varieties, the offspring are remarkable. The mating European ♀ × Japanese ♂ produces in the F_1 normal males, and females which show a number of modifications in the direction of maleness, *i.e.*, the females are all imperfect, intersexual. The reciprocal cross, European ♂ × Japanese ♀ produces normal males and females in the usual proportions, but if such F_1 individuals are then interbred, there appears in F_2 a certain proportion of males showing modifications in the direction of the female type of organisation, *i.e.*, males which are intersexual. As a result of much experimental breeding, Goldschmidt (1923) was able to group his strains into "weak" and "strong" classes, according to their "strength" in mating. For example, a male of a "strong" strain mated to a female of a "weak" strain produced 50 per cent. normal males and 50 per cent. intersexual individuals which were females modified in the male direction. A "weak" male mated to a "strong" female produced a normal generation of offspring. A "very strong" male mated to a "weak" female produced offspring all of the male type of organisation. It will be noted that this idea of efficiency in genetical action introduces the conception of "fractionation" of genes. This can readily be avoided by calling on the aid of "modifying" genes which act upon the "principal" ones. However, for the sake of simplicity the results are interpreted as grades of relative efficiency of the principal genes themselves. On the basis of his results Goldschmidt was soon able to predict with precision the consequence of mating individuals from different cultures. If "strong" race A gave moderate intersexuality when mated with "weak" race P, whilst with race Q it had strong intersexuality, and if a "strong" race B had given moderate intersexuality with Q, then it could be safely predicted that B with P would give only a slight degree of intersexuality. Goldschmidt accounts for the results of his extensive breeding experiments by introducing a quantitative notion of "efficiency" distinguishing the sex-determining genes of different local races of Lymantria. By efficiency is inferred the rate at which the sex-determining genes produce in the germinal organisation their sex-differentiating substances which influence the differentiation of the sex-organisation of the individual, substances perhaps of the nature of enzymes which produce one of the two types of metabolism, male or female, in the developing embryo, creating thus one or two sorts of internal environment.

In moths the male has the constitution XX, the female XY. If the gene which produces the male-differentiating substance is borne upon the X-chromosome then in the male it will be produced in double dose, in the female in single dose. Goldschmidt found that the gene which produced the female-differentiating substance exists in the same dosage in all ova, and suggested first that this gene was transmitted in the cytoplasm of the egg. But in a cross of two strains, Tokyo ♀ × Hokkaido ♂, a female was produced which when back-crossed with a pure Hokkaido ♂ produced none but females, one half of which were normal while the other half were abnormal, exhibiting certain male genetic characters, and having two X-chromosomes and no Y. The eggs of these, therefore, were formed in the entire absence of a Y-chromosome. Goldschmidt's interpretation of this situation is that the female-determining factor is resident in the Y, and that in this case it became transferred to the X through crossing-over between the X and the Y. Similar results were obtained in crossing a female carrying a factor (c) for dark colour in the X-chromosome with a light male. This mating gave dark sons and light daughters, but in addition one light son and one dark daughter appeared. These are explained similarly as being the result of crossing-over between the X and the Y.

For these reasons Goldschmidt has definitely placed the female-determining factor on the Y-chromosome. He suggests that the functioning of the Y-borne female-determining gene-complex is prezygotic. The oocyte has the sex-chromosome constitution XY, and if it is assumed that the Y-borne factors are active at this stage of oogenesis, before the disjunction of the X and the Y occurs, then the female-differentiating substance will have been elaborated and will be included in both the X- and the Y-bearing ova.

If M represents the gene determining maleness and F that determining femaleness, the male will be MMF, the female MmF. As F is transmitted through the mother only, the eggs of the female will be of two sorts—MF (the X-bearing ovum) and mF (the Y-bearing ovum), while the males will liberate gametes all bearing M. The conception of Goldschmidt can be illustrated by assigning arbitrary numerical symbols to the sex-determining factors. Those which are here employed are those used by Hogben (1923) and are merely illustrative and are not identical with those originally employed by Goldschmidt in his rather intricate presentation. In the production of males and females, 2M must be greater than 1F and 1M less than 1F respectively.

M = male-determining gene resident on the X-chromosome. M_1, M_2, M_3, M_4, M_5, etc., are male-determining genes of relatively different efficiency. M_1 is a weak M, M_5 a relatively very strong M, and so on. Since a male has two X-chromosomes, he carries two Ms and these may be of different grades of efficiency.

F = female-determining gene resident in the Y and producing its sex-differentiating substances before the X and Y disjoin and the mature eggs X and Y respectively are produced. F_2, F_3, F_4, etc., are female-determining genes of relatively different efficiency. The same grade of F will be present in all the eggs produced by one and the same individual.

The following table shows how racial differences can be illustrated and the results of inter-racial crosses interpreted:—

A "Strong" Race—	♂ $M_3M_3F_4$	×	♀ M_3mF_4
Gametes	M_3		M_3F_4 mF_4
F_1	$M_3M_3F_4$		M_3mF_4
	A male		A female
	$M > F$		$M < F$

A "Weak" Race—	♂ $M_2M_2F_3$	×	♀ M_2mF_3
Gametes	M_2		mF_3 M_2F_3
F_1	M_2mF_3		$M_2M_2F_3$
	Female		Male
	$M < F$		$M > F$

A Cross—

A "strong" male	$M_3M_3F_4$	×	M_2mF_3	A "weak" female
Gametes	M_3		mF_3 M_2F_3	
F_1	M_3mF_3		$M_3M_2F_3$	
	Intersexual female		Male	
	$M = F$		$M > F$	

Reciprocal Cross—

A "weak" male	$M_2M_2F_3$	×	M_3mF_4	A "strong" female
Gametes	M_2		M_3F_4 mF_4	
F_1	$M_2M_3F_4$		M_2mF_4	
Gametes	M_2 M_3		M_2F_4 mF_4	

F_2	$M_2M_2F_4$	M_2mF_4	$M_3M_2F_4$	M_3mF_4
	Intersexual male	Female	Male	Female
	$M = F$	$M < F$	$M > F$	$M < F$

($>$ = greater than; $<$ = less than).

By the use of such symbols it is easy to illustrate the production of an F_1 generation consisting of 50 per cent. males and 50 per cent. females whose bodily characteristics are male:—

P_1 Strong male	$M_5M_5F_6$	×	M_2mF_3	Weak female
Gametes	M_5		M_2F_3 mF_3	
F_1	$M_5M_2F_3$		M_5mF_3	
	Male $M > F$		Female (MmF) but $M > F$, so all with male organisation.	

The sex-characters of these intersexual females are remarkable. They start their development as females and at a critical point change their mode of life and finish as males, and since the hard parts of an insect are external and are composed of chitin, any of them which are hardened before the change remain unaltered by it, so that from an examination of the parts which normally are different in the two sexes it is possible to decide in the case of any particular intersexual individual exactly when the change occurred. The intersexuality in the Lymantria hybrids does not show an intermediate condition of sex-differentiation of such features as the shape, size, and colour of the body, the feathering of the antennæ, the structure of the legs. The intersex is a sex-mosaic, and the character of the structure which displays sex-differentiation is related to the time at which it makes its appearance in development. The intersex is a sex-mosaic in time. The female with the least degree of intersexuality has only the feelers modified in the manner of the feathered male type. Those displaying a further degree of intersexuality will have the male colouring of the wings in addition. A further stage will consist in male type of copulatory organs as well, although the sex-glands are still of the female type. A still further stage is that in which the size of the abdomen and hair of this region are of the male type. The final stage of all is that in which the ovaries are replaced by testes: in such cases sex-reversal is complete. The importance of these observations lies in the fact that the last characters to be differentiated in the pupa and the first to become intersexual are the branching of the antenna and the wing coloration, while the first organ to be differentiated and the last to become intersexual is the sex-gland. Goldschmidt infers with reason that the sexual characterisation of any particular organ of the sex-equipment depends on whether one or the other type of sex-differentiating substance is effectively in excess at the time when the organ arises in development. He interprets the mosaic character of the intersex by the assumption that the amount of sex-differentiating substances produced in virtue of the presence of the corresponding sex-determining genes is not constant throughout life: that at one time the male-differentiating substance is in excess, at another, the female. In the male of the moth $M > F$ and the male-differentiating substance is effectively in excess until the period of development is completed. In the female $M < F$ and the female-differentiating substance is effectively in excess during development. But if it should so happen that the sex-differentiating substances are produced at different rates, and if some genes possess the property of producing more sex-differentiating substance in a given time than others, then there exists the possibility that sex-mosaics in time will be produced.

A male of a race in which the sex-determining genes work at a faster rate is crossed with a female of a race in which these genes work at a slower rate. The female-determining factor F is always inherited through the mother and in all the offspring there will be this factor F and the female-differentiating substance will be produced all at the same rate. The male offspring, on the other hand, will receive one M from their mother and the other, the quickly producing M, from their father, so that in a given time the male-differentiating substance will be effectively in excess during development. The female offspring will have the M from the father and, as a consequence, the amount of male-differentiating substance will increase relatively to the amount of the female-differentiating substance, overtake it, and finally supplant it, and from this point onwards any sex-characters which still have to develop will be of the male type. The individual will be a female intersex. It is not the absolute but the relative rates of production of male- and female-differentiating substances that control the modelling of the sex-equipment, so :—

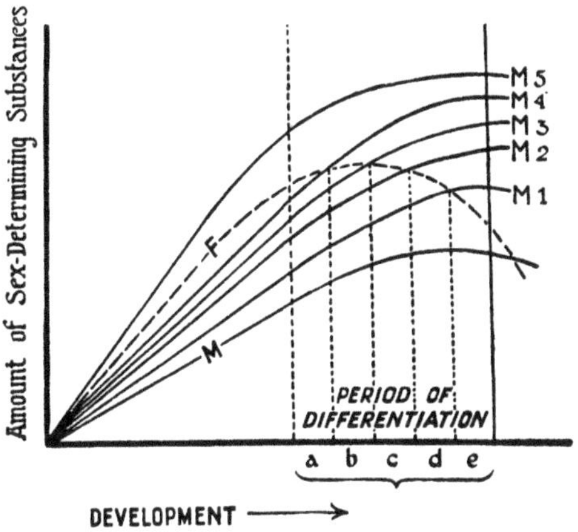

FIG. 55. (*After* Goldschmidt.)

There are two sorts of sex-determining genes, male-determining, borne on the X, and female-determining borne on the Y. The male genetically is MMF and the female MmF, since the action of the Y-borne genes is prezygotic. The sex-determining substances elaborated by these genes are known as male-differentiating and female-differentiating substances. These are elaborated at different rates by different male-determining and female-determining genes respectively; the introduction of more quickly and of more slowly elaborating genes into a genotype can result in a disturbance of the previous quantitative relation of the two sorts and so yield the intersexual condition.

In general the point at which the curves for production of male- and of the female-differentiating substances intersect lies beyond the stage at which differentiation occurs. But if the growth rate could be changed so that the point of intersection occurred during or before the period of differentiation, then it should be possible to produce a partial or complete reversal of sex and to produce individuals genetically of one sex (XX or XY, that is), but somatically, phenotypically, of the other. Goldschmidt by rearing Lymantria at very low temperatures produced intersexes, thus verifying this inference. Sex-reversal in these cases is due to genetic causes—the fertilised egg contains inevitably within itself the seed of its eventual transformation in the form of a quantitative disharmony of the sex-determining factors. It should be defined as genetic or ontogenetic sex-reversal.

Heslop Harrison (1914) working with Biston species crosses obtained results very similar to those of Goldschmidt and accepts the latter's hypothesis in interpretation.

Sexton and Huxley (1921) found in the amphipod crustacean Gammarus an instance of progressive change of an animal from one phenotypic sex to the other—consecutive inter-sexuality—closely similar to that described in Lymantria, but the causes of this are not known. As Gammarus moults throughout life, it was possible to show that the intersexes start their life as females, for when a certain degree of femaleness has been reached it is retained throughout life. The animal then switches over to maleness, the male-differentiating substance progressively increases and the individual becomes more and more phenotypically male with successive moults.

The types of genetic intersexuality encountered in the cases of Drosophila and of Lymantria, types which may be distinguished as "balanced" and "consecutive," are both based on a particular quantitative relation between the sex-determining factors, on the X and on the Y in Lymantria, and on the X and the autosomes in Drosophila. In Drosophila the female-determining factor appears to reside in the X; in Lymantria it is the male-determining factor that is X-borne. Unusual quantitative relations between the two sorts of sex-determining factors result in the production of intersexual forms. In the case of Lymantria the situation can be summarised as follows. Genetic intersexuality is the condition in which as a result of genetic causes the differentiation of the sex-organisation of a genotypic male or of a genotypic female, having been pursued up to a point in a manner appropriate to that sex, is switched-over, so that after this point it follows the plan appropriate to the opposite sex. An intersex is an XX (or XY) individual which as a result of an abnormal sexual differentiation comes to possess more or less completely the sex-equipment appropriate to the alternative XY (or XX) individual. Not every part of the body is involved in this condition; only the structures of the sex-equipment are concerned and of these only those the differentiation of which is not complete at the time of the switch-over are affected; the earlier in development the switch-over occurs, the more structures will be affected and the greater will be the degree of the intersexual condition, and *vice versa.*

Intersexuality results when the male and female sex-determining genes are quantitatively incorrect in harmony, one set with the other. It does not occur when, as in the case of the determined female which attains a typical female organisation, the female-determining reactions are predominant throughout this period. Intersexuality occurs when during the course of this phase of differentiation the male determining reactions overtake and supplant the female differentiating reactions and so control the remainder of the process, or when the female-differentiating reactions replace the previously predominating male reactions.

Hormonic Intersexuality.

Another type of intersexuality is that known as hormonic, which is not established at the time of the formation of the zygote, but which is produced later as a result of the action of specific hormones, the origin of which is localised in the differentiated gonad. It follows that before these so-called sex-hormones are elaborated, sex must be determined and the sex-glands differentiated. In insects the quantitative relation of the male-determining and female-determining genes in each cell leads to the establishment of a certain physiological state—maleness or femaleness—in the presence of which differentiation is pursued. In the mammals, on the other hand, the control of sex-differentiation is removed from the individual cells of the body and has become localised in the sex-gland. It is not improbable that the relative efficiency of the gonadic hormone or the relative time during development at which the glands of internal secretion (including the gonads) begin to function are based upon the genotype, so that actually this type of intersexuality may also be genotypic, genetic, in origin. However, for purposes of description it is convenient to distinguish the two classes.

The Case of the Free-Martin.

The part played by the sex-hormones in the production of this kind of intersexuality is best illustrated by the work of Keller and Tandler (1916) and of Lillie (1917) on the bovine free-martin, a genetic female (XX) co-twin to a normal male, the reproductive system of which becomes abnormal during the period of sexual differentiation as a result of the action of the sex-hormone of the male *in utero*. Twins may be monovular or identical, and these, arising from one and the same egg, are always of the same sex and very similar in their characters, or they may be binovular or fraternal, resulting from the synchronous fertilisation of two separate ova by separate spermatozoa. In the latter case they may or may not be of the same sex and do not resemble one another any more closely than do brothers and sisters born at different times. Twins in cattle may consist of two normal males, two normal females, one male and one female each normal, or one male and the other an individual with an abnormal reproductive system and known as a "free-martin." In all save one of 126 cases of twins in cattle thoroughly examined, two corpora lutea were found. This shows that twins are almost invariably binovular in this animal, since two ova are concerned in the pregnancy, for when an ovum is discharged from the mammalian ovary, the follicle of the ovum remains as a glandular structure known as the *corpus luteum*, which apparently functions as a gland of internal secretion.

The two fertilised ova pass into the bicornuate uterus and become attached to the uterine mucosa. If they have been discharged from the same ovary the zygotes usually develop in one and the same uterine horn. As the ova increase in size, the embryonic membranes of the two fœtuses meet to adhere and in many cases to fuse. If such fusion occurs, an anastomosis (an intermingling) of

FIG. 56.—The Bovine Free-Martin. (*After* Lillie.)

their blood-vessels can result, so that a common vascular inter-communication may become established.

Thus the situation arises in which the sex-hormone of each developing individual is at liberty to pass into the tissues of its co-twin. The sex-hormone is the instrument which models the sex-organisation and the sex-organisation alone. The internal secretions of the pituitary, thyroid, adrenal, and so forth, can also pass from each individual to the other, but these are mainly concerned in the general and not in the special development of the individual and will be alike in both twins.

But if it so happens that the twins are bisexual and that the fusion of the chorions occurs, and further, that a vascular inter-communication becomes established, as it does in seven cases out of eight, the sex-differentiation of both individuals will be directed by that sex-hormone which is exhibited earlier or which is more potent. The testis becomes differentiated at an earlier stage of development than the ovary, and so the sex-hormone of the male is liberated before that of the female. The female twin (*i.e.* genotypic female) will pursue her sex-differentiation under the direction of the male sex-hormone of her co-twin and will therefore come to possess more or less completely the organisation of the male. The assumption of the male characters in the case of the fœtuses examined is imperfect: the external genitalia are of the female pattern, the internal organs of reproduction more or less completely male. The male sex-hormone is liberated before the embryonic gonads of the genotypic female have undergone differentiation into ovaries: such differentiation is prevented and so there is no question of a competitive action between male and female sex-hormones. The end-result will have a relation to the time of exhibition of and to the efficiency of the male sex-hormone. The variation in the size of the testes of the male co-twin and of the extent of vascular inter-communication seems to point to the conclusion that the amount of the hormone is not a significant factor in the production of a free-martin, but that there is a minimum stimulus and the reaction is of the "all or none" type. It is seen that the tissues of the genotypic male respond completely to the stimulus of the testicular sex-hormone, whereas those of the genotypic female fail to do so. Now it is known that genotypic male and female tissues are to be distinguished by differences in their chromosome content, and it is reasonable to assume that because of these differences they differ also in their physiological constitution. It is probable, therefore, that though both kinds may be capable of responding to one and the same sex-hormone stimulus, they will respond differentially. The male co-twin develops testes because he is a genotypic male and becomes a phenotypic male because he develops testes. His embryonic gonads became testes because their differentiation was pursued under the direction of the male-differentiating substances elaborated by the male-determining factors in the sex-determining factor complex. The sex-hormone elaborated by the testes, passing into the body of the genotypic female, swings her sexual differentiation in the male direction, but the swing is not complete because the sex-hormone of the testis is not equivalent physiologically to the male-differentiating substances elaborated by the sex-determining factors and because her tissues are constitutionally different from those of the genotypic male. In the assumption of any character three variables are involved, the efficiency of the stimulus, the degree of response, and the sufficiency of nutrition.

That this is the correct interpretation of the case of the free-martin seemed to be supported by the work of Minoura (1921) who claimed to have produced an equivalent condition in the chick. A small window was made in the shell of a seven to nine days' incubated fertile hen's egg and on to the vascular area of the chorio-allantoic membrane were grafted small pieces of testis or of ovary from embryo chicks and adult fowls. In a certain proportion of cases the operation did not interfere with the further development of the chicks and the grafts survived and grew. The embryos which had received ovarian and testicular grafts, it was claimed, showed modification in their sex-organisation; fourteen individuals were affected as a result of ovarian grafts and sixteen by testicular. In the case of male embryos which had received an ovarian graft, modification in the direction of the female condition was seen in the right testis being smaller than the left (in the female the right gonad atrophied and disappeared), while the Müllerian ducts persisted instead of atrophying as in the male. In females grafted with testicular tissue, the right and left ovaries were equally developed and the male genital ducts persisted. In this way Minoura claims to have produced free-martins of both sexes and the conclusion is that sex-differentiation in birds as in mammals is introduced by the production of a gonad of one or the other type manufacturing an internal secretion. It is not clear, however, whether Minoura's results might not have been due to a simple retardation of sex-differentiation by operative interference. Anyone who is well acquainted with chick embryology knows that there is a very great variation in the process of sex-differentiation. Moreover, Greenwood (1925) repeating this work has completely failed to confirm Minoura's conclusions.

Moore (1919) has shown that it is possible in the rat to remove one testis and replace it by an ovary and that following this both testis and ovary continued to produce functional gametes. It is possible, therefore, to secure a balance of the male and female hormones in one and the same individual and so to produce an artificial hermaphrodite although such an individual could not function as a male and a female. Sand has recently demonstrated the effects of simultaneous implantation of ovary and testis into an infantile castrated guinea-pig and of implantation of ovaries into the testes of rats and guinea-pigs, and has shown that artificial hermaphroditism with pronounced bisexuality of the psycho-sexual characters could be produced associated with the synchronous development of both male and female sexual organs.

The Case of Inachus and Sacculina.

Another instance of intersexuality is that of the crab Inachus attacked by the parasite Sacculina. Sacculina, an internal parasite, is a cirripede Crustacean, and part of its body projects to the exterior under the abdomen of the crab in which it is living, while root-like processes which absorb the juices of its host ramify to all parts of the crab's body, avoiding the vital organs and absorbing nourishment chiefly from the blood. It attacks males and females, and in both it causes atrophy of the sex-glands and consequent sterility. The only effect of this in the female is acceleration in the assumption of the adult sex characters. Parasitised males, however, gradually take on more and more of the female characters, their great claws become smaller and smaller, the abdomen broader, the swimmerets enlarge and become fringed with the hairs to which, in the female, the eggs are attached. Most of the affected crabs die, but in a few the parasite disappears and the reproductive organs are regenerated. In a female a normal ovary develops, in a but partially feminised male, a normal testis; but in a fully feminised male a sex-gland is regenerated, in which both ova and sperm are found: real male intersexuality is produced. Geoffrey Smith (1906) who investigated this problem, found that the blood of the normal female crab differs in chemical constitution from that of the male. It contains fatty substances which are absorbed by the ovaries and used in the production of the yolk of the egg. These fatty

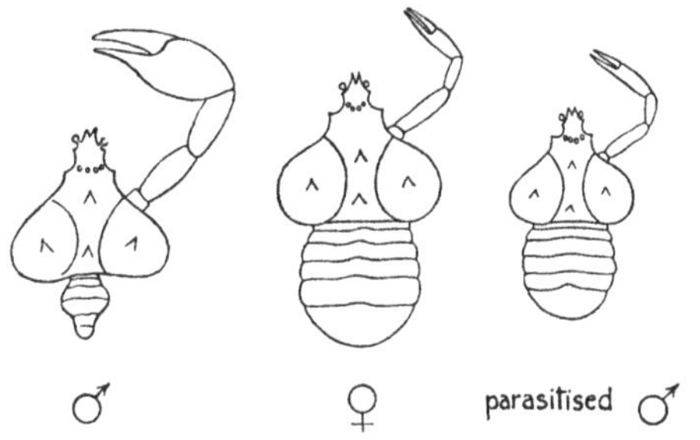

FIG. 57.—Inachus. (*After* Smith.)

substances form an important part of the food of the parasite Sacculina. That which Sacculina absorbs cannot be used in yolk formation, and as the eggs cannot develop the ovary degenerates. In the male these fatty substances are present in but small quantities. The parasite demands more, and the whole physiology of the male crab is altered to meet this demand; the male thus assumes the female type of metabolism, and consequently the characters of the female.

Such was Smith's interpretation of the condition in Inachus and, as is seen, this theory of metabolic stimuli is opposed to the sex-hormone theory of differentiation. Instead of adding something to the circulation, the sex-glands, according to Smith, remove something from it. It is possible, however, that the altered metabolism is not the cause of the alteration in the sexual characterisation but merely a part of this process of alteration. Goldschmidt points out that the case of the intersexual female Lymantria is somewhat similar. In the female caterpillar large deposits of fat are laid down, and these are used up in the pupal stage during the growth of the ovary. If the male-determining reactions supersede the female just at the time of pupation the ovary is not differentiated, and so the fat is not used up.

In the presence of testes the plumage of the fowl (genotypic male or female alike) is cocky, unless the testis is that of a breed such as the Campine or Sebright, in which both sexes are henny-feathered. In the presence of ovary the plumage is henny. In the absence of gonadic tissue of either sort the plumage is capony and similar in the castrated male and ovariotomised female. In a hemi-castrated henny-feathered cock the plumage is intermediate in character, and this kind of plumage, containing scattered cocky feathers among a henny ground, is not uncommon among the male progeny of the mating between henny and cocky-feathered breeds. If ovarian tissue is implanted into a cock, then in the presence of both ovarian tissue and testicular the plumage becomes henny, if testicular tissue is implanted into a hen, then in the presence of both kinds of gonadic tissue the plumage remains henny. It is difficult for the sex-hormone hypothesis to accommodate these varied facts and a simpler interpretation can be found. If it is assumed that the gonad, in the course of its own functioning, exerts a demand upon the general economy of the individual and that the demand on the part of the ovary is greater than that of the ordinary testis, as would be expected since the food storage of the egg is so much greater than that of the sperm, then ovary and testis in their functioning will establish distinct physiological states—there will be a male and a female type of metabolism—and this difference can be mirrored in the different plumage characterisation. It must be further assumed that the physiological demands of the testis of the henny-feathered cock are nearer akin to those of an ovary than to those of the testes of a cocky-feathered cock. Granting these assumptions, which can be tested readily enough by blood-fat and basal metabolism estimations, the facts outlined above can be reconciled. Gonadectomy removes all demands and the physiological level is the same in male and female. Hemi-castration of a henny-feathered cock lessens the demand, and if this coincides with the renewal of portions of the plumage there will be partial cocky feathering. The supplementing of ovary with testis in a hen merely emphasises the demands of the ovary so that henny-feathering persists. The supplementing of testis with ovary in a male raises the demand with the result that the plumage becomes henny. The intermediate character of the plumage of the hybrid from a cocky x henny mating is to be interpreted as the result of the bringing together of two types of physiological constitution which in their inheritance obey the Mendelian scheme.

The alimentary castration of Pézard produced by feeding fowls on a strictly carnivorous diet might be explained as a result of lipoid deprivation. Theoretically it might be possible to affect the type of plumage by controlled feeding (*cf.* the production of henny-feathered cocks by thyroid feeding by Horning and Torrey, 1919).

The sum total of the physiological processes of the body produce a characteristic type of metabolism different in male and female. Stecke (1912) has shown that there is in many cases a demonstrable, fundamental, physiological difference between the male and female of the same species. He found that in certain moths the blood of the males was yellow, that of the females green. When tested by the precipitin test there was as much difference between the blood of the two sexes of one species as between the blood of the same sex of different species. Farkas (1898) has shown that in the male of moths there is a greater energy-consumption than in the female, so that the adult weight of the latter is both relatively and absolutely greater. In the human the basal metabolism of the female when all corrections have been made for surface and weight, is less than in the male. The difference between male and female metabolism is indicated in a remarkable way by the intense phagocytosis of ovarian tissue when a Lymantria female intersex passes into the male phase (Goldschmidt, 1923).

Pseudo-Intersexuality in the Mammal.

A different sort of hormonic intersexuality is encountered in the domesticated mammals which further illustrates the rôle of the sex-hormones in the differentiation of the sex-equipment of the individual.

Abnormality of the reproductive system taking the form of an intimate mixture of male and female structures belonging to the accessory sexual apparatus is not uncommon among the domesticated mammals, and many cases have also been recorded in the human subject. The typical history in these cases is that an individual, regarded as a female during the earlier part of its life, later assumes many of the characters of the male. This peculiar type of abnormality is particularly common in the goat and pig. Cases are known in which an individual, which actually won prizes as an immature female, from the time of sexual maturity became more and more like the male: its beard grew, its head became male-like, and about it there hung the pungent smell so characteristic of the male. In its behaviour it resembled the "rig," a male with mal-descended testes, but its external genitalia retained the form of a vulva-like aperture with an abnormal clitoris. When the internal genitalia from such a case are examined there are found paired gonads lying in the situation of ovaries or somewhere along the track of the migrating testes, which on section show the structure typical of the mal-descended testis; and an accessory sexual apparatus composed of more or less well-defined epididymes, vasa deferentia, seminal vesicles, prostate, Cowper's glands, uterus and vagina, the latter in some cases having failed to establish communication with the vulva.

A number of cases were examined by Crew (1923) in the goat, pig, horse, cattle, and sheep. All the cases were very similar in the details of their anatomy. The external genitalia in a few cases had the form of an unremarkable vulva and clitoris, in other the erectile organ was abnormally large, though female in type, in others it was peniform but imperfectly canaliculised. In no instance was there a typical scrotum, though in several the gonads could be palpated beneath the skin of the inguinal or peritoneal regions. The internal genitalia in all cases consisted of paired testes with a histological structure varying with the position of the organ, and situated somewhere along the line between the primitive position and the imperfect scrotum, and a double set of structures of the accessory sexual apparatus. It is worthy of note that the testes in these cases, even though in the scrotum, always showed indications of fatty degeneration. The relative degree of development of the structures derived from the Wolffian and Müllerian ducts respectively, varied in different cases. The secondary gonadic characters were definitely male in all cases though imperfectly so in some.

The diagrams on page 229 illustrate the series which these cases formed. They are all from the goat.

The fact that all the cases readily form a series suggests that each is a grade of one and the same condition, and that between them all there is a time relation. There are but four possible interpretations of such abnormality: the abnormal individual might be a free-martin; it might be a female, not a free-martin, in which more or less complete sex-reversal had taken place; it might be a genetic hermaphrodite in which during the early stages of sex-differentiation both ovarian and spermatic tissues were present but in which the ovarian tissue had later disappeared; or it might be a genetic male in which the differentiation of the sex-organisation had been abnormal.

A free-martin is a genotypic female, co-twin to a male, and the abnormality of her sex-equipment is produced by the action of the sex-hormone of the male, which passes into her body through the vascular inter-communication established in the fused embryonic membranes. For the production of a free-martin it is necessary that there should be bisexual twins and fusion of the chorions. The abnormal individuals included single births, co-twins to normal females as well as to normal males, or one of triplets, the others being normal, either males or females. Though certain of these cases could be interpreted on the same principles as the bovine free-martin, all cannot be so explained.

It is known that an individual which formerly possessed

the organisation of one phenotypic sex, and actually functioned as such, may undergo a complete transformation, and come to possess, more or less completely, the organisation of the other. But in all such cases the history of the transformation is written more or less clearly in the characterisation of the individual, and in the vertebrate there are certain evidences of the existence of gonadic tissues of both kinds to be found. In the cases under discussion there is no history of the individual ever functioning as a female, and no evidence to show that it ever possessed only the female type of organisation.

The degree of development attained by the uterus in some of these cases supports the idea that these individuals may be hermaphrodites similar in many ways to those in which both ovarian and spermatic tissues are found associated with the same combination of accessory sexual apparatus, imperfect external reproductive organs and secondary gonadic characters. But there is never any trace of ovarian tissue in these cases and no suggestion that any has ever been present.

The remaining interpretation is that these individuals are males in which the differentiation of the sex-organisation has been abnormal, and this for the present would seem to be the most satisfactory.

Sex is determined by the nature of the factors which are brought into the zygote by the conjugating gametes and by the interaction of these within a given internal environment. Sex-differentiation is the process during which the further development of the sex-equipment of the individual is pursued under specific control. It consists of two phases: (1) the differentiation of the embryonic gonads into testes or into ovaries; and (2) the modelling of the remaining structures of the sex-equipment under the control of the testis or of the ovary according to one of the two plans, the male or the female respectively.

The time relation in the differentiation of the structures of the sex-equipment in the goat would seem to be as follows. In the earliest stage there are paired genital glands and paired solid Müllerian and Wolffian ducts. Then the

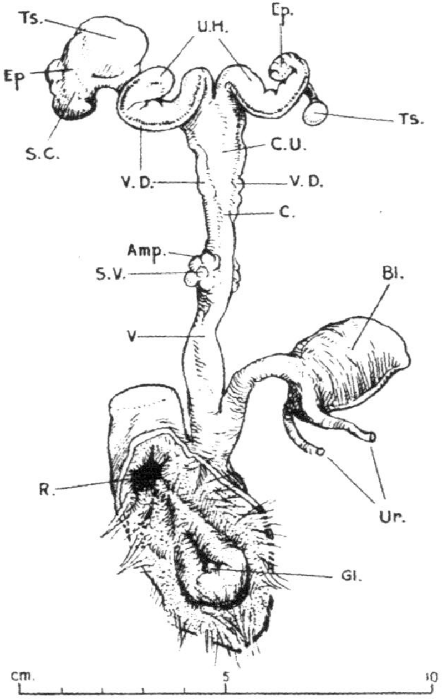

FIG. 58.

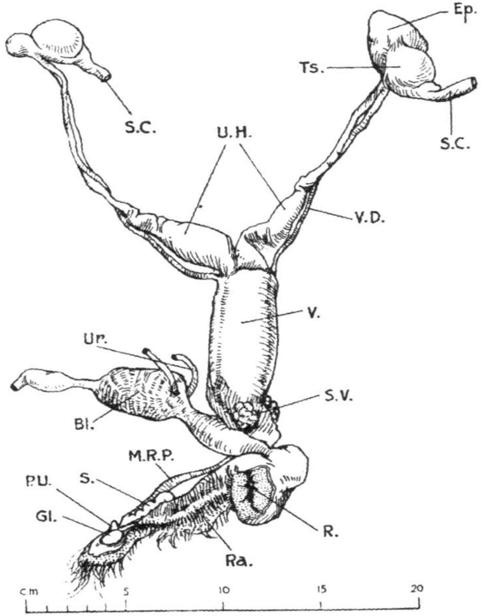

FIG. 59.

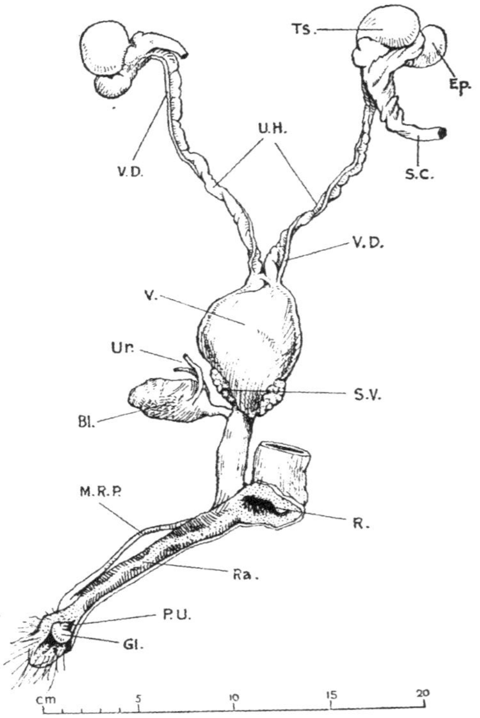

FIG. 60.

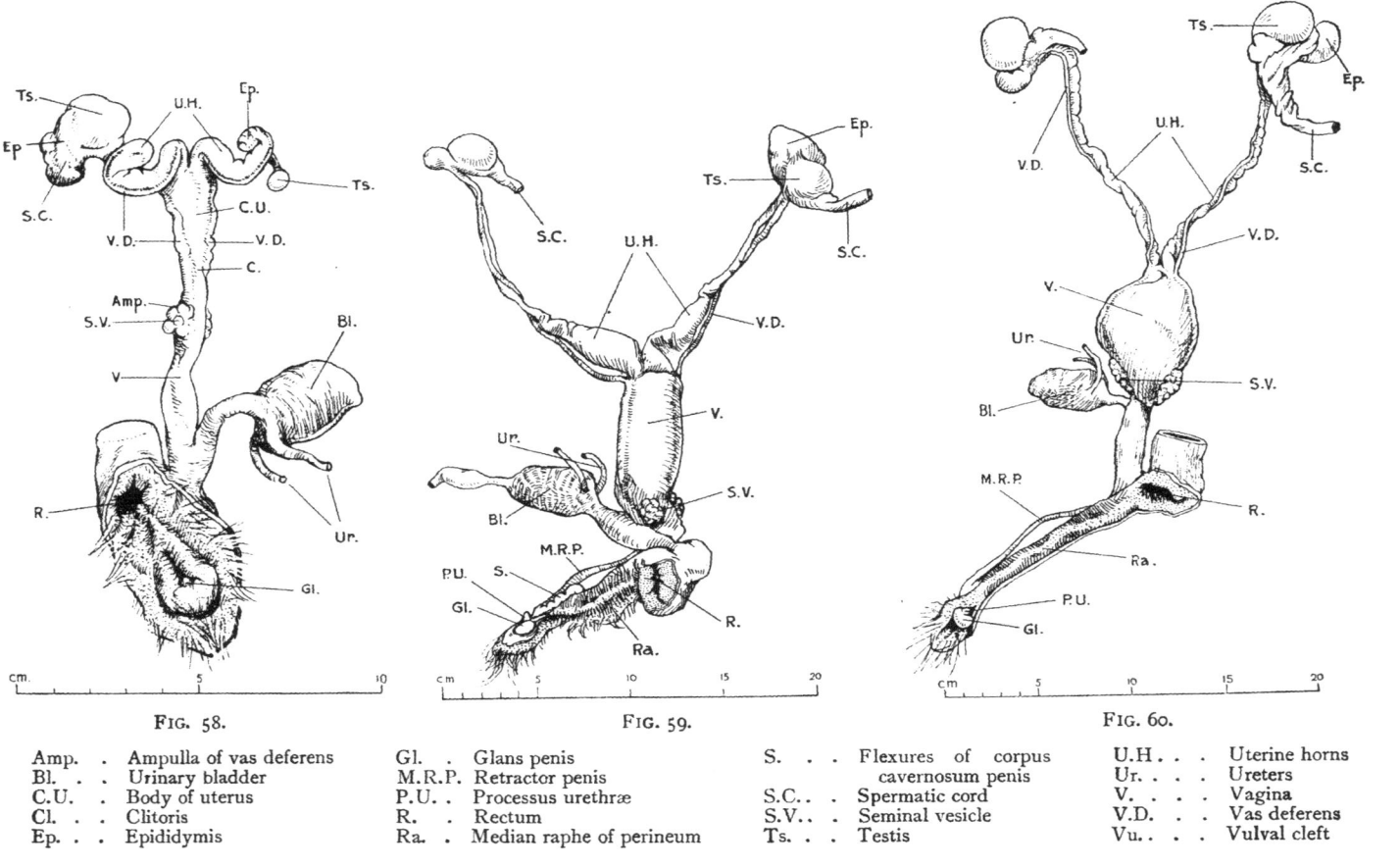

Amp. .	Ampulla of vas deferens
Bl. . .	Urinary bladder
C.U. .	Body of uterus
Cl. . .	Clitoris
Ep. . .	Epididymis
Gl. .	Glans penis
M.R.P.	Retractor penis
P.U. .	Processus urethræ
R. .	Rectum
Ra. .	Median raphe of perineum
S. . .	Flexures of corpus cavernosum penis
S.C. . .	Spermatic cord
S.V. . .	Seminal vesicle
Ts. . .	Testis
U.H. . .	Uterine horns
Ur. . . .	Ureters
V. . . .	Vagina
V.D. . .	Vas deferens
Vu. . . .	Vulval cleft

genital glands become either ovaries or testes, and interstitial tissue appears, while the Müllerian and Wolffian ducts are more or less equally developed in both sexes. Next, in the female, the caudal part of the Wolffian ducts disappears, and the two Müllerian ducts fuse to form the beginnings of the uterus and vagina. In the male, on the other hand, at this stage the Müllerian ducts atrophy. In both sexes there is a common type of external genitalia. Lastly, in the female, cervix, vagina and vulval cleft are formed; in the male the scrotum and penis, while the testis migrates to the internal abdominal ring. The first structure of the sex-organisation to be differentiated is the gonad, the last those of the external genitalia.

Though at present experimental evidence is incomplete on this point, there are numerous clinical indications that the full development of many of the structures of the sex-organisation, or at least the rapidity with which they develop, is conditioned by the action of the internal secretion of other glands of the endocrine system, such as the pituitary, the adrenal and the thyroid.

The appropriate secondary gonadic characters and sexual behaviour are exhibited later as the individual approaches sexual maturity. Since the sex-hormone is present long before this time, it would appear that a certain degree of undifferentiated growth is necessary before the threshold of response to the stimulus of the sex-hormone is reached.

The fact that at one time one set of structures of the sex-equipment is affected by the functioning of the sex-gland, and at another a different set, and also the fact that the relation between the intersexual condition of the accessory sexual apparatus and the degree of imperfection of the external genitalia in the cases now being described is not constant, suggest that (1) the sex-determining substances are not produced in constant amount throughout the life cycle, and (2) there is a different threshold of response to the sex-differentiating stimulus at different stages in the development of any organ which is susceptible to such a stimulus.

It is known that in the adult female mammal vestiges of the Wolffian ducts and of the structures developed therefrom are commonly found, and that in the adult male there are to be seen the remains or the derivatives of the Müllerian ducts. The degree of development of these structures varies widely in different cases. It follows, therefore, that either the time of the exhibition of the stimulus that controls the differentiation of the sex-organisation or else the potency of the stimulus is variable.

In the case of the intersexual individuals of Lymantria, Goldschmidt encountered a similar sort of seriation as is described here and comments upon it as follows: "If we now try to formulate a rule which governs this strange seriation we find the most important fact, that this series is the inverse of the order of differentiation of the organs in development. The last organs to differentiate in the pupa and the first to become intersexual are the branching of the antennæ and the coloration of the wings. The first imaginal organ differentiated and the last in the series to be changed towards the other sex is the sex-gland. And if we apply this law to the minute parts of a single organ we find it to hold here also."

In the case of the intersexual mammal it is possible to apply a somewhat similar interpretation of the seriation of events if it is recognised that the stimulus to differentiation of the sex-equipment becomes localised in the sex-gland; that the abnormalities pertain only to the earlier stages of sexual development; that the influence of the gonad in the mammal at this stage is such as inhibits the further development of the accessory sexual structures of the alternate sex, which would develop unchecked in the absence of such inhibition; and that in all probability there exists a different threshold of response to the sex-differentiating stimulus in the case of different structures of the sex-equipment, and at different times during the development of one and the same structure.

In the absence of the proper endocrine control during the period of differentiation Wolffian and Müllerian ducts pursue an equal and parallel development under the common stimulus of nutriment, and the urogenital sinus with its genital tubercle increases in size to form a large cleft with a phallus in its ventral commissure. The fact that in these circumstances epididymes, vasa deferentia, and seminal vesicles are developed from the Wolffian ducts, and uterus and vagina from the Müllerian, shows that the development of these structures is not conditioned by the endocrine control at all, and that the action of the sex-differentiating stimulus is limited to the inhibition of the development of one and the encouragement of that of the other of these paired ducts. It should be noted, however, that a difficulty arises here. It is known that after ovariotomy the uterus shrinks in size, and it is difficult therefore to argue that the uterus can become fully developed in the absence of the ovary. It is possible, however, that in the case of a late differentiation of the testes the uterus having grown is maintained in its size by the presence of gonadial tissue of either kind.

If such undirected growth continues, then, after a time, the structures concerned will have lost all embryonic plasticity, and even though the proper endocrine stimulus be then exhibited, they will no longer be able to respond. The degree of the development of the structures derived from the Müllerian ducts found in a male, and the degree of imperfection of the external genitalia will provide, therefore, some indication as to the time during development at which the sex-hormone became operative.

Moreover, if it is assumed that the testis, and the structures concerned in its migration, pursue a corresponding and parallel development up to the point at which descent normally occurs, and that if the proper development of the testis is retarded in any way, this association of testis and gubernacular apparatus is prevented, then mal-descent of the testis can be interpreted in terms of abnormal differentiation of the sex-organisation.

The text-figure on the opposite page gives a speculative interpretation of the phenomena along the lines suggested by Goldschmidt. The hypothetical amount of the sex-differentiating stimulus is plotted along the ordinate and the time of differentiation along the abscissa. There is undoubtedly an orderly sequence in the differentiation of the different structures of the sex-equipment in a genotypic male, and this can be shown for purely illustrative purposes as consisting of three somewhat overlapping periods: (1) the atrophy of the Müllerian ducts, (2) the further development of the accessory sexual apparatus, and (3) the modelling of the external genitalia. For the sake of simplicity it is assumed that for all these structures concerned there is one and the same minimum stimulus which, provided by the sex-differentiating substance elaborated by the testes, will evoke the specific response toward appropriate development. It is also assumed that when once the undirected

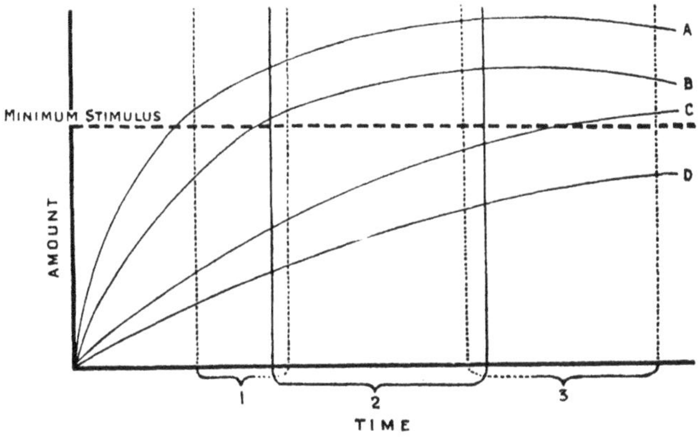

FIG. 61.

development of any structure has proceeded so far, then that structure is no longer capable of responding to the stimulus provided by the testis.

In A (Fig. 61) the minimum stimulus necessary for proper differentiation of the sex-organisation was exhibited before the time for differentiation had been reached, and as a consequence the differentiation would be such that a completely male organisation would be established. In B in consequence of a retardation in the elaboration of the sex-hormone, or of the production thereof at a slower rate, the growth of the Müllerian ducts would be partially unchecked and the end result of sex-differentiation would be a male in which a *uterus masculinus* would be present. In C the end-result would be a male with abdominal testes, a double set of structures of the accessory sexual apparatus, and external genitalia of the male type but imperfect. In D in which the required stimulus was never exhibited there would be no differentiation.

There is then an embryonic but full-grown form of the sex-equipment, and in the cases being described, the Wolffian and Müllerian derivatives attain a considerable size, and the external genitalia have the form, in the higher grades of the intersexual condition, of a urogenital cleft and a phallus. In such a case the individual, so far as external sexual characters are concerned, will resemble a female very closely indeed, and will be regarded as a female during the earlier part of its life.

The primary cause of the abnormality might be: (1) a complete absence of the interstitial tissue in the embryonic testis, or a complete non-functioning of this tissue during the period of differentiation of the sex-organisation; (2) a quantitative, or qualitative, insufficiency of the sex-hormone during this period; or (3) a mal-development, or a mal-functioning of the other endocrine glands, the action of which, in addition to that of the sex-gland, is necessary for the proper development of the structures of the sex-equipment during this period.

It has not been possible, as yet, to define the exact cause, for only well-grown individuals have been available for examination, and in these nothing remarkable in the thyroid, pituitary, adrenal, and other glands of the endocrine system has been found.

Whatever may prove to be the exact primary cause, the condition can certainly be interpreted as the result of the absence during the period of sex-differentiation of the proper endocrine control in a genotypic male and in view of Goldschmidt's work it is reasonable to regard it as being due to an insufficiency of the sex-differentiating stimulus.

Granting this, and assuming that the threshold of response on the part of the structures of the secondary gonadic characters is lower than that of the structures of the accessory sexual apparatus, it can be seen that, as the individual approaches sexual maturity, it will assume the secondary gonadic characters of the male, and exhibit the male behaviour. The structures concerned in the development of these characters are the only ones of the sex-equipment which are capable of responding, and in most cases the secondary gonadic characters of the male are but the result of the further development, at a certain time, of structures possessed in common by the embryonic full-grown form, the female, and by the immature male. The normal exhibition of the secondary gonadic characters by these individuals can be explained equally well, on the assumption that the primary cause of the intersexual condition is not an insufficiency of the sex-differentiating stimulus but a retardation in its exhibition.

The frequency of the occurrence of this type of abnormality in certain strains of goats and pigs, and the fact that it is more common among the offspring of certain individuals than among those of others, suggest that as in the case of Lymantria, the condition is genetical in origin. In the goat there is considerable evidence to show that this kind of abnormality is related to the importation, in 1897, of three Toggenburg she-goats in kid. These goats figure largely in the back part of the pedigree of most modern British goats, according to Davies (1913), and it is reasonable, therefore, to hold that this peculiar intersexual condition is the result of the mating of two races, or individuals, which differ one from the other in the nature of the factors which play their part in the determination of sex, and in the mechanism which controls the rate of sexual development.

Sex-Reversal.

In the case of the Gipsy moth sex-reversal based on genetic causes has already been described. It was shown that the genotype of the individual contained all the elements necessary for this phenomenon, and that the transformation of a genotypic female into a phenotypic male or *vice versa* was but the inevitable result of further development. Sex-reversal was as inevitable as growth, and was but the expression of the factorial constitution of the individual. Reference has also been made to the faint possibility of the development of a functional, phenotypic male *in utero* from a determined genetic female, through the interference of a sex-hormone as in the case of the free-martin. The weight of opinion is decidedly against such a possibility. However, there can be no question whatsoever that complete sex-transformation can be the final stage of the condition of intersexuality occurring in embryonic and fœtal life. It remains to consider the phenomenon of sex-transformation occurring in post-natal life among vertebrates, cases in which an individual during the earlier part of its life has been a functional male, and later has undergone a complete transformation and has become a functional female, or *vice versa.* Of such post-natal sex-transformation there are already several well-authenticated instances.

Essenberg (1923) records that sex-reversal occurs in the viviparous teleost fish, *Xiphophorus helleri* (the sword-tailed minnow), and that many instances of this have been reported by fish breeders and fanciers. In Essenberg's cases, two females ceased to produce young when about three years old, and during the course of several weeks took on the sex-characters of the male. Cytological examination revealed the presence of ripe sperm in all parts of the gonad which, however, was juvenile in comparison to the size and age of the fish. Essenberg was able to show that there is a type of differentiation in the female which readily provides a morphological basis for the change-over. He also shows that there is a complete reversal of the sex-ratio in a population, this being 50:100 among immature fish and 200:100 among mature, a fact which supports the suggestion of sex-transformation of 50 per cent. of the females. In many males, moreover, the shape of the testes closely resembles that of the ovaries, and the grades suggest a transformation of pre-existing ovary into testis. It would seem from Essenberg's observations that sex-reversal is extremely common in this fish and that it is genetic in origin, there being a form which through genetic action is destined merely to pass through a female phase and later proceed to a male type of sex-differentiation. The case is very similar to that of Lymantria, save that even in a well-grown individual a remodelling of the sex-organisation can take place, there being no permanent hard parts.

Other cases of what would seem to be sex-reversal in fishes have been recorded by Herzenstein (quoted by Essenberg) in the cyprinodonts *Gymnocipris potanini* and *Schizopygopsis güntheri*, in which females assumed the sexual characters of the male. Phillippi (1904) reported a similar case in the viviparous teleost, *Glaridichthys caudimaculatus*, and three others in *Glaridichthys januarius*, whilst Newman (1908) described a significant case of hermaphroditism in *Fundulus majalis*.

Among Amphibia there is the case of complete sex-transformation in *Triton alpestris Laur.* recorded by Champy (1921) who found that a male, on being fed intensively after the winter's starvation assumed the external characters of the female, and that in place of the testis there was an ovary as that of a young female. Abnormality of the reproductive system in frogs and toads is relatively common. All grades of "maleness" and "femaleness" in the external sexual characters and in the gonads and accessory sexual apparatus have been recorded. Crew (1921) collected these cases and by arranging them in a series, at one end of which was a nearly complete female, at the other an almost perfect male, was able to put forward the suggestion that the gradations found were but stages in the process of complete sex-reversal probably from female to male. For reasons that could not be defined, the ovaries of an adult female underwent degenerative changes and in the altered conditions spermatic tissue developed along the median border of the gonad. One of the specimens described had functioned as a male and of his progeny by a normal female every one was a female, as would be expected if this individual had been a genotypic female with the sex constitution XX, which had undergone a process of masculinisation. Witschi (1921) has been able to show that such an hermaphrodite individual can elaborate both functional sperm and ova. In this case both sperm and ova were all X-chromosome-bearing and therefore yielded an abnormal sex-ratio in the next generation.

Harms (1923) has found that if young castrated male toads are fed on a diet containing an excess of fat, lipoids and lecithin for a considerable period of time, the caudal portion of Bidder's organ becomes an ovary and the cephalic portion a new Bidder's organ. Oviducts and uteri are developed and the pointed shape of the head in the male is gradually transformed into the wide blunt head shape of the female.

In the case of birds, sex-reversal has been recorded in the ring-dove (Riddle, 1923) and in the domestic fowl. A ring-dove laid eleven eggs at times exactly observed between 27th January and 15th April 1914. During the six months following she and a male mate three times began incubation of nest without producing eggs, and raised young of other parents. During the following nineteen months her sex-behaviour and method of growing changed to that of a male—frequently forcing her male mate to act as a female in copulation. At twenty-two and a half months, after producing her last egg, this bird and mate were transferred to a pen with a few other spent inactive doves. The male of this pair died three and a half months later: weights and dimensions of testes were obtained. Twenty-one months after transfer the bird died, showing very advanced abdominal tuberculosis. Two testes were found, removed, and weighed. If any residue of the original ovary remained it was wholly included in a tuberculous mass, involving spleen and liver. At the time of autopsy this bird was supposed to be the original male of the pair, and therefore the testes were not saved for demonstration. The bird had lived forty-four and a half months after producing the last egg, became tuberculous, assumed male behaviour, the curve for the body weight during three years underwent a remarkable change, and at death it possessed two unmistakable testes. Riddle interprets this transformation as the result of the increased metabolism which followed the destruction of the ovarian tissue and the presence of tuberculosis. He has adduced considerable evidence to show that sex and metabolism are intimately related, that a high metabolism is associated with maleness and a low metabolism with femaleness from the stage of the gamete to the adult.

Many instances of the more or less complete assumption of the sexual characters of the male by the old female bird, wild and domesticated, have been recorded, but in the great majority of such cases no accurate knowledge of the previous history of the individual has been available and each has been considered as an isolated case. Rare cases of "hermaphroditism" have been encountered. A bird at the age of four to six months, instead of developing the distinctive male or female characters grows slowly into a creature which is neither a pullet nor a cockerel and its characters remain indefinitely intermediate. These possibly are gynandromorphs. Rare cases are known of an otherwise perfectly normal laying hen with cocky plumage. In certain of these, the plumage following successive moults has been cocky-henny-cocky. The explanation is that at the time of the moult the ovary is not functioning and that under these circumstances the plumage becomes cocky. The condition is that of temporary ovariotomy. The exhibition of the male type of sexual behaviour by a laying hen of perfectly normal external female characterisation is exceedingly common among the more highly fecund strains and especially when no male is kept in the pen. This behaviour is corrected by removal into fresh company or by the introduction of a male bird. There is no anatomical basis for this abnormal behaviour. The assumption of the male type of head furnishings—the large comb (or the erect comb in certain breeds) and wattles—and the greater development of the spurs, are by no means uncommon among two to three year old hens of heavy laying strains. A hen, previously a heavy layer, ceases to lay, her head furnishings rapidly increase in size, the spurs grow; the plumage, bodily conformation and carriage remain henny; the bird makes efforts to crow but exhibits no sexual behaviour and seeks solitude. This is associated with ovarian atrophy. Such a bird occasionally, following irregular moults, puts up more or less completely the type of plumage characteristic of the male of her breed. This is associated with the complete removal of active ovarian tissue. Very exceptionally such a bird as this apparently undergoes a complete sex-transformation. She begins to exhibit the signs of a functional male activity; the crow becomes challenging and the disposition bellicose towards cocks, courteously masterful towards hens. The bird treads hens and fights cocks, and save for an indefinable difference in shape and carriage is readily distinguishable from a "real" male only when compared side by side.

Cases of this kind have been described by Tichomiroff (1887), Brandt (1889), Shattock and Seligmann (1906), Pearl and Curtis (1909), Boring and Pearl (1918), Hartman and Hamilton (1922) and Crew (1923).

Crew examined in detail eight cases. All these birds were kept under observation for eighteen months. The most interesting case was that of a Buff Orpington 3½ years old, a good layer, and a mother of chickens. On examination it was seen that the head of this bird was somewhat male-like, for her comb and wattles were rather larger than those of the typical hen. At this time the bird exhibited the classical signs of early ovarian disease. She had ceased to lay in the preceding autumn, and had moulted; she had spurs 3 mms. long on the left leg, 2 mms. long on the right; the plumage was entirely henny. She crowed weakly as one practising and her sexual behaviour was indifferent.

Two months later the comb, wattles, and spurs had progressively increased in size, and the bird had begun to moult irregularly. The feathers of the neck, saddle-hackle, and tail, as they were renewed, were seen to be cocky in structure, and ultimately she had become entirely cocky-feathered, though she could never retain the tail-sickles. The spurs were now about 1 cm. in length, the left one being slightly longer than the right, and the legs had assumed the red tinge which characterises the male of the Buff Orpington. In the following spring she was crowing lustily and with a challenging note, was readily attracted by hens which would squat on her approach, and the sexual act would be performed. The bird fought with any and every male in the yard and was gently courteous to the hens. In fact, only by one accustomed to poultry or when placing it alongside a "real" cock could it be told that this bird was different from a typical male. Its stance differed from that of a cock; the bird was shorter on its legs, which formed a different angle with the body.

The bird was placed with a hen, a virginal Buff Orpington, in a pen far removed from all other birds. This hen was laying; the eggs which she laid during the fortnight previous to her mating were incubated and found to be infertile. Every egg she laid after the mating was incubated. Her mate performed the sexual act daily; fluid passed into the cloaca of the hen was withdrawn and examined; a few living spermatozoa were identified in the fluid. The hen became broody and nine of her own eggs laid during the preceding eighteen days were placed under her. Two chickens were hatched: the other eggs were clear.

Post-mortem examination of the abnormal bird revealed, lying in the situation of the ovary, a rounded mass with its purple surface marked with raised areas of yellow. Incorporated in the dorsal aspect of this mass there was a structure exactly resembling a testis, whilst another similar in appearance was situated in the equivalent position on the other side of the body. On the left a thin, straight oviduct could be identified, having a diameter of 3 mms. in its widest part near the cloaca; paired vasa deferentia were clearly discernible.

On sectioning, the structure of the gonads confirmed the conclusion that they were functional testes in a phase of reduced activity. The tumour proved to be the ovary, almost completely destroyed by tubercular disease.

The bird just described had been up to the age of $3\frac{1}{2}$ years an unremarkable hen; she had laid many eggs and raised many of her own offspring. Her history was known, since her owner kept but few fowls. She began to suffer from ovarian disease, which became recognisable. The disease was tuberculosis of the ovary which progressively removed the ovarian tissue and so produced the effects of pathological ovariotomy. But it would seem that this tumour-growth in its effects so altered the general metabolism of the individual that the conditions favourable to the differentiation and growth of spermatic tissue were created. New sex-cords developed from the germinal epithelium, and spermatic tissue was differentiated both in the left gonad and also in the incompletely atrophied right. The bird became anatomically equipped to function as a male, for with the development of the testes the Wolffian ducts were apparently stimulated to form functional vasa deferentia and the cloacal apparatus of the male was developed. Synchronously with the replacement of the ovarian tissue by spermatic the oviduct atrophied. This bird functioned as a male and became the father of two chickens. If this is indeed a case of complete sex-reversal in the fowl, in which a genotypic female as a result of the disturbance of metabolism by tumour-growth had become a phenotypic male, and if the fowl has the Abraxas type of sex-constitution, the sex-ratio of the offspring of this bird and a normal hen should be 50 : 100, so—

P_1	XY		XY	
Gametes	X	Y	X	Y
F_1	XX	XY	XY	YY (an infertile egg or a dead zygote)
	♂	♀	♀	
	1	2		

Of the two offspring of the mating, both typical Buff Orpingtons, one was a male and the other a female. These were interbred and their progeny were typical Buff Orpington chickens.

The histological study of the gonads in this case and in seven others showing different stages in transformation, demonstrated beyond doubt that the birds were originally hens, the ovaries of which atrophied at some period of life and were then invaded by peritoneal tissue. This tissue in some birds consummated development by giving rise to mature seminiferous tubules, and others produced undifferentiated epithelial cords which either continued to grow indefinitely, thus developing into tubules of an embryonic or immature type, or forming a malignant tumour. Traces of the proliferation of sex-cords from the germinal peritoneum were met with in most of the ovaries.

The cases displayed a consistent seriation illustrating the conversion of an actively functioning female into an actively functioning male, and into this series could be placed the cases described by other investigators. A fowl which previously had been equipped with the sex-organisation of the female and had functioned as such may undergo such a transformation as to come to possess the sex-organisation of the male, and actually to function as a male. Ovarian tissue is replaced by testicular, and the type of differentiation of the rest of the sex-equipment pursued under the direction of the functional ovary gives place to that type which is pursued under the direction of the functional testis. It is necessary to bring these facts into line with the established principle of the zygotic determination of sex in the fowl and with the more general problem of the over-riding of the sex-chromosome mechanism.

The actual sex-chromosome constitution of the fowl has not been finally demonstrated, but the indisputable evidence of sex-linked inheritance affords strong reason for holding that sex in the fowl is determined at the time of fusion of the gametes by a sex-chromosome mechanism of the Abraxas type, the sex-chromosome constitution of the male being symbolised as XX, that of the female as XY. If this is so, then, as in the case of Drosophila, it might be expected that any agency disturbing the balance between the two sets of sex-determining factors—*i.e.* those borne upon the X-chromosome, and those borne on the autosomes, in the cytoplasm, or possibly on the Y-chromosome—would produce a greater effect in the XY individual, in this case the hen. The fact that one of these fowls, kept under closest observation, had during the first three years of its life the appearance, behaviour, and functional powers of a hen and then later assumed the attributes of a cock, makes it clear that the type of sex-organisation and of the reproductive functioning of the individual are not irrevocably decided by the sex-chromosome constitution. It is certain that an XY individual—a "determined female"—can produce sperms just as efficiently as it can produce ova. The crude definition that a female is an individual which elaborates ova, and a male one that produces spermatozoa, requires profound modification: the transformation of the sex-organisation of an individual, a determined male or a determined female, into that ordinarily possessed by an individual which has the alternative sex-chromosome constitution is an established fact.

It would seem that the cytological features of the oocytes or of the spermatocytes depend, as does the character of the somatic structures of the rest of the sex-equipment of the individual, on the balance of conflicting physiological factors determined by the sex-chromosome constitution of the body as a whole, or, in the case of mammals, locally through the action of the interstitial cells of the gonad. On this assumption Goldschmidt's conception of a timing mechanism puts the discussion as to whether ovum-like bodies in a testis are oocytes or not on an entirely new footing, and shows that such questions as the homology of Bidder's organ to an ovary or the transformation of a characteristically female definitive gonad to one of the male type do not in the least conflict with the view that genetical factors play an important rôle in sex-differentiation. If it is agreed that the essential difference between the male and the female lies in the timing mechanism which decides whether, whilst a given organ is developing, the male- or the female-differentiating reactions are predominant, if it is agreed that at some point in the development preceding or following the stage of differentiation the female-differentiating reactions are predominant in a genotypic female and *vice versa*, then such questions as the above are resolved into a mere verbal quibble, and the efficiency of environic agencies to co-operate with the genetical factors offers no difficulty. The provisional hypothesis outlined by Goldschmidt to account for his Lymantria intersexes then brings into one coherent scheme the occurrence of oviform cells in the pro-testis of Anura (or among Myriopods as steps in normal spermatogenesis), and the cases of intersexuality and of sex-reversal to which reference has been made.

In the case of the fowl it has been shown that there are successive invasions of the organ by sex-cords derived from the peritoneum. The histological appearances suggest that so long as growing oocytes are present these invading sex-cords do not develop further into functional germinal tissue, perhaps being transformed into "luteal" cells. But in the absence of growing oocytes these cords are apparently converted regularly into seminiferous tubules. It would seem that the physiological conditions which in the female embryo at the time of differentiation of the sex-organisation induce the primitive germ-cells to assume the characters of oocytes—and it will be remembered that these are laid down before birth in the fowl—no longer obtain in the mature bird, so that if what may legitimately be regarded as some inhibiting influence of the functional ovary upon the invading sex-cords be removed, as is the case in ovarian atrophy and disease, or, to put the matter differently, if by ovarian disease the conditions favourable for the continued development of the sex-cords are created, the germ-cells inevitably take on the characteristics of spermatogonia, spermatocytes, and spermatozoa.

The phenomenon of sex-reversal in the case of the female of the domestic fowl interpreted in terms of Goldschmidt's hypothesis can be illustrated as in Figs. 62 and 63.

During embryonic life the female-determining substances are effectively in excess and the differentiation of the gonad and the rest of the sex-equipment proceeds under the influence of the female-differentiating reactions: the oocytes are laid down. Ordinarily during the succeeding years of the individual's life the growth of the oocytes precludes the operation of the male-differentiating reactions which are increasing in efficiency. But should the conditions be unfavourable for their growth, or should the conditions favourable for the continued development of the sex-cords arise as a result of the physiological exhaustion consequent upon excessive egg-laying or from hæmorrhage or tumour-growth, then, in the absence of the inhibitory influence of the growing oocytes, the male-differentiating reactions become effective, spermatic tissue is differentiated and the

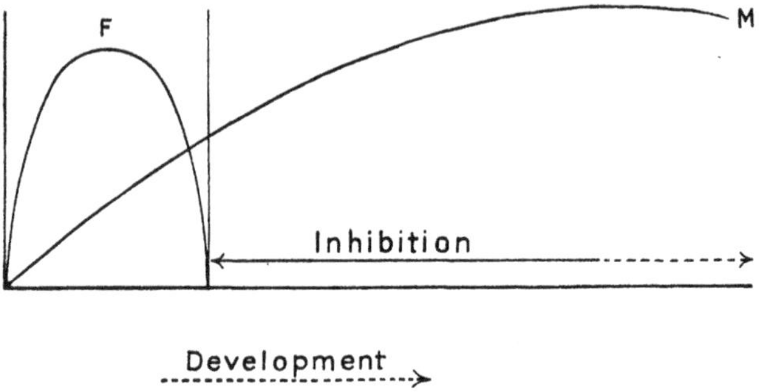

FIG. 62.

characters of the individual become those of the male (Fig. 63). It can be expected that almost any hen of a

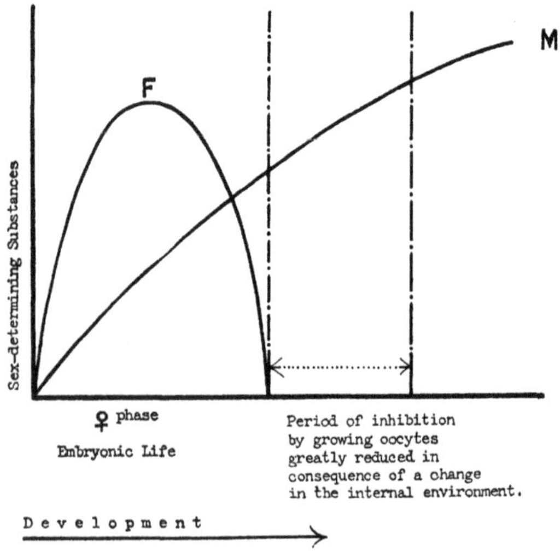

FIG. 63.

highly fecund strain will sooner or later develop some degree of the male characterisation.

It has been suggested that since the right gonad of the female chick never presents the histological structure of an ovary (it undergoes atrophy after about the eighth day of incubation), and since it does on occasion, in the ovariotomised hen, spring again into activity and become a testis, it is a testis from the beginning, but that its complete development is inhibited by the action of the differentiated left functional ovary. But it is sufficient to postulate that the right gonad is an incompletely differentiated gonad that still retains sufficient embryonic plasticity in certain cases to be capable of differentiating into either an ovary or into a testis. It is a fact that in the fowl it does not become an ovary, whilst the left gonad is functioning (it does so in birds of prey quite commonly, however), and a differential blood supply of pressure can explain this; it does become a testis in certain cases after the left ovary is removed by the knife or by disease, but this is to be explained by the fact that ovariotomy results in a drastic change in the internal environment, so that the conditions which encourage differentiation of germinal tissue into testicular rather than into ovarian are created. It is a significant fact that only the products of the secondary proliferation of germinal epithelium in the female chick develop into ovarian tissue. Any other proliferation yields testicular tissue. It would seem that the internal environmental conditions within the female chick at about the sixth day of incubation alone are favourable for differentiation into ovarian tissue.

Gynandromorphism in Birds.

The condition of gynandromorphism is possible only in those forms in which the control of the processes of sex-differentiation is not removed from the individual cells of the body and localised in the gonads. The gynandromorph is a sex-mosaic phenotypically because it is a mosaic genotypically. Its significance has been made clear by the work of Morgan and Bridges (1916) and others on Drosophila. The condition is based upon a disturbance of the sex-chromosome sex-determining mechanism, being the result of an accidental loss of an X-chromosome during the segmentation divisions of the fertilised egg. The gynandromorph of Drosophila is a female, an XX individual and a bilateral gynandromorph, with one side of the body including the sex-gland phenotypically male and the other phenotypically female, results when the elimination of the X-chromosome occurs at the first segmentation division of the zygote, so that one of the daughter-cells comes to possess but one X-chromosome and the other two. All the descendants of the first will possess but one X-chromosome and are therefore, as the result of this accidental loss, genotypically male. The relative amount of male characterisation varies according to the stage of embryonic development at which the loss of the X-chromosome occurs.

Among birds several cases of gynandromorphism have been recorded. Weber (1890) described a finch, Poll (1909) a bullfinch, Bond (1913) a pheasant, and Macklin (1923) a fowl. In the finches and the fowl the right side of the body was phenotypically male and the gonad on this side was a testis; the left side was phenotypically female and the gonad was an ovary. In the pheasant the right side was phenotypically female, the left male, whilst the single gonad was an ovo-testis.

If it is postulated that the differentiation of the sex-organisation of the bird is pursued under the control of specific sex-hormones elaborated by the testis and ovary respectively, then the avian gynandromorph cannot be explained. If it is assumed that the avian gynandromorph is a genotypic male, (XX) in sex-chromosome constitution, in which one X-chromosome is lost during the segmentation divisions of the zygote, an interpretation is possible on the understanding that the processes of sex-differentiation are pursued under the control of substances elaborated locally in every cell of the body and that the gonads do not differ in this respect from any other component structure of the sex-equipment.

Following the accidental loss of one X-chromosome certain foundation tissues become genotypically female (X) while others remain genotypically male (XX). The former will inevitably develop the appropriate secondary genotypic characters and will be phenotypically female, the others will become phenotypically male. The XX gonad will become a testis, the X gonad an ovary, or, if the gonad is a mixture of XX and X tissues, it will become an ovo-testis. Experiment has shown that ovarian and spermatic tissues can flourish in one and the same body, and in their growing affect the general physiological state of the individual. If this state is of a certain kind, then the genotypically female tissues will assume the female characterisation, the genotypically male will become phenotypically male. It is to be granted that the genotypic male and female tissues would respond differentially to male and female internal secretions were these elaborated by the ovarian and spermatic tissues present in these cases, but this does not explain the presence of these two kinds of tissues in one and the same body. According to this hypothesis there could exist a bird able to fertilise its own eggs. The conditions present in the artificial hermaphrodite possessing both ovarian and spermatic tissues is different, for such a bird is genotypically either a male or a female and the modification of the general plumage characterisation can be regarded as the reflection of a disturbed physiological state.

In the case of Bond's pheasant and of Macklin's fowl, it is of importance to note that the male side of the body was larger than the female. It has already been stated that the skeletal size character is a secondary genotypic and not a secondary gonadic character. Another point of considerable interest emerges from the case of the pheasant, for whereas the bird was a bilateral gynandromorph its tail was remarkable in that one half of the vane of each feather was phenotypically female, the other being phenotypically male. This fact is of great interest, bearing as it does upon the question of the developmental physiology of the feather, and it is related to the situation which exists in the parti-coloured breeds of fowls where commonly the two halves of the feather are coloured differently, one half being black and the other gold or silver, or red or white. Different regions of the bird and different regions of the feather behave as discrete units, their threshold of response to one and the same stimulus differs. If this is so, the extraordinary mosaic seen in the gynandromorph is understandable.

It is unfortunate that the chromosomes of the bird are so numerous and so small. Those of the fowl do not number less than 35 and the XY pair cannot readily be recognised. It is difficult therefore to secure cytological confirmation of the suggested explanation of the avian gynandromorph.

Hermaphroditism in the Mammal.

The essential feature of the condition of hermaphroditism in the mammal is that both ovarian and testicular tissues shall be present synchronously or consecutively in one and the same individual. A mammal can possess both kinds of gonadic tissue, but since its external reproductive organs cannot be both male-type or female-type it cannot function both as male and female. Moreover, ovarian tissue will not flourish in the normal position of the testes nor spermatic tissue within the abdominal cavity and a completely functional ovo-testis in the mammal is impossible.

Many cases of hermaphroditism have been described in the case of the pig, one gonad may be an ovary, the other a testis or an ovo-testis, or both may be ovo-testes. In rare cases there have been found two ovaries within the abdominal cavity and two testes in an imperfect scrotum. When one gonad is an ovary, it is invariably the left; in an ovo-testis, the ovarian tissue is always anterior to and sharply separated by a well-defined belt of connective tissue from the posterior testicular portion. Invariably the spermatic tissues are degenerate, the ovarian apparently normal. The relation of ovarian and testicular tissues in the ovo-testis found in the human and in the goat is not so well defined as that in the pig.

Many are the theories that have been advanced to interpret the condition, but it has to be confessed that as yet no completely satisfactory explanation is forthcoming. The following purely speculative hypothesis is put forward merely to attract further attention to the advantages of the pig as experimental material for use in this particular field of biological inquiry (Crew, 1924).

The abnormality of the accessory sexual apparatus and of the external genitalia is due to exactly the same cause as that of pseudo-intersexuality already described. There is a retardation in the exhibition, or an insufficiency of the sex-hormones following a retardation in the differentiation of the gonad.

The abnormality of the gonads can be explained if it is assumed (1) that in these cases the sex-determining factor complex included "quickly or early elaborating" female-determining factors and "slowly or late elaborating" male-determining factors, and that the individuals are genetically determined males; and (2) that the differentiation of the gonads in the pig is not synchronous but consecutive, the left one responding to the differentiating stimulus before the right as a general rule, and that the differentiation of one and the same gonad is not instantaneous but passes as a wave from cephalad (that nearest the head of the animal) to caudad (that nearest the tail) poles.

If these individuals are males genetically, it can be expected that sooner or later the male differentiating reactions will be in excess, but as the male-determining factors in these cases are relatively "slowly elaborating," the situation will be such that during the earlier stages of gonadic differentiation the more "quickly elaborated" female differentiating substances will direct that differentiation, and ovarian tissue will be laid down. The relative amounts of ovarian and testicular tissues in the gonads will provide an estimate of the time during the period of gonadic differentiation at which the male differentiating stimulus replaced the female.

This suggested interpretation can be illustrated graphically (Figs 64 *a*, 64 *b*, 64 *c*.)

The conditions in which two intra-abdominal ovaries and two testes beneath the skin of the inguinal or perineal region are found is interpreted as the result of the pulling apart of ovarian and testicular tissues in the case of paired ovo-testes.

As a result of the synchronous presence of ovarian and

testicular tissues both male and female sex-hormones will be elaborated, and the assumption of the secondary gonadic

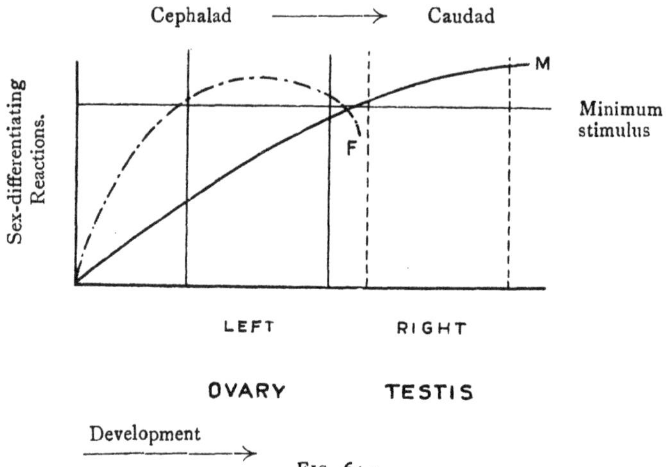

FIG. 64 *a*.

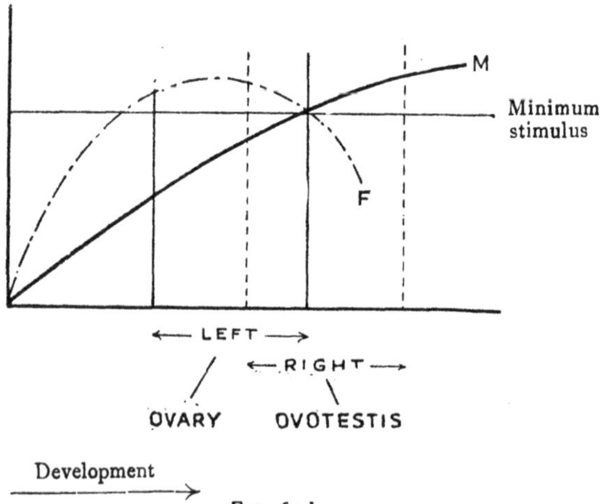

FIG. 64 *b*.

characters and sexual behaviour may thus be expected to be unusual. The characters of the accessory sexual apparatus and of the external genitalia will depend on the time relation that exists between these structures during the period of differentiation, and on whether the abnormal differentiation of the gonads is abnormal in time. If the differentiation of the gonads is delayed, as in the case of the pseudo-intersexual, then the characterisation of the accessory sexual apparatus and external genitalia will be as that of the pseudo-intersexual goat if the time relation in differentiation is the same in pig and goat; whereas, if the differentiation of the gonad occurs at the proper time, then the differentiation of the structures of the external genitalia and accessory

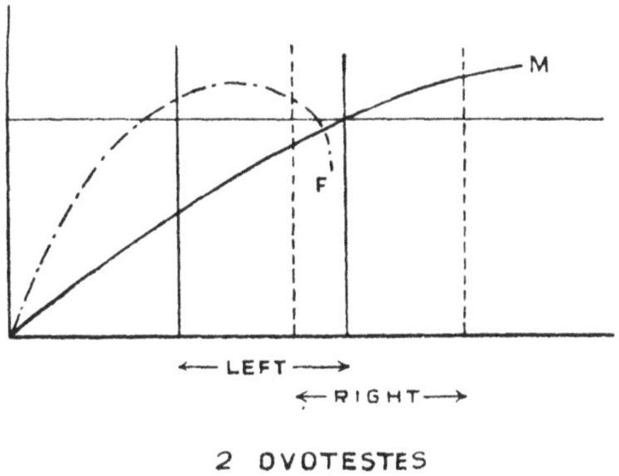

FIG. 64 *c*.

sexual apparatus will take place in the presence of both kinds of sex-hormone. If the individual, however, is a genotypic male it may be expected that the external genitalia will respond preferentially to the stimulus of the sex-hormone of the testis and a male-type of external reproductive apparatus should be developed. Bearing on this point is the fact that in these abnormal individuals there is always a more or less well-defined preputial area. In the presence of the conflicting influences of both kinds of sex-hormone the accessory sexual apparatus will ultimately consist of more or less well-developed derivates of both Müllerian and Wolffian ducts.

CHAPTER VIII

THE SEX-RATIO AND THE QUESTION OF ITS CONTROL

THE sex-ratio is the relative numerical proportion of the sexes within a group. In any bisexual species there must be a sex-ratio at all times after sex is determined, but it is convenient to take conception, birth, and maturity as the three salient points in the life-history of the individual at which to consider the sex-ratio of the species, and the sex-ratios which obtain at these three stages are known as the primary, the secondary, and the tertiary sex-ratio respectively. The secondary sex-ratio is measured by taking the number of males per hundred females born, and is the one usually considered. The primary sex-ratio is a demonstration of the sex-determining mechanism in operation, while the tertiary will provide an estimate of the postnatal survival value of the two sexes. The difference between the primary and secondary sex-ratios will provide an indication of the pre-natal survival value of the sexes. Since an exact knowledge of the processes involved in the establishment of the sex-ratio may possibly lead to the development of breeding practices by which the stock-breeder may control at will the production of progeny of one sex rather than of the other among his stock, the subject possesses more than a purely scientific interest. To the dairy farmer or to the egg farmer any striking increase in the number of males produced by his stock must foreshadow disaster, whereas any notable increase in the relative number of females born must prove highly advantageous.

A review of the established facts of sex-linked inheritance allows of no escape from the conclusions that sex is determined at the moment of fertilisation, that there must exist a mechanism which tends to preserve the production in every new generation of equal numbers of males and females, and that this mechanism is inherent in the gametes in virtue of the production by one sex, the female in the Abraxas group, the male in the Drosophila, of two kinds of reproductive cells, male-producing and female-producing respectively. Cytology, in revealing the sex-chromosome differences in the two sexes, has demonstrated this mechanism and has shown clearly that in the absence of disturbing agencies the sex-ratio should be 1 : 1, since one sex is constitutionally heterogametic, elaborating two sorts of gametes in equal numbers, the other homogametic. It is established that in the case of the domesticated mammals, the male is the heterogametic sex, in the case of the domestic fowl, the female.

However, the sex-ratio, though fairly constant and not far from equality, is distinctly variable and rarely coincides with the expected 1 : 1; in view of what is known concerning the sex-determining mechanism it is necessary to examine this variability and to explain it.

This sex-ratio varies with the species. The secondary sex-ratio of most mammals has not been determined experimentally, for with few exceptions the mammals are unsuitable for experiments on a large scale, and that which is known has been culled from different Breed Registers. The following data have met with general approval (Cuénot (1899), Schleip (1913), Lenhossék (1913), Hertwig (1912), Doncaster (1914), *et al.*):—

Man . .	103-107	100	Pig . .	111·8	100
Horse . .	98·3	100	Rabbit .	104·6	100
Dog . .	118·5	100	Mice .	100-118	100
Cattle . .	107·3	100	Fowl .	93·4-94·7	100
Sheep . .	97·7	100	Pigeon .	115·0	100

The sex-ratio varies with the race, breed, and strain, and there are reasons for holding that the production of a profoundly unusual sex-ratio is characteristic of a particular individual. Instances, not a few, are known in which a male of some monotocous species has produced in different matings none but female, or none but male offspring. But the monotocous female, producing usually but one offspring at a time, is not a suitable material with which to test this hypothesis. An appeal must be made to the polytocous rodent. King (1918) has found that in the case of the albino rat it was possible, starting with two pairs of rats from the same litter, to found two strains, one of which produced a high proportion of males, the other a preponderance of females. The progeny of one pair (pair A) were bred brother to sister without selection for six generations in order to build up a homozygous and uniform race. After this, selection was practised, the brothers and sisters being chosen from litters which showed a preponderance of males. In line B the selection after the sixth generation was made from litters showing a preponderance of females. After fifteen generations of such in-breeding and selection, the sex-ratio at birth in line A was 125 : 100, in line B 83 : 100. The habitual production of an unusual sex-ratio can be the expression of a genetic constitution. It is possible to breed for a preponderance of one sex.

Month.	Number of Puppies.	Dogs.	Bitches.	Secondary Sex-Ratio.
January	726	382	344	111 : 100
February	593	318	275	112 : 100
March	906	468	438	106 : 100
April	794	408	386	105 : 100
May	1129	587	542	108 : 100
June	892	486	406	110 : 100
July	932	480	452	106 : 100
August	669	354	315	112 : 100
September	314	173	141	122 : 100
October	250	122	128	90·6 : 100
November	209	107	102	104 : 100
December	122	57	65	87·6 : 100

The sex-ratio varies with the season of the year. It is not improbable that the breeding season is one in which the general physiological condition of the individual is above the average, and it is of interest therefore to compare the secondary sex-ratio following conception during the breeding season with that following conception at other times. The human birth-rate actually shows a slight variation in spite of the fact that nearly all traces of the primitive breeding season have been obliterated by social habits. It is found that the sex-ratio is low for births resulting from conceptions at the seasons of greatest fertility and high at the times of lowest birth-rate.

Dighton (1922) gives the figures (page 256) for the greyhound.

Heape (1908) and Wilckens (1886) supply the following data :—

	Numbers.	Secondary Sex-ratio, Whole Year.	Warm Months.	Cold Months.
Horse	16,091	97·9 : 100	96·6	97·3
Cattle	4,900	107·3 : 100	114·1	103·0
Sheep	6,751	97·4 : 100	102·1	94·0
Pig	2,357	111·8 : 100	115·0	109·3
Dog	17,838	118·5 : 100	126·3	122·1

It should be mentioned that Bonnier (1923) maintains that the Swedish vital statistics do not confirm Heape's conclusions.

Parkes (1924) gives the following figures for the albino mouse—

Month.	Numbers.	Males.	Females.	Secondary Sex-ratio.	Percentage of Males.
March	25	12	13	100	49·7 ± 1·78 (March–June)
April	82	42	40	105·0 : 100	
May	90	44	46	95·7 : 100	
June	157	78	79	98·8 : 100	
July	163	88	75	117·4 : 100	56·5 ± 1·27 (July–October)
August	231	138	93	148·5 : 100	
September	187	100	87	115·0 : 100	
October	96	56	40	140·0 : 100	
	1031	558	473	118·0	54·2 ± 1·04

King's (1915) figures for the rat also support the contention that the season of the highest birth-rate is that of the lowest proportion of males. Sumner, M'Daniel, and Huestis (1922) suspect a seasonal variation also in the case of the deer-mouse, Peromyscus, which however gives the highest sex-ratio in the season opposite to King's.

The sex-ratio varies in different matings and the disturbance seems to be related to the relative physiological condition of the parents at the time. In the experience of many poultry breeders, the first lot of eggs laid by a pullet yields a preponderance of male chickens, whereas as the season advances and the pullet ages, the proportion of males steadily decreases. Jull (1923) using a sex-linked cross in order to preclude errors, recorded the sex of the chickens hatched from eggs of 45 hens during their first year of production. The observations were repeated for three years and the secondary sex-ratio was found to be 48·41 expressed as a percentage. Analysis of the figures gave the following table—

Eggs.	Secondary Sex-ratio.
0 to 20	62·91 ± 1·44
21 " 40	57·46
41 " 60	45·00
61 " 80	44·61
81 " 100	37·65
101 " 120	32·53 ± 1·15

Statistical evidence has been presented, sometimes supporting, at other times contradicting, the suggestion that the sex-ratio is affected by the relative ages of the parents, the offspring being mostly of the same sex (or of the opposite sex) as the older (or as the younger) parent. Hofacker (1828) and Sadler's (1830) law—that the sex of the offspring was that of the older parent—finds no support in the result of critical inquiry: it is contradicted by the work of Schultze (1903) on mice, for example. According to some data, the age of the mother has a relation to the sex of the offspring, younger mothers producing a preponderance of males (or of females.) It must not be forgotten that in the majority of cases the data upon which these theories are based have not been collected by biometrical experts, nor can their genuineness be absolutely guaranteed. Other data seem to suggest that the sex of the offspring tends to be that of the more (or of the less) vigorous parent. For example, the theory of Starkweather

(1883) suggested that the "superior" parent tended to beget offspring of the opposite sex, but since it is impossible as yet to define "vigour" and "superiority" in accurate physiological terms, such theories are not suitable for scientific discussion. There is no experimental basis for such conceptions.

It has been suggested that the sex-ratio varies with the time of service during the œstrous period. Pearl and Parshley (1913), in testing this theory first propounded by Thury (1863) and later by Düsing (1884) collected data from stock-breeders, and found that out of a total of 480 calves, 255 were male and 225 female, and that the sex-ratio among calves resulting from service early in the heat was 98·4; among calves resulting from service during the middle period of the heat was 115·5, and in the case of service late in heat, 154·8. Later data collected by Pearl (1917) did not support the suggestion that service early in heat resulted in a female calf, late in heat in a male.

The suggestion that there is a relation between the sex-ratio and the size of the litter in polytocous animals is not supported by the results of Wentworth (1914) in the case of dogs and pigs, of King (1915) in the case of rats, of Parker and Bullard (1913) and of Machens (1915) and also of Parkes (1923) in case of pigs.

It would seem that the sex-ratio varies with the parity, with the chronological number of the pregnancy, for in the case of the human, the dog, and the mouse, it has many times been noted that there is a continuous drop in the sex-ratio at each succeeding pregnancy, Wilckens (1886), Punnett (1903), Bidder (1878), Copeman and Parsons (1904). King (1915) found that the same rule obtained in the case of the rat:—

Sequence of Litters.	No. of Litters in the Series.	Individuals.	Males.	Females.	Secondary Sex-ratio.
1	21	131	72	59	122·0
2	21	162	85	77	110·4
3	18	127	64	63	101·6
4	15	96	41	55	103·1

Parkes (1924), working with mice, gives the following table:—

	Total.	Males.	Females.	Secondary Sex-ratio.	Percentage of Males.
First births . .	242	134	108	124·2	55·4 ± 2·14
Subsequent births	190	114	76	150·0	60·0 ± 2·89
	432	248	184	134·9	57·3 ± 1·60

Parkes points out, however, that most of the second and higher births occurred at the end of the breeding-season when the sex-ratio is at its highest, and that too much must not be inferred from his figures until the experiment has been repeated.

It has been suggested that the sex-ratio varies with the time relation of successive conceptions. Rumley Dawson (1921), for instance, maintained that in the case of the monotocous female the right ovary elaborated only male-producing ova, the left only female-producing, and that the ovaries function alternately, ovulation occurring in one ovary at one œstrous period, in the other at the next. Knowing then the sex of the first offspring of the female, and keeping a record of all œstrous periods, including those suppressed by the first pregnancy, it is possible, according to this theory, to arrange services so that subsequent offspring produced by this female shall be of the selected sex and likewise to foretell their sex. In order that an offspring of the same sex as the first shall be produced, all that is necessary is to see that conception shall coincide with an œstrous period which, when referred back to the one associated with the conception of the first offspring, is an odd number, 9th, 11th, 13th, and so on. If progeny of the opposite sex are desired, then conception must be made to coincide with œstrous periods with even numbers, 10th, 12th, and so on. It should be stated that a considerable number of experienced stock-breeders in this and in other countries claim that their observations entirely support this theory. Nevertheless it cannot be brought into harmony with established scientific facts, and therefore cannot be accepted on its present-day evidence. The theory is supported by a collection of selected statistical data applied without proper statistical treatment, and those cases which do not fit into the scheme are airily dismissed, whilst the great body of established facts which supports other theories and cannot support this particular one is neglected. Variations of this theory are numerous, and like it are based upon the conception that in the human, the horse. and in cattle, the female is heterogametic. Many believe that offspring of either sex can be obtained at will by persuading the semen of the male to flow to the right or to the left of the body of the female—towards the left ovary or to the right, that is. This is ensured by the female lying on one side or the other after coitus, or standing on a slope. The matter has been tested experimentally and found wanting. Doncaster and Marshall (1910) have shown that unilateral ovariotomy in the rat does not result in the production of offspring of one sex only, and the cogency of these experimental results cannot be dismissed by the statement that it is too far a cry from the rat to the human female. If the breeder really desires to have this theory tested, the way is simple, for it can readily be shown that unilateral ovariotomy in the horse or in the cow is not followed by the production of offspring of one sex only, and that the production of both male and female progeny is not to be explained by any regeneration of the imperfectly removed ovary. As it is, the believer in this theory may well be content, for a calf must be either male or female; some matings undoubtedly produce a preponderance of female calves, and in any case if a calf of the wrong sex appears the breeder can always find some satisfying explanation for the unexpected.

In the case of the rabbit it has been shown that the sex-ratio is related to the chronological order of the service of the buck; in the first service group there is a preponderance of males and then an increasing preponderance of females as the number of services increases. Hays (1921) obtained the following results:—

Service . . .	1st	5th	10th	15th	20th
Sex-ratio . . .	56·33	43·50	44·44	54·64	21·87

The sex-ratio is profoundly disturbed as a result of interspecific and intervarietal crosses. Haldane (1922) has pointed out that in any such cross the sex that is absent, rare, or sterile, is the heterogametic sex.

Mother.	Father.	Males.	Females.	Author.
INSECTS. (In Lepidoptera the female is heterogametic ; in Drosophila, the male.)				
Nyssia græcaria . .	*Lycia hirtaria* . .	65	0	Harrison (1916)
" *zonaria* . .	" " . .	208	0	"
" " . .	*Pœcilopsis isabellæ* . .	32	0	"
" " . .	" *pomonaria* .	90	0	"
" " . .	" " (inbred)	71	7	"
" " . .	" *lapponaria* .	93	0	"
" " . .	" " (inbred)	62	3	"
Lycia hirtaria . .	" *pomonaria* .	86	65	"
" " . .	" " .	190	14	"
Pœcilopsis isabellæ . .	*Lycia hirtaria* . .	38	32	"
" *lapponaria* .	*Pœcilopsis pomonaria* .	38	39	"
Oporabia diluta . .	*Oporabia autumnata* .	6	0	"
Tephrosia bistortata .	*Tephrosia crepuscularis* .	378	12	"
Drosophila melanogaster —	*Drosophila melanogaster* —			Lynch (1919)
(fused) . . .	(normal)	0	823	"
(fused XXY) . .	"	9	77	"
(rudimentary) . .	"	10	952	"
(rudimentary XXY) .	"	93	647	"
Drosophila melanogaster .	*Drosophila simulans* .	2	3552	Sturtevant (1920)
BIRDS (female heterogametic).				
Turtur orientalis . .	*Columba livia* . .	13	1	Whitman and Riddle (1919)
Streptopelia risoria . .	" " . .	38	0	"
" *alba-risoria* . .	" " . .	11	0	"
" *risoria* . .	*Zenaidura carolinensis* .	16	0	"
Gallus domesticus . .	*Phasianus colchicus* .	100	...	Lewis Jones (quoted by Haldane)
Phasianus reevesi . .	" *torquatus* .	{161	6}	Smith and Haig Thomas (1912)
" " . .	" *versicolor* .			
Tetrao urogallus . .	*Tetraoteipennis* . .	40	8	Suchetet (1897)
Gallus domesticus . .	*Pavo nigripennis* . .	2	0	Trouessart (1907)
MAMMALS (male heterogametic).				
Bos taurus . . .	*Bison americanus* . .	6	39	Boyd (1914)
" *taurus* . . .	" *bonasus* . .	1	3	Ivanov (1913)

Genetic Causes of a Disturbed Sex-Ratio.

It can be accepted that the sex-determining mechanism is such as should give equal numbers of males and females provided that both kinds of gametes elaborated by the heterogametic sex are produced in equal numbers, that they are equally viable, that random fertilisation occurs and that the resulting zygotes are equally viable.

The heterogametic sex can be identified cytologically in many cases, by the results of breeding experiments involving sex-linked characters, and by the fact that crossing-over either does not occur, or if it occurs, it does so to a much less extent in the heterogametic than in the homogametic sex.

In the case of the mammal, in which group the male is the heterogametic sex, there are two kinds of spermatozoa, the X-chromosome bearing and the Y-chromosome bearing (or the no-X-bearing). Sperm-dimorphism has been demonstrated in the following cases cytologically. XY type: man, monkey, opossum (Painter 1922); rabbit (Bachuber 1916); guinea-pig (Stevens 1911). XO type: horse, pig (Wodsedalek 1913); bull (Wodsedalek 1920); cat (Winiwarter and Sainmont 1909), but see p. 171; rat (Allen 1918); mouse (Yocum 1917); dog (Malone 1918). Wodsedalek (1913), Zeleny and Faust (1915) and Parkes (1923), as a result of measuring the length of the sperm-head, have brought forward evidence to show that there are two intergrading classes of sperms, one class being of larger size than the other. It is assumed that in those cases in which this size difference can be detected, as in the horse and the boar, the larger class contains the X-bearing sperm, *i.e.*, the female-producing, and the smaller size class the Y-bearing (or no X-bearing sperm), the male producing.

The primary sex-ratio is affected by the differential production of the two sorts of gametes by the heterogametic sex. That such differential production exists there can be no doubt, though the cause for this is not well understood. In the case of the human, it is known that the primary sex-ratio is higher than the secondary and that the secondary is higher than the tertiary. It is estimated that the primary sex-ratio in the human is about 120 : 100. In the case of the bird and moth the egg contains the X- and Y-chromosomes in conjugation before the polar-bodies are formed. Into the first polar-body goes either the X or the Y. If it is but a matter of chance which way this chromosome pair lies on the spindle, then equal numbers of X-bearing and of Y-bearing eggs will result. But if in a particular line this pair should habitually be so orientated on the spindle that the X passes into the polar-body more often than the Y, then in this line a preponderance of female offspring would be observed. Such a differential production can be obtained experimentally, as is shown by the work of Seiler (1920) on the Psychid *Talæporia tubulosa*, in which the female is the heterogametic sex. Seiler was able to show that the ratio of the eggs in which the X-chromosome passed into the polar-body to those in which it remained, was exactly the same as the sex-ratio. Moreover, since in the course of these observations it was possible to detect the moment of the disjunction of the sex-chromosomes, it became possible to attempt to influence this disjunction experimentally and so to disturb the sex-ratio. Seiler by varying the temperature during the maturation division obtained the following significant results—

Temperature.	X-chromosome remained in the egg.	X-chromosome passed into the polar-body.	Sex-ratio.
18° C.	61	45	136 : 100
35-37° C.	52	84	62 : 100
3·5° C.	48	31	155 : 100

Riddle (1916) submits that it is possible to distinguish between the two sorts of eggs in the pigeon, and has adduced a considerable amount of evidence in support of his contention. According to this authority, in pure species of pigeons the first egg laid, smaller and containing less chemical energy than the second, is destined when fertilised to become a male, the second a female. Cuénot (1899) and Cole (1915), however, disagree with this conclusion. Heape (1907) kept two aviaries of canaries under very different conditions and found that the sex-ratio in the two cases was markedly different. One aviary was well lighted, the temperature equable, and the birds did not receive specially rich food; the other was darker, the temperature varied, and the food was abundant and rich. The percentage of males produced by the first aviary was more than three times that obtained from the second, in which the environmental conditions were not so favourable. Since the birds were interchanged without the sex-ratio being altered, it was concluded that the difference in the ratios was due to a selective action upon the production and survival of the two sorts of gametes of the heterogametic sex—in this case the female.

Bearing upon this question is the fact that in the Aphids the no-X-bearing gametes degenerate, that in the male bee three out of the four gametes fail to develop, and that in Hydatina one of the primary spermatocytes yields two female-producing gametes, the other spermatocyte, failing to divide, degenerates. In all these cases fertilisation yields only females.

The sex-ratio is affected by the relative degree of maturity of the ovum at the time of fertilisation in those cases in which the female is the homogametic sex. It is possible experimentally to modify profoundly the sex-ratio, as seen in the case of the frogs of Hertwig (1912) and of Kuschakewitch (1910), or of trout of Mrsic (1923), and this may be explained on the assumption that the over-ripeness of the ovum is associated with extrusion of the X-chromosome into the polar-body, thus leading to the production of males. Hertwig allowed a male frog to fertilise half the eggs of a female and removed him from the nuptial embrace. The female does not lay her eggs in the absence of the male and so after an interval of any duration, the male can be put back and will then fertilise the remaining eggs. The sex-ratio of the frogs hatched from the first half of the eggs was in every case near equality; with the rest the degree of disturbance of the sex-ratio varied with the length of the interval. Kuschakewitch, Hertwig's pupil, repeated and confirmed these results—

Hours	0	6	18	24	36	42	54	64	89
Hertwig	58	54	...	55	...	...	...	...	...
	49·0	...	...	...	58	...	59	...	...
	48·5	...	37	...	...	58	...	88	...
Kuschakewitch	55	...	...	...	...	...	...	...	100

Kuschakewitch (1910) showed quite definitely that this result was not due to a differential mortality and Hertwig has described an actual histological remodelling of the gonad in these cases, showing that in the late-fertilised zygote the gonad develops in a way quite distinct morphologically from that seen in the normal male. Bearing on this point is the observation of Adler (1917) that the thyroid of the late-fertilised zygote is markedly hypertrophied, which, if confirmed, may throw some light on the physiology of sex-differentiation.

The quantitative difference that exists between the X- and the Y-chromosome-bearing spermatozoa in many mammals, for example in the mouse, rat, pig, bull, horse, and man, may possibly supply an explanation of the differential production of the two sorts of gametes by the heterogametic sex; but it is likely that a disturbed primary sex-ratio is more commonly the result of a differential activity, susceptibility, or mortality on the part of the two sorts of sperm. It is necessary and not unreasonable to suggest that the Y-bearing sperms of the mammal possess some advantage during the period coition-fertilisation. It may be that the male-determining sperm is the more active. If this is so, there exists the possibility of artificially separating the two kinds, the X- and the Y-bearing, or of further handicapping the X-bearing by treatment of the female passages. In the case of the heterogametic female, environic conditions, as is seen from Seiler's work, can cause a differential production of the two sorts of eggs as the result of a differential maturation division. Conditions may be such as to induce, for example in the case of the first egg of the pigeon, the female-producing genetic complex (= the Y) to be extruded into the polar-body more often than the male-producing genetic complex (= the X), whilst as a result of further egg-laying the conditions become such that the male-producing genetic complex is more frequently extruded. There is evidence which seems to show the existence of a differential chemical constitution in the early and the later egg, and it seems probable that this difference is mirrored in the different reaction systems in the dividing oocytes. Riddle has found that by forcing the female bird to lay eggs at more than the normal rate the proportion of females among her progeny is increased; Pearl's (1917) work yielded suggestions that this might also be the case in the fowl, for significantly more females were produced by hens which had laid very heavily immediately prior to mating. The matter needs further investigation. It is well to bear in mind, however, the possibility that the differential production of gametes may be characteristic of a particular individual or strain, the result of some heritable mutation affecting the maturation division of the egg or leading to the suppression of one sort of sperm. This probably lies at the basis of such results as those of King in her in-breeding experiments with rats, in which she was able to shift the sex-ratio in either direction.

A disturbed primary sex-ratio may be the result of a differential mobility and vitality of the X and Y spermatozoa, or of a differential attraction for sperm by the X- and the Y-eggs of the heterogametic female. Such a conception as this postulates that there is a competition among the sperm. Cole and Davies (1914) have shown that this is the case. A rabbit was served by two very different bucks in rapid succession. In the litter which resulted the majority claimed one of the two bucks as their sire. In repeated matings this was always so. But when the sperm of this buck were alcoholised they could not compete with those of the other buck, though it was shown that when employed alone they could and did fertilise ova. It is reasonable to assume that if differences in the size of the sperm are associated with differences in motility, activity, or resistance to unfavourable conditions within the genital passages of the female, then chance would favour fertilisation by one rather than by the other kind of sperm. There can be no doubt that an unusual secondary sex-ratio may be but the reflection of a disturbed primary ratio.

The sex-ratio may be profoundly disturbed by the selective elimination of the zygotes, *e.g.*, a differential mortality of the males or females in their embryonic or fœtal stages. Prenatal mortality due to the action of an unbalanced sex-linked lethal factor falls upon the heterogametic sex. When more than one sex-linked lethal are present in the genotype, the sex-ratio will depend on the linkage value between them. For example, in *Drosophila melanogaster*, lethal 1 is located at 0·7, lethal 3 at 26·5 on the X-chromosome, and therefore about 25 per cent. of crossing-over will occur. The female with each of these lethals in the simplex state will have the constitution $(l_1L_3X)(L_1l_3X)$ and will elaborate four sorts of eggs in the following proportions:—

(l_1L_3X)	(L_1l_3X)	(L_1L_3X)	(l_1l_3X)
3	3	1	1

and when these are exposed to fertilisation by the sperms elaborated by a wild-type male $(L_1L_3X)Y$ the following zygotes will result:—

$(l_1L_3X)(L_1L_3X)$	$(L_1l_3X)(L_1L_3X)$	$(L_1L_3X)(L_1L_3X)$	$(l_1l_3X)(L_1L_3X)$
3	3	1	1
(l_1L_3X) Y	(L_1l_3X) Y	(L_1L_3X) Y	(l_1l_3X) Y
3	3	1	1
(die)	(die)	(lives)	(dies)

so that only one male in every eight will live and a sex-ratio of 12·5 : 100 will result. It is probable that sex-linked lethals and semi-lethals (which allow a few of the XY individuals to come through) are at the bottom of most of the excess of male fœtal mortality. Jewell (1921) found that the fœtal sex-ratio in cattle was 123 : 100, so that there must be a selective elimination of male fœtuses. The specific action of a lethal is not to be demonstrated if that action is exerted during the earliest stages of embryonic development; it has to be assumed that the physiological derangement or the anatomical abnormality was such that, becoming expressed in the earliest stages of development, it rendered the zygote incapable of pursuing the further developmental stages. Parkes (1923) has shown that prenatal mortality in mice falls preponderatingly upon the male, while in the case of the bison × cattle cross it has been shown that the lethal effect is such as to lead to severe dystocia preventing the birth of the male calf. The abnormal sex-ratio following interspecific crosses may be due to some such cause as the action of a sex-linked lethal complex.

In the case of *Drosophila melanogaster*, it has been shown also that primary and secondary non-disjunction lead to a profoundly unusual sex-ratio, and in these cases there is some definite abnormality in the chromatin content and in the genotype of the individuals that succumb.

Selective mortality of the developing zygotes may be based upon a differential susceptibility to disease. Federley (1911), for example, obtained in two successive generations of *Pygæra pigra*, the chocolate-tip moth, none but females, and found that the lack of males was due to an inherited disease which had the effect of making the blood of the male larvæ abnormal, so that they were killed off in the larval stage. The females were unaffected but transmitted the disease to their male offspring. In such a case as this the action of a sex-linked lethal factor demonstrates a physiological distinction between the sexes. Goldschmidt (1923) was able to show that in the case of the caterpillars of the gipsy moth attacked by Flacherie, a disease which affects the caterpillar about the time of the fifth moult, it did not affect the males as these were already in the pupal stage and thus secure from infection, but that it did affect the females, causing among them a high death-rate and resulting in a profoundly disturbed sex-ratio. It is seen then that differences in the life history of the two sexes may provide an opportunity for the partial or complete elimination of one.

This selective elimination is also affected by favourable and unfavourable conditions during the pregnancy. Parkes (1924) has shown that mice which are allowed to become pregnant immediately after parturition and whilst still suckling their young produce smaller litters in which the proportion of females is markedly raised. Corpora lutea counts showed that in such cases the number of fœtuses was not unusual, and that the smaller litter-size was due to an intensified selective elimination of the males. The same explanation can be applied to the fact that the secondary sex-ratio among illegitimate children is lower than that among legitimate—the lack of prenatal care and hygiene resulting in an intensifying of the forces that always make it relatively difficult for the mammal to beget male offspring. The secondary sex-ratio is highest among those peoples and those herds in which the highest degree of prenatal hygiene is practised. It is highest among the Jews, and would be found to be higher among race-horses than among the overworked beasts of burden of the uncivilised.

The difference that clearly exists between the secondary and the tertiary ratios is simply the result of a selective postnatal mortality. In the case of the human it is well established that more boys than girls die during the years of infancy. It is probable that this is but a delayed expression of sex-linked semi-lethal factors. Gunther's (1923) figures of mortality in the German Empire bear upon this question:—

	Years.	Sexual quotient (number of ♀ deaths : 1 ♂ death).
Postnatal	3-5	0·92
	2-3	0·91
	1-2	0·89
	0-1	0·74

The sex-ratio among live and still-births shows a similar difference:—

			Sexual quotient.
Live births . .	106 ♂	100 ♀	0·945
Still-births . . .	130	100	0·77

The constant differences between the sex-ratios of different species cannot be regarded as the result of a constant difference in the amount of prenatal mortality, unless it is assumed that each species is remarkable for its own lethal factor complex. The difference is more probably due to differences in the physical and physiological properties of the two sorts of gametes elaborated by the heterogametic sex. Seasonal variation of the sex-ratio in a species is to be explained similarly, the differences between the two sorts of gametes becoming more pronounced in the extra-breeding season. The relation of unusual sex-ratios and litter-size is to be explained by selective prenatal mortality. Small litters are those that have been depleted prenatally; large litters are those which have not, and amongst which therefore there has been a conservation of the males. The influence of parity on the sex-ratio is entirely one of selective post-conceptional elimination of fœtuses; the number of abortions and of still-births increases with the age of the mother and with the serial number of the pregnancy.

The work of Baltzer (1914) on the marine worm Bonellia, of Goldschmidt (1923) on the gipsy moth, of Essenberg (1923) on the fish Xyphophorus, of Witschi (1922) and of Crew (1921) on the frog, of Champy (1921) on the triton, of Riddle (1924) on the pigeon, of Crew (1923) on the fowl, of Tandler (1916) and of Lillie (1917) on the bovine free-martin, has shown the way in which an unusual sex-ratio may be the reflection of complete sex-reversal. It is an established fact that an individual with the chromosome constitution of one sex, a genotypic male or female, as the case may be, may come to possess the functional sex-equipment and capacity of the opposite. A hen, XY in genotypic constitution, may function as a male, and mated with a hen will produce offspring, the sex-ratio amongst which will be 50 : 100. If, on the other hand, a female amphibian or mammal, XX in genotypic constitution, functions as a male, its progeny will consist solely of females.

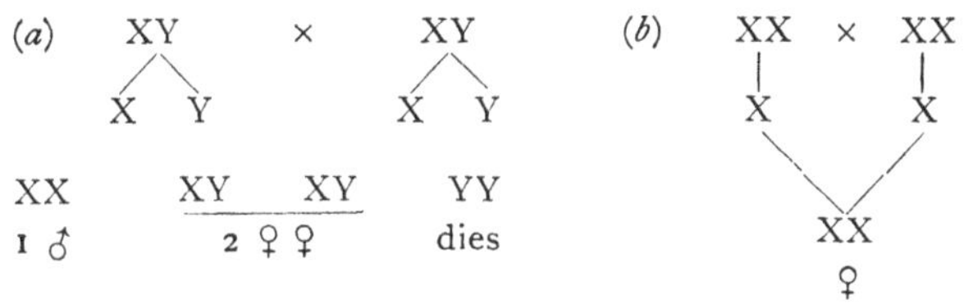

The problem of the control of the secondary sex-ratio is that of the control of the primary, and this involves a control of the differential production of the two sorts of gametes elaborated by the heterogametic sex. This can be done most effectively, as is seen, by controlling sex-reversal. This is as yet not practicable, and for the present at least the problem will be approached by breeding on lines known to give a preponderance of one sex. The selective elimination of one genotypic sex is possible, but it is doubtful that it would be profitable. The most promising field would seem to be that of creating those conditions in the mammal in which fertilisation by one rather than the other kind of sperm is favoured, and in the bird of those conditions that favour the production of one rather than of the other kind of egg.

In the case of the domestic fowl it is not possible to distinguish the two sorts of eggs by inspection. It has been claimed that differences in size indicate differences in sex, but this claim has not been substantiated. Size of egg is a character based on genetic constitution and modified by environmental agencies. If traced to its ultimate analysis it would be found that egg-size is a reflection of some anatomical and physiological relation of the reproductive organs which governs the formation of the egg: in this sense egg-size is the result of a character and not itself one. But size of egg and the conditions that decide it are both expressions of the same genotype, and by measuring the egg it is possible to gather impressions of the mechanism that produced it. In the case of Drosophila many of the mutant stocks exhibit a distinguishing egg-size character. Egg-size is not affected therein by the size or age of the female nor by environmental forces, it is as characteristic of the female as is any one of her external characters, and is fixed before egg meets sperm, and cannot be affected by any genes contributed by the male. An F_1 female of a mating of different egg-size stocks has the same egg-size character as her mother, and it is only in the F_2, as Warren (1924) has shown, that the action of the genes brought in by the P_1 sperm is evidenced. Many genes in all the chromosomes are involved, and an egg-size difference of but 0·2 mm. was shown by Warren to be a character in the Mendelian sense.

CHAPTER IX

EXOGAMY AND ENDOGAMY

ENDOGAMY is that system of breeding in which closely related individuals are mated. In inbreeding the closest types of mating possible are practised, sire to daughter, dam to son, brother to sister; in line breeding the matings are between individuals within one line of descent, excluding those which constitute inbreeding. Exogamy or out-breeding is that system of mating in which the individuals concerned are unrelated, in which consanguinity is deliberately avoided. The terms can be used only in a relative sense, for if one holds to the evolutionist's conception of the origin of species, all species and all members of all species are related in some degree. Endogamy merely implies that the individuals concerned possess fewer different ancestors in some particular generation or generations than the maximum possible number for that generation or generations.

Inbreeding.—The records of the breeds of domestic animals show that close inbreeding and line breeding of good stock, if associated with the usual elimination of the weakly, may be practised for many generations without any undesirable consequences. Endogamy and vigorous selection are the tools which have fashioned the breeds of to-day, but the material thus fashioned was in the great majority of cases the product of outbreeding and of the crossing of different local breeds. Endogamy during the formative period of the breeds was practised extensively, and the evidence would seem to show quite plainly that some degree of narrow breeding is an essential to the attainment of outstanding success in animal breeding. Inbreeding is not necessarily harmful therefore, in fact it can be definitely advantageous, leading to the establishment of a uniform and true breeding stock. But benefit does not always follow endogamy. Often there is advance, but sometimes there is disappointing regression, a diminution of vigour, lowered power of resistance, decreased fertility, even reduction in size. It is necessary to inquire why it is that endogamy in some cases results in definite improvement whilst in others it is disastrous. The experiences of the stock-breeder cannot be considered in this inquiry because his stock is not suitable material for scientific investigation of this sort. We must turn to the laboratory animals.

King (1919) took 4 slightly undersized but otherwise normal albino fancy rats, 2 males and 2 females, as a foundation of two lines, A and B, of inbred individuals. 25 generations were raised by brother to sister matings and in every generation after the 6th, 20 females were selected for further breeding. In the first 6 generations the animals suffered from faulty feeding but this was then corrected. It was clearly demonstrated that by selection within an inbred race, vigorous uniform strains could be built up, larger, longer-lived, and more fertile than many strains of the control stocks. Through selection the strain A was slightly more fertile, attained sexual maturity earlier and lived longer than strain B. Variability gradually became reduced as the experiment progressed.

Castle (1906) bred Drosophila for many generations of continuous brother × sister matings. After 59 generations fertility did not appear to be reduced below that shown by the original stock. During the generations 6 - 24 there were between 17 to 80 per cent. of totally sterile matings: between the 25th - 42nd, 18 to 47 per cent., and between the 45th - 59th only 37 per cent.

On the other hand, Crampe (1883), starting with a litter of 5 young rats obtained from the cross albino ♀ × white and grey ♂, practised close in-breeding for 17 generations. During the course of the experiment many individuals showed marked susceptibility to disease, many exhibited anatomical abnormalities, fertility was much reduced and many individuals were actually sterile. Ritzema-Bos (1894), likewise starting with 12 rats obtained from a cross albino fancy ♀ × wild norvegian ♂, continued to inbreed for six years, obtaining some 30 generations in this time. He found that there was a gradual decrease in size of the litters and a gradual increase in the percentage of infertile matings—

Years of inbreeding	1	2	3	4	5	6
Average number in litter	7·5	7·1	7·1	6·5	4·2	3·2
Percentage of infertile matings	0	2·6	5·6	17·4	50·0	41·2

Weismann (1898) inbred a stock of white mice for 29 generations and found that the average number of young for the three 10-year periods to be 6·1, 5·6, and 4·2. Von Guaita (1898) then crossed some of these highly inbred mice with Japanese waltzers and then inbred for 6 generations to find that the average number of young in the successive generations was 4·4, 3·0, 3·8, 4·3, 3·2, 2·3.

But the experiments of Crampe, Ritzema-Bos, and von Guaita cannot be regarded as critical tests of the effects of inbreeding because in each case the original material resulted from wide out-crossing; the experiments were started with hybrid stock and hybridisation involves the complication of Mendelian recombination. To examine the effects of inbreeding as such, the material must have been inbred already *to reduce the genetic constitution of the animals to an approximately homozygous condition.* King's work fulfils this necessary condition, for her rats were from a stock already closely inbred and therefore approximately homozygous.

Another investigation which fulfils the conditions is that of Rommel and Sewall Wright on the guinea-pig. The experiment was started in 1906 with 33 pairs of stock guinea-pigs which had been more or less inbred previously. After the closest inbreeding for some 20 generations 16 of these families were still in existence in 1917. The inbred race considered as a whole produced smaller and fewer litters, while the mortality among the young had increased. At birth the young weighed less than the controls and they grew more slowly. But when considered family by family some still compared most favourably with the original stock, others had degenerated and become extinct during the course of the experiment. In the case of those that remained, Wright was able to show that there were many genes affecting fertility, growth rate, sexual maturity and longevity, and that different combinations of these distinguished one family from another. Moenkhaus (1911), Hyde (1914), and Wentworth (1913), have all investigated this problem in Drosophila, and all are agreed that though sterility is increased in the earlier stages it tends to be eliminated after a time. Inbreeding results in strains of unequal fertility and the less fertile are eliminated by differential productiveness, a result to be anticipated since inbreeding leads to homozygosity.

The conclusion to be drawn from these experiments is that inbreeding accompanied by vigorous selection is not necessarily harmful. *The effects depend on the genetic constitution of the individuals concerned and not upon any pernicious attribute of inbreeding in itself.* The results of inbreeding can be interpreted readily in terms of Mendelian recombination. But the critical test cannot be made with bisexual species for the problem is complicated by biparental inheritance. One must turn to the autogamous plant there to find many forms which are almost invariably self-fertilised and yet lack nothing in the way of fertility and viability. Shull (1908) has shown in the case of maize that though the progeny of self-fertilised plants are less vigorous, smaller and less fertile than those of a cross-bred plant of the same stock, this regression did not proceed uniformly but that it actually becomes less and less with the succeeding generations which might be expected as homozygosity was approached.

East and Jones (1919) experimenting with over thirty different varieties of maize, and with several lines in each variety, have extended Shull's conclusions. In every case there was a reduction in the size of the plant and in the yield of grain, but the several inbred lines originating from the same variety became strikingly differentiated in their structural characters, the result of different genetical combinations. They obtained dwarf plants, plants deficient in chlorophyll, malformed plants, plants exhibiting marked susceptibility to disease. This variability of the inbred lines with respect to these characters decreased as the experiment proceeded. After 4 generations the grosser characters were fixed; after 8, the different lines became remarkably uniform in all their distinguishing characters. These authors concluded that inbreeding the naturally cross-pollenated maize plant has these results—

(1) There is a reduction in size and in productiveness which continues up to a certain point. In no sense is there actual degeneracy.

(2) There is an isolation of subvarieties differing in their characters.

(3) As these varieties become more constant in their characters the reduction in growth ceases to be noticeable.

(4) Individuals are obtained with such characters that they cannot be reproduced, or if so, only with extreme difficulty.

These results show that inbreeding has but one demonstrable effect on the individuals subjected to its action —*the isolation of homozygous types.* The diversity of the resulting types depends directly upon the number of heterozygous hereditary characters present in the individuals with which the process is begun. The degree of diversity among the resulting types will vary directly with the amount of cross-breeding to which the foundation stock has been subjected. The rapidity of the isolation of homozygous types is a function of the intensity of the in-breeding. In the case of the maize, a most variable cultivated plant, cross-pollination is the rule. Each individual is heterozygous for a large number of its characters and this heterozygosis is maintained by the continual crossing and recrossing. But if such heterozygous material is inbred there will be automatic isolation of homozygous combinations such as occurs in the F_2 and F_3 and further generations of a typical Mendelian breeding experiment. Stability and uniformity will be reached when homozygosis has been attained. But with the decrease in heterozygosis there is a decrease in size and productiveness. Combinations of recessives become extracted and the extracted recessive is often the undesirable. Lethal factors in the duplex condition will increase the percentage of sterile matings until such matings become impossible as these types are eliminated, and different genetical combinations will produce individuals strong growing or weak, fertile or sterile, normal or abnormal, and so on.

Rigorous selection among the resulting types will isolate strains which will compare very favourably with the original stock. Consanguinity in itself is no bar to mating. If in-breeding results in disappointment, then all that has happened is that characters previously hidden have been brought to light. In-breeding ultimately must purify a stock, though the process may be disastrously expensive if the ingredients of genetic combinations which will result in undesirable or even non-viable types pre-exist.

When homozygosis is attained, and it is attained most quickly in the autogamous plants and parthenogenetic animals (for in such when the individual has become homozygous its progeny must be similarly constituted), the nearest approach to the "pure line" has been reached and selection alone within a pure line is without avail, as was found by Johanssen (1909) in his study of the inheritance of seed-weight in beans. If, for instance, 500 beans are taken at random from a great quantity—*i.e.*, a random sample of a population—and are weighed, the majority will be found not to diverge considerably from the average weight of the population as a whole. There will be a constantly decreasing number of individuals as the upper and lower extremes of weight are approached and a curve in which seed-weight is plotted against frequency will in general be of the same shape as the ordinary probability curve. If a bean of a weight above or below the average of the whole is selected and allowed to germinate seed by self-fertilisation, and if the weights of the resulting progeny are plotted similarly, a frequency curve of the same shape will be obtained. But the average will be greater or less and the weight which gives the highest frequency likewise will be greater or less than that for the original population as a whole. The descendants of such a bean constitute a "pure line" and if individuals within this line are selected and selfed, their progeny have a frequency curve with the same maximum whether the parent was the heaviest or the lightest or the average bean. No matter whether the largest or the smallest beans within a pure line are selected, the results will be the same. Variability in the weight of the progeny there will be, but this variability is the result of difference in nurtural conditions and is not of genetic significance.

The curve of variation of the population as a whole is compounded of a series of curves showing the variability of a number of genetically different strains. An apparently homogeneous race or "population" is a congeries of pure lines but it is not possible to distinguish a pure line from a population by inspection, since both may be phenotypically alike and fluctuations about the average occur in both cases. These differences occurring within a pure line are simply instances of somatic variability probably caused in general by differences in some environmental agent, while differences occurring within a population include both these modifications and also true variations of germinal origin in the pure lines of which the population is composed. Johannsen has made the distinction between pure lines and population clear by means of the figure in which five pure lines of beans are combined artificially to form a population. The beans which make up the pure lines are represented enclosed within inverted test-tubes and the beans in any one tube are all of one size. Tubes in the same vertical line also contain beans of similar size. Thus it may be seen that what may be a rare size of bean in one line, *e.g.*, that in the left-hand tube of pure line 3, may be identical with the most common size in another line, as pure line 2. The five pure lines are combined in a population at the bottom of the figure, making a phenotype that hides the five genotypes. If in selection the beans from the extreme left-hand tube in the population are chosen, all would belong to one pure line 2; or, if the

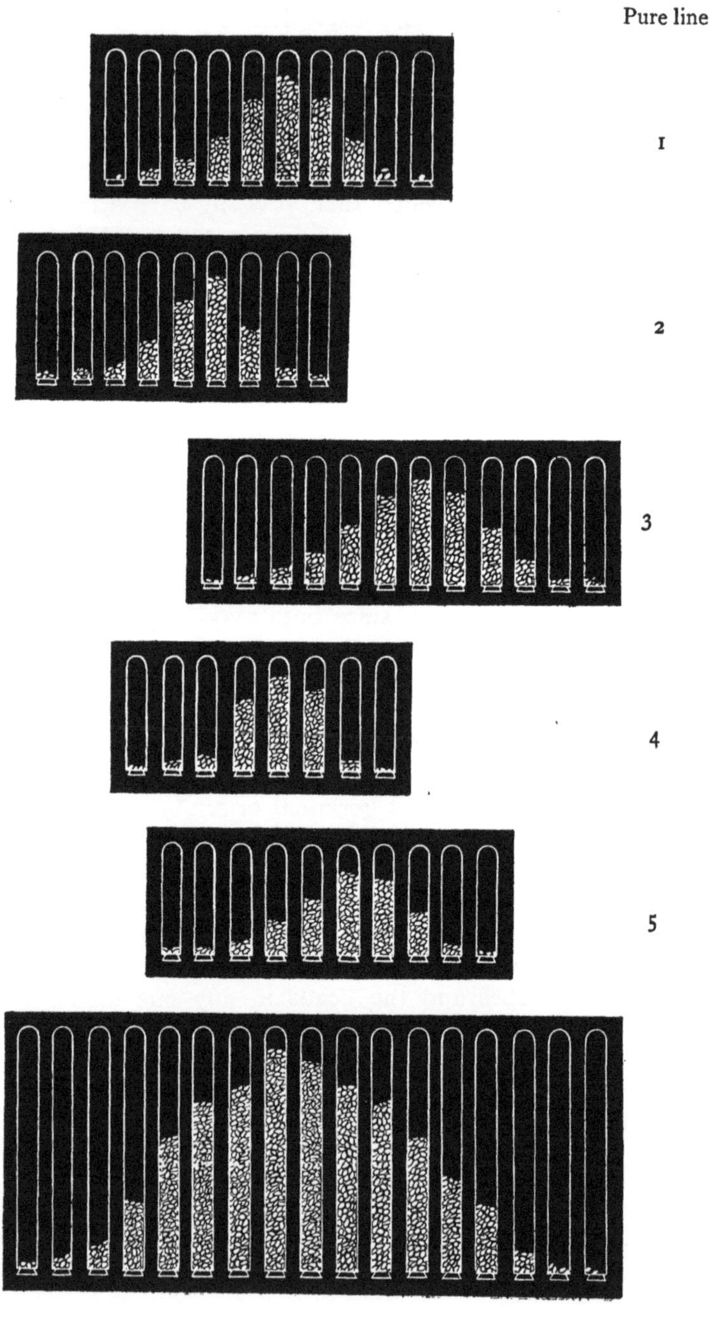

FIG. 65.

beans are chosen from the extreme right-hand tube, they all belong to pure line 3. This would constitute the isolation of pure lines from a population.

Johannsen defined a pure line as the progeny of a single self-fertilised individual. The basic idea of the pure line concept is that every member of any given pure line is genetically identical with every other member of the same line. This condition is met with also in the case of parthenogenesis, in the offspring of two individuals homozygous for their different characters, and in the case of clones. A clone is the progeny produced by asexual reproduction, by continued fission of the original individual and in this case as in parthenogenesis the genotype is unchanged from generation to generation. A pure line implies constancy of genotypic constitution and this is attained in homozygous matings. It is well-nigh impossible to find two individuals among bisexual species which are homozygous in all particulars. The nearest approach to such a condition would be found in identical twins. But the breeder is able to consider a few chosen characters out of the hundreds which make up his stock and it is essentially possible to speak of homozygosity under these conditions.

Selection.—Selection has been the greatest agent in the permanent improvement of the domesticated animals. The accidental discovery of some "prepotent" sire or dam, or the intuition on the part of certain breeders to see more in their stock than their competitors, has laid the foundation of all the famous herds. But to-day this phenotypic selection—the choosing of the best looking—has given place to another type of selection altogether. The sire in the milking herd is judged by the average performance of all his daughters, and his possible value is estimated from a consideration of the performance of his dam and other relatives. The modern advanced registry book allows one to hazard a considered opinion concerning the value of an untried animal, but the value of the sire of the milking herd is only recognised when the milk-yield of his daughters is known. For this it is necessary, unfortunately, to wait three years or so.

One of the great problems of the breeder—if not the greatest—is the control of the genotype, and this in the established stock can only be done by selection. By deliberate, untiring enlightened selection of desirable characters he can fix these in the homozygous state and then he is not dealing with phenotype any longer but with the genotype.

The aim of selection is to obtain "pure lines"—groups of individuals with the same hereditary formula and all the factors in this formula in duplicate.

In dealing with allogamous species in which, when starting with a mixed population of unknown genetic constitution, it is necessary to mate two individuals, the original selection must be made on the basis of phenotypic similarity. With domestic animals the repetition of such selection through a large number of generations has produced the pure or pedigreed breeds, which approximate more or less closely to pure lines and hence should be expected to breed fairly true to type. The length of time required to produce approximately pure lines will depend upon the genetic constitution of the stock concerned.

An important consequence of Mendelian principles in relation to the selection problem is the continuous diminution in the proportion of heterozygotes through successive generations of self-fertilisation. For simplicity consider the effect of self-fertilisation in the progeny of a cross involving one pair of factors:—

								Heterozygotes.
F_1				Aa				100
F_2	1AA			2Aa			1aa	50 %
F_3	1AA	½AA		1Aa		½aa	1aa	25 %
F_4	1AA	½AA	¼AA	½Aa	¼aa	½aa	1aa	12½%

This is evidently a geometrical series and the percentage of heterozygous individuals in the 8th generation is therefore $100\,(\frac{1}{2})^{8-1} = \frac{100}{128}$ or less than 1 per cent., and in the 21st generation there should be $100\,(\frac{1}{2})^{20}$ or less than 0·00005 per cent. heterozygotes. In the case of two pairs of independently heritable factors, the following results would be expected (h = homozygote, H = heterozygote):—

						Heterozygotes.
F_1			AaBb			100%
F_2	1AABB	2AaBB	2AABb	4AaBb	2Aabb	75%
	1h	2H	2H	4H	2H	
	2aaBb	1aaBB	1AAbb	1aabb		
	2H	1h	1h	1h		
F_3	1h	1h : 1H	1h : 1H	1h : 3H	1h : 1H	43·8%
	1h : 1H	1h	1h	1h		

This series converges less rapidly than the preceding one, so that with linkage the proportion of heterozygotes in a population diminishes more rapidly than in the case of independent factors. Reimers (1916) gives the empirical formula $\frac{(2^n - 2)^m}{2n}$ for the proportion of homozygotes in the nth generation of a cross involving m independently heritable factors.

A mixed population consists of a number of distinct genotypes—groups of individuals all having the same genotypic constitution. In autogamous species which require only one individual to accomplish sexual reproduction, for example, the normally self-fertilising plants, these genotypes are pure lines to begin with, while in allogamous species which require two individuals to accomplish sexual reproduction (the same term is applied to plants which, though capable of self-fertilisation, yet are normally cross-fertilised), it is only by continued intensive selection that existing genotypes can be differentiated one from another so that they breed true.

The breeder's art has been concerned with mass-selection from a population, and this will certainly produce temporary change in any allogamous species, as is seen from Johannsen's illustration. If one should select individuals from the fifth tube from either end, it is clear that the individuals might belong to several genotypes. If selection in the same direction were continued, a strain would be established with a mode distinct from the mode of the original population, and these strains could be maintained by continued selection and in time a single genotype might be isolated, when selection would be said to have changed the type permanently. But selection will not produce anything new, it will only isolate a certain already existing genotype from the population.

The results of artificial selection in the case of the domesticated animals and plants are to be explained in terms of modifying genes. It is known that the action of a given gene—the principal gene—may be profoundly influenced by the action of another. The gene "cream," for example, does not disturb the action of the genes which determine the normal red-eye character of Drosophila, but it does affect the action of the gene which results in white eye-colour—a fly with the genes for both cream and eosin has much paler eyes than a fly with only that for eosin, as has been shown by Bridges (1919). Similarly, the gene "whiting" has no effect on red eye but makes eosin entirely white. Cream and whiting require some eye colour on which to exert their effects; they are modifiers of eosin.

Muller (1914) has shown, in the case of the "truncate" character of Drosophila (short wings with straight cut ends), that such a stock includes flies with very truncate wings, flies with wings of practically normal size and shape, and flies of every intervening grade, and that by continuous selection of individuals with the stumpiest wings he could, in the space of three years, produce a true-breeding strain in which the wings were much shorter than the body.

Such a result at first sight seems to show that selection can modify the gene, can alter its organisation. But Muller was able to show, by means of linkage experiments, that he was dealing with modifying genes. At least three such were present in his original stock, and he was able to pick them up by linkage and incorporate them as he wished into his strains. Bar (eye) and "beaded" wings are other characters which are affected in the degree of their expression by the action of modifying genes. The fancier is dealing with such modifying genes. He is not concerned, for example, with the inheritance of the character Rosecomb in fowls, he is especially concerned with the transmission of the genes which modify this character, the genes which in their action make all the difference between a comb that scores full points in the show-pen and the Rosecomb as at present dealt with by the geneticist. The breeder seeks duplicity in respect of the modifiers of the basal character. Selection has indeed produced most wonderful results, but it has not altered the gene, it has unwittingly dealt with modifying genes which affect the action of the principals.

Line breeding.—Line breeding is generally credited with all the benefits of inbreeding without entailing its disadvantages; it has been and is a popular system of breeding. The breeder who vehemently condemns inbreeding in theory usually practises line breeding, yet the latter is but a less intense form of close breeding than inbreeding. The difference between the two methods is but one of degree. The slightly wider relationship of the individuals mated permits the introduction into the experiment of the genetic constitutions of two slightly different lines of descent. Homozygosis is not so easily attained and, therefore, undesirable recessive characters are not disclosed or are not disclosed so soon. But, for the same reason, the homozygous condition of the desirable characters cannot be attained so readily as by inbreeding, so that, if the disadvantages of inbreeding are avoided, the advantages are also postponed or even precluded.

Endogamy is the supreme test of a stock, for it illuminates the constitution of the individuals. From the study of its effects one is forced to regard the different physiological properties of the individual as characters which in their mode of inheritance obey the Mendelian scheme. Just as one selects for the morphological characters so must one also select for the physiological.

This distinction between a pure line and a population explains why it is that the stock-breeder must constantly select among his stock in order to maintain the standard he desires. So soon as this selection is relaxed the "pure line" becomes merged into the population and the "strain will run out"—there will be "reversion." Only by the isolation of pure lines can character constancy be maintained, and when a pure line has been isolated, then all the members of it, regardless of any phenotypic differences, are equally efficient in maintaining the characters of the line. Moreover, this selection cannot be mere mass selection but must be individual. In 1899 an experiment was begun at the Maine Agricultural Station, which had as its object the improvement of fecundity in the Plymouth Rock. Hens which had laid 150 or more eggs in their pullet year, cocks whose mothers had laid at least 200 eggs were chosen. Mass selection was carried on until 1908 and it was found that fecundity had declined slightly. Mass selection had chosen certain females which owing to favourable circumstances had exhibited their maximum laying power, and these depressed the average yearly production. But by individual selection after 1909 the average egg-yield of the flock was quickly raised.

Exogamy.

Outbreeding as usually practised between members of the same species, of the same stock, is generally followed by manifest benefit. Hybrid vigour (heterosis) was noticed and described in great detail by many of the older writers, such as Kolreuter (1763), Knight (1799), Gärtner (1849) and others, all plant breeders and all concerned with a wider (inter-specific) sort of out-crossing than was undertaken by the animal breeder who was mainly concerned in the maintenance of the existing qualities of his stock (though it is true that the mule with its excellent qualities had been known for centuries). Naudin (1865), the contemporary of Mendel, whose name is linked by French writers with that of Mendel, gave excellent examples of the beneficial results of hybrid vigour from inter-specific crosses, whilst Mendel himself, in describing his tall-dwarf pea experiments, records that "the longer of the two parental stems is usually exceeded by the hybrid, a fact which is possibly only attributable to the greater luxuriance which appears in all parts of plants when stems of very different length are crossed. Thus, for instance, in repeated experiments, stems of 1 foot and 6 feet in length yielded without exception hybrids which varied in length between 6 feet and 7½ feet." Darwin investigated this subject both with plants and with animals and his views are as follows: "The gain in constitutional vigour derived from an occasional cross between individuals of the same variety but belonging to different families or between distinct varieties has not been so largely or so frequently discussed as have the evil effects of too close interbreeding. But the former point is the more important of the two inasmuch as the evidence is more decisive. The evil results from close interbreeding are difficult to detect, for they accumulate slowly and differ much in degree with different species, whilst the good effects which almost invariably follow a cross are from the first manifest. It should, however, be clearly understood that the advantage of close interbreeding as far as the retention of character is concerned is indisputable and often outweighs the evil of a slight loss of constitutional vigour."

It is true that the effects of inbreeding may not be very noticeable in F_1 and that the effect of outbreeding is, but, as East and Jones have clearly shown, Darwin was mistaken in assuming that the evil effects of inbreeding accumulated as the method was continued.

Outbreeding between individuals within a pure line is without effect, but the mating of two distinct genotypes almost invariably results in the exhibition of heterosis, usually most clearly demonstrated by an increase in size. In maize the effect is seen in the increase of the number of seeds produced, in some cases as much as 180 per cent. increase in yield of grain over the inbred parental forms being obtained. Earlier flowering, increased longevity, greater viability, greater resistance to disease, are often the peculiar properties of the hybrid. In the silkworm, Drosophila, and fishes, experiment has demonstrated that heterosis follows outbreeding particularly when the strains crossed had been inbred previously. In poultry it is indeed recognised that increased size and more rapid growth usually follow the crossing of two distinct strains or breeds and for the production of table poultry this system of outbreeding is commonly practised. In the growing of "beef" cattle, in the production of mutton, the fact that outbreeding results in heterosis is widely recognised, the cross-bred offspring combining large size with more quality.

An experiment on commercial lines with pigs as the material, carried out at The Lord Wandsworth Institution, Long Sutton, Hampshire, showed that a first cross may be mature more quickly and more economical to feed. 9 pure-bred Large Black pigs were compared with 9 Berkshire and Large Black F_1 individuals. The individuals were each eight weeks old at the beginning of the experiment, and received similar food and management throughout. For the first two months both lots received the same quantity of food but it was found necessary, since the cross-breds thrived so much better, to feed them more generously after this and the pigs were given just as much as they would clear up eagerly at each meal.

The weights of the pigs were as follows—

	Pure-breds.	Cross-breds.
8 weeks	232 lb.	271 lb.
„ + 28 days	408 „	451 „
„ + 56 „	655 „	718 „
„ + 84 „	964 „	1083 „
„ + 116 „	1279 „	1502 „

The pure-breds gained 1074 lb. and consumed 3419 lb. of mixed meals, 456 lb. skim milk, 116 lb. green kale, 73 lb. mangels, or a total of some 3503 lb. of mixed meals.

The cross-breds gained 1231 lb., consumed 3767 lb. of mixed meals, 456 lb. of skim milk, 116 lb. of green kale, and 73 lb. of mangels, or a total of 3851 lb. of mixed meals.

For each pound of live weight increase in the case of the pure-breds 3·3 lb. of meal were required, whereas in the case of the cross-breds 1 lb. of live weight required only 3·1 lb. of meal.

Though there is no doubt as to the results of outbreeding in the case of farm-stock, the experimental investigation of this subject has dealt with laboratory animals. Castle and Wright

(1916) crossed the domestic guinea-pig (average weight 800 grms.) with a wild one, *Cavia cutleri* (average weight 420 grms) The offspring of this mating weighed about 85 grms. at birth, *i.e.*, rather more than the young of either parental race, and retained this lead throughout life. At maturity they weighed on the average 890 grms. F_2 individuals of both sexes were smaller than the F_1 individuals, indicating that the heterosis observed in F_1 had not been maintained, but the curve of the growth-rate of the individual of F_2 rises sharply at first showing that, at least, they had a good start, being the offspring of vigorous parents.

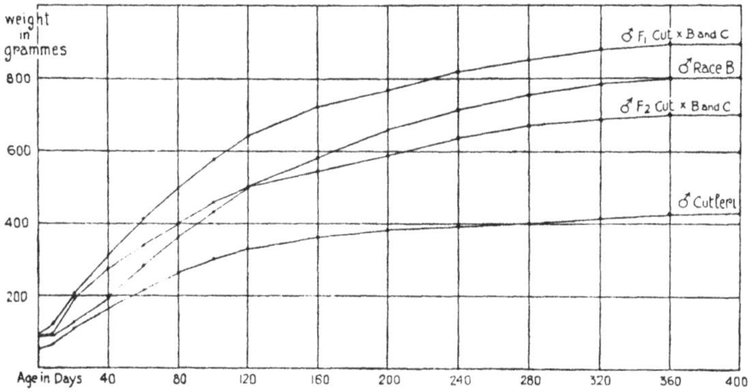

FIG. 66. (*From* Castle and Wright.)

The cross-bred guinea-pigs in Wright's experiments were distinctly superior to their inbred relatives; they produced bigger and more frequent litters, stronger offspring heavier at birth, gaining in weight more quickly, and maturing earlier.

Castle found that in crosses between two small breeds of rabbits, such as Polish and Himalayan, the F_1 was larger than either P_1 form, but that this increase was lost in the F_2 which in average size was strictly intermediate.

The effects of inbreeding have been interpreted in terms of homozygosity, the advantages being the result of homozygosity with respect to desirable characters, the disastrous being the result of homozygosity with respect to recessive undesirable characters.

Mendelian analysis suggests very strongly that the characters—morphological and physiological—result from the action of the genes residing on the chromosomes and that in the production of each character more than one gene is concerned. No one individual possesses all the favourable characters, each is a random sample of good and bad. Usually, normality is dominant over abnormality. This being so, the F_1 individuals must contain the maximum number of different genes. Heterosis is related to heterozygosis.

East and Jones illustrate this point by means of a hypothetical case in which two individuals, each with three pairs of chromosomes, and duplex for different genes producing the same effect, attain the same development of a measurable character of six units, two of which are determined by the genes on each of the chromosomes. It is assumed that the nine genes are as effective in the simplex as in the duplex condition.

P_1	A A	G G	M M		a a	g g	m m
	b b	h h	n n		B B	H H	N N
	C C	I I	O O		c c	i i	o o
	d d	j j	p p	×	D D	J J	P P
	E E	K K	Q Q		e e	k k	q q
	f f	l l	r r		F F	L L	R R
Number	1 1	2 2	3 3		1^a 1^a	2^a 2^a	3^a 3^a
		6 units				6 units	

F_1	A a	G g	M m
	b B	h H	n N
	C c	I i	O o
	d D	j J	p P
	E e	K k	Q q
	f F	l L	r R
	1 1^a	2 2^a	3 3^a
		12 units	

The F_1 individual receives different genes from each parent, but all these genes in their action are additive so that the F_1 individual will attain twice the development of either parent.

The F_1 will produce gametes as follows :—

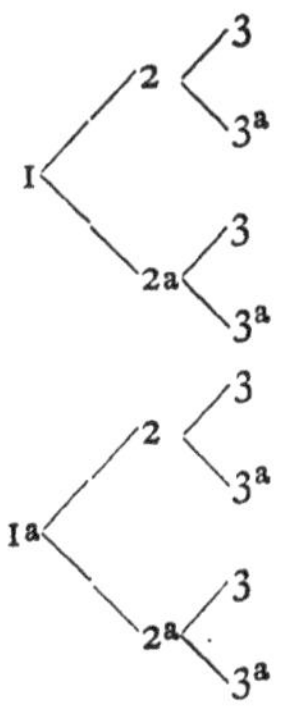

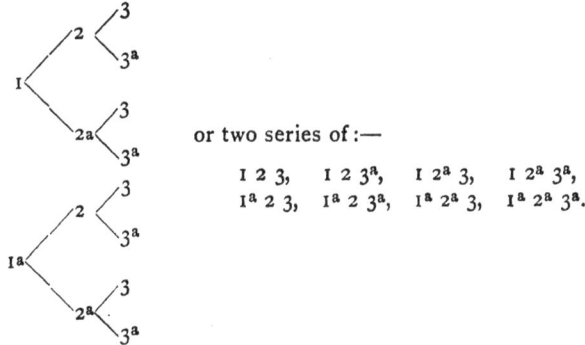

or two series of :—

$1\ 2\ 3$, $1\ 2\ 3^a$, $1\ 2^a\ 3$, $1\ 2^a\ 3^a$,
$1^a\ 2\ 3$, $1^a\ 2\ 3^a$, $1^a\ 2^a\ 3$, $1^a\ 2^a\ 3^a$.

In F_2 there will be :—

No. of Individuals.	Categories.	Units.	Total Development.
1	1 1 2 2 3 3	2 + 2 + 2	6
2	1 1a 2 2 3 3	4 + 2 + 2	8
2	1 1 2 2a 3 3	2 + 4 + 2	8
2	1 1 2 2 3 3a	2 + 2 + 4	8
4	1 1a 2 2a 3 3	4 + 4 + 2	10
4	1 1 2 2a 3 3a	2 + 4 + 4	10
4	1 1a 2 2 3 3a	4 + 2 + 4	10
8	1 1a 2 2a 3 3a	4 + 4 + 4	12
1	1 1 2 2 3a 3a	2 + 2 + 2	6
2	1 1 2 2a 3a 3a	2 + 4 + 2	8
2	1 1a 2 2 3a 3a	4 + 2 + 2	8
4	1 1a 2 2a 3a 3a	4 + 4 + 2	10
1	1 1 2a 2a 3 3	2 + 2 + 2	6
2	1 1 2a 2a 3 3a	2 + 2 + 4	8
2	1 1a 2a 2a 3 3	4 + 2 + 2	8
4	1 1a 2a 2a 3 3a	4 + 2 + 4	10
1	1a 1a 2 2 3 3	2 + 2 + 2	6
2	1a 1a 2 2a 3 3	2 + 4 + 2	8
2	1a 1a 2 2 3 3a	2 + 2 + 4	8
4	1a 1a 2 2a 3 3a	2 + 4 + 4	10
1	1a 1a 2a 2a 3 3	2 + 2 + 2	6
2	1a 1a 2a 2a 3 3a	2 + 2 + 4	8
1	1a 1a 2 2 3a 3a	2 + 2 + 2	6
2	1a 1a 2 2a 3a 3a	2 + 4 + 2	8
1	1 1 2a 2a 3a 3a	2 + 2 + 2	6
2	1 1a 2a 2a 3a 3a	4 + 2 + 2	8
1	1a 1a 2a 2a 3a 3a	2 + 2 + 2	6
64			

Distribution of F_2 individuals according to development attained :—

Classes.		Frequency.				No. of Individuals.		Mean Development.
6	×	8	=	48				
8	×	24	=	192				
10	×	24	=	240				
12	×	8	=	96				
				576	:	64	=	9

The distribution is symmetrical and the mean development in F_2 is 9, as compared with 6 in P_1 and 12 in F_1: there is diminution of 50 per cent. Similarly in F_3 there will be a diminution of 50 per cent. and so on, until by the 8th generation the diminution is a negligible quantity.

Heterosis results from heterozygosis which implies a pooling of the genes of both parents. Each P_1 individual will be homozygous for different unfavourable characters, the F_1 will then be heterozygous for such. The less favourable characters as met with in Drosophila are recessive characters, so that the F_1 individual will be heterozygous instead of homozygous and the dominant allelomorph will be advantageous. No doubt there have been many dominant unfavourable characters, but the homozygote and heterozygote in respect of such would be eliminated by selection. The homozygous recessive would likewise be eliminated if the recessive characters were seriously unfavourable: the heterozygous would be spared and these will outnumber the homozygous forms.

In outbreeding each genetic constitution is complemented by the other, and so heterosis results. Linkage tends to preclude the possibility of the segregation and recombination of the genes in the production of F_2. But linkage is not inevitable, crossing-over occurs, and there is then the chance of producing in F_2, F_3, and so on, individuals homozygous instead of heterozygous for the desirable characters. When the homozygous condition has been attained, inbreeding will not reduce it. But the production of such a homozygous form is extremely difficult, as can be seen from the following breeding experiment.

A female of Drosophila with dachs legs, Grey body, purple eyes, and Long wings, is mated to a male with normal Long legs, black body, Red eyes, and vestigial wings. The F_1 are Long-legged, Grey-bodied, Red-eyed, and Long-winged, and are far more vigorous than either parent—

d	d		D	D	
B	B	×	b	b	(all the genes are on Chromosome II)
p	p		P	P	
V	V		v	v	

d	D
B	b
p	P
V	v

If these genes were not linked then in F_2 one should get one individual with the constitution DDBBPPVV ; but linkage does exist. In the case of F_1 females crossing-over between dachs and black is 10 per cent., between black and purple, 6 per cent., between purple and vestigial, 13 per cent., and only one egg in 2000 will have the constitution DBPV In the male no crossing-over occurs and the sperms of F_1 males will be either dBpV or DbPv in constitution. The chances of choosing the required genotypes in F_2 for the production of homozygosis in F_3 are infinitesimally slight, yet Drosophila is relatively a simple organism from the genetical point of view. Unless the genes concerned are few in number and the crossing-over percentage is high, it is almost impossible to produce individuals of maximum heterosis which will be unaffected by inbreeding.

Prepotency.

It has long been known to animal breeders that certain individuals possess the power of impressing their characteristics upon their offspring to a much more marked degree than do others. A study of the records of the breeds will show that in all a few individuals have stamped the breed with their own peculiar characters. It is also a fact, however, that truly prepotent sires are extremely rare, there are very few indeed which beget progeny with uniformly high characterisations.

Prepotency is not a peculiar virtue of an individual; it is the property of its several characters. If a certain character is dominant then its possessor will prove to be "prepotent" when mated with individuals exhibiting the corresponding recessive. A homozygous dominant will prove twice as "prepotent" as a heterozygous dominant although the two may be indistinguishable on inspection. But so simple an interpretation of prepotency is not always applicable since all cases do not consist of the association of dominant and recessive characters. Such an interpretation can be applied, however, to the success which follows the formation of a co-operative bull association. Pure-bred bulls (*i.e.*, individuals relatively homozygous for the characterisation of the herd to which they belong) are used upon relatively heterozygous cows. In the matter of milk-yield, these bulls cannot increase the production of the cows but they may double the production of their daughters. It is quite possible that in such cases as this linkage between morphological and physiological characters is involved.

There are reasons for thinking that the "potency" of a given gene, using the word in the sense that it was employed in the discussion of the Lymantria inter-sexes of Goldschmidt, varies with the source from which it is derived, that a gene derived from one family has a different degree of potential expression to the same gene derived from another. Moreover, it is known that a recessive character, when a member of a certain combination of characters, may be exhibited in F_1, though the corresponding dominant character is exhibited by the other parent, this reversal of the usual apparently resulting from the interaction between the gene for this recessive character and the genes for the dominant characters in the combination. For example, "truncate wings" in Drosophila is a recessive character when tested against its normal allelomorph, but in association with the character "black" the character "truncate" behaves as a dominant. Genetic inter-relations therefore affect the "potency" of the genes, and the larger the group of inter-related genes the greater is the possibility that the ordinary expression of the action of any constituent gene may be reversed. Prepotency may then depend on the extent of genetic inter-relationship.

One sex (the XX) may be more prepotent than the other (the XY) as far as the sex-linked characters are concerned. Absence of crossing-over in the case of one sex will also affect the relative prepotency of the two sexes, since that sex in which crossing-over does not take place will necessarily transmit its chromosomes with their genes intact.

Bearing on this subject of prepotency is the phenomenon known as "nicking." Two individuals not remarkable in themselves beget superior offspring. This result is to be explained on the assumption that the mating brings together the chance association of complementary or supplementary factors which correspond to characters that are greatly esteemed.

CHAPTER X

THE GENETIC ASPECTS OF FECUNDITY AND FERTILITY

FECUNDITY is the term used to define the potential reproductive capacity of an individual and is measured by its ability to elaborate functional gametes, ova or sperm. Fertility is the term used to define the ability of a pair (male and female) to produce living offspring and is measured by the rate at which these are produced compared to the average rate of production of the species or group to which the individuals under consideration belong. Sterility is the negation of fertility; infertility may be absolute, when the individual is sterile, or it may be diminished to a greater or lesser degree, when compared with the average of the group to which the individual belongs, and in these cases fertility is relative. In different instances there may be found every grade between complete fertility and sterility. Fertility is based primarily on fecundity and grades of fertility may be but reflections of corresponding grades of fecundity.

In the construction of a standard of fertility the following facts have to be considered: (1) Different species exhibit a true-breeding difference in the frequency of the periods of special reproductive activity during which conception may occur; thus there are the monœstrous species, in which during the year there is but one œstrous cycle, and the polyœstrous species which exhibit during the sexual or breeding season several diœstrous cycles. For descriptive purposes the sexual season is divided into *anœstrum*, the phase during which the female reproductive organs are at rest, though the oocytes are gradually maturing; *proœstrum*, the phase of "coming in heat" or "coming in season," in which the uterus becomes congested and during which in many cases there is a flow of blood from the vagina; *œstrum*, the phase of desire and acceptance of the male; and *metœstrum* (if conception does not occur) during which the activity of the reproductive organs subsides and which leads to *anœstrum* again, directly or after a phase of pseudo-pregnancy. If there is but one such cycle during the breeding season, then the animal is known as *monœstrous*. But often after a short anœstrous phase of a few days the cycle may be repeated. The short intervening phase of inactivity is known as *diœstrum* and an animal that has several such diœstrous cycles is known as polyœstrous. It is obvious that polyœstrous and monœstrous females must be judged by different standards. (2) Different species have markedly different duration of life, a character in the Mendelian sense, and as the reproductive period bears a definite relation to the whole life, it follows that the fertility of the long-lived should be judged by a different standard than that of the short-lived. (3) Some species are polytocous, producing several at a birth, others monotocous, and the standards of fertility in the two sorts must be different.

It is certainly possible to increase the number and intensity of the diœstrous cycles in a polyœstrous animal, but there is no evidence that special treatment of any kind has ever transformed the constitutionally monœstrous into the polyœstrous. It is an established fact that the number of diœstrous cycles in the polyœstrous mammals is affected by environic agencies. In the sheep, for example, the wild species behaves as though it were monœstrous; the domestic sheep developed from them are polyœstrous to different degrees; the Scottish Blackface ewe on the Northern hills exhibits two diœstrous cycles each of three weeks' duration, whilst in the Lowlands, she may have as many as six, each lasting about a fortnight. In the Dorset Horn, which often produces two crops of lambs in one year, diœstrous cycles may continue from autumn right on to the spring, whilst in the case of the Australian Merino the sexual season appears to embrace the whole year. Food and climatic conditions undoubtedly are to a very great extent responsible for this diversity. It is known that the practice of flushing, or special feeding, affects the onset and intensity of activity of the reproductive organs during the sexual season. But though environic agencies affect the œstrous cycle, it is certain that differences in the nature of this cycle fundamentally are specific and breed characters.

The number of young produced by the polytocous female is affected by the general physiological condition of the mother during pregnancy. All fertilised eggs do not complete their development, atrophic embryos and fœtuses are commonly found in the uterus and more corpora lutea than fœtuses. In the case of the pig, Hammond (1914) tentatively suggests that the number of fœtuses that should attain full development is limited by the conditions of nutrition, though the evidence is such as to indicate that the cause is a deficiency in the quality rather than in the quantity of the nutriment. Corner (1923) has found that about 10 per cent. of the ova of the pig, though reached by spermatozoa, and in healthy uteri, do not segment, that another 10 per cent. degenerate before implantation, and yet another 5 to 10 per cent. degenerate during implantation and the subsequent course of pregnancy. He is satisfied that the cause of this lies within the zygote and not in its environment, being genetic in origin.

It has to be remembered also that the possibility of conception following sexual congress is affected by differences in the nature of ovulation. In the mare, cow, ewe, sow, and bitch, ovulation has no relation to coitus, whereas in the cat, ferret, rabbit, it is coitus which determines the onset of ovulation.

The duration of the period of reproductive activity bears a definite relation to the length of the individual's life; it is the period between sexual maturity and senescence. Pearl, Parker and Gonzalez (1923) have recently investigated the inheritance of length of life. Two P_1 forms of Drosophila, normal wings and vestigial, with average lives respectively of $44{\cdot}26 \pm 0{\cdot}44$ and $14{\cdot}08 \pm 0{\cdot}23$ days respectively, produced an F_1 with an average length of life of $51{\cdot}55 \pm 0{\cdot}47$ days and all with normal wings. In F_2 there were 639 normal-winged flies, and their average length of life was $43{\cdot}33 \pm 0{\cdot}42$, and 148 vestigials with a life of $14{\cdot}6 \pm 0{\cdot}57$ days. In order to show that the difference in life-length of the P_1 strains was genetic and not the result of physiological differences arising out of the inability of the vestigial to fly, the wings of normal flies were clipped and their life-length contrasted with other normals, unclipped. There was a difference in the life-length of the two groups, but this difference was explained entirely satisfactorily as a result of operative injury. More recently, Pearl and Parker (1924) have made an interesting experimental and statistical analysis of the duration of life in Drosophila under conditions of complete starvation. Having formerly shown that, under conditions of feeding, the wild flies had an expectation of life practically three times as great as in the mutation with vestigial wings, they now find that under starvation conditions the mean length of life is the same in both, *i.e.*, about forty-four hours for males, and fifty hours for females. Under conditions of starvation, the variability in length of life is also much reduced, but the relative difference in length of life of the sexes remains the same under conditions of feeding or of starvation.

The size of the litter is limited by the number of ova available for fertilisation by the always abundant spermatozoa. This in all probability is based on genetic factors. Lush (1921) and Simpson (1912) found that in the mating of wild pig × Tamworth the litter size of the F_1 female was the same as that of the wild pig. In the ewe one, two or sometimes three, ova are extruded from the ovaries synchronously, so that a ewe cannot as a general rule produce more than three lambs at a time. It is apparent that the polytocous female has an advantage in the matter of propagation over her monotocous rival. The number of offspring produced at one birth is also related to the length of gestation: the longer, the fewer, is the general rule. The first litter of animals producing several young at birth is usually smaller than the second and third. The number increases with successive pregnancies to a maximum and thereafter falls again. In the case of the pig, one set of records shows that the first litter is the smallest and the fourth the largest. Hammond (1914) has shown that this is based on a differential fecundity which varies with the age of the individual. For some unknown reason the season 1922-3 was peculiar, in that quadruple and even quintuple births in the goat were remarkably and disastrously common.

Captivation, as opposed to domestication, results in lessened fecundity and lowered fertility. There are wild animals which can be domesticated' and those which can not, and the latter though kept in perfectly sanitary conditions and in perfect bodily health, even when kept in their own native country, will not breed, though the reproductive system is anatomically and histologically normal. Faulty nutrition may result in a deficiency of functional gametes, but in many cases it would seem that confinement precludes the action of those stimuli which in nature call forth the sexual instinct. There are male wild birds which when kept in captivity never assume the typical male plumage in spite of many moults.

Herbert Spencer in his *Principles of Biology* elaborates the thesis that the power to sustain individual life and the power to reproduce are inversely proportional, *i.e.*, Individuation and Genesis vary inversely. With an abundant food supply and a favourable environment the cost of Individuation—the production and maintenance of the individual—is low and the rate of genesis consequently high. The less expensive in energy consumption the habit of life, the higher the fertility of the species. Domestication, therefore, results in increased fertility. For example, the wild rabbit which breeds four times a year produces less than six young at a time; the tame rabbit breeds six or seven times a year and produces more at a birth. There is increased fecundity as a result of the more favourable conditions of domestication, acting upon individuals carefully selected for these characters. An ancestor of the domestic fowl, *Gallus bankiva*, lays the minimum number of eggs necessary for the propagation of her species, a matter of a dozen or so in the year. The modern hen lays between 200 to 300 a year; so may the modern domestic duck, though its wild ancestors lay but 5 to 10. Yet if the ovaries of sexually immature specimens of the ancestral and modern fowls are examined, there will be found therein a more or less equal number of oocytes, *e.g.*, about 3000. Each is equipped anatomically with the material for a 3000 egg-yield during her lifetime, yet one lays about 1000, the other 200 at most. The morphological basis of fecundity in each is similar, but in the case of the domesticated hen very many more of the oocytes develop into functional ova. The modern hen has been encouraged to lay, and is provided with plentiful food; she lays for man, not for the species. Yet even in the case of the domestic hen there is a rhythm in her egg-yield, the maximum production occurring in March and April, the minimum in October and November. The high fecundity of certain strains is the result of the addition of an extra laying season, as it were; all hens lay in spring, but only some lay in winter. The difference is genetic in nature.

Grades of fertility are definite racial and breed characters and are transmitted in inheritance. For example, the Dorset Horn sheep, the Hampshire, are *relatively* highly fertile breeds; others, such as the Blackface, as at present constituted, is *relatively* infertile. Moreover, within one breed there are strains far more fertile than others, and in a flock or herd there are individuals more fertile than their sisters; in the sheep it has been found possible to increase fertility of a flock by selecting ewes for breeding which possess a higher degree of fertility than the rest. Alexander Graham Bell (1904) bred his sheep for some twenty-five years with a view to getting the ewes to produce more at a birth, and selected each year those ewes which had more than the usual two nipples. Ultimately none of the ewes had less than four and many had six nipples, and twins were the rule. Hayden (1922) describes the case of a pure-bred Holstein-Friesian cow which produced twin calves five times out of seven and by three different bulls. Pearl (1912) records the case of a Guernsey which produced 14 calves in 8 pregnancies, triplets twice, twins twice, and singles four times. Wentworth (1912) records twins in 3 generations of cows. The exact mode of inheritance of fecundity and fertility in the case of the sheep was obscured by the fact that it was found that such conditions as time of attaining maturity, extra feeding, time of mating, influenced the production of twins. Weinberg (1909) studied this question statistically, and concluded that fertility was a character in the Mendelian sense, but that its expression was modified very greatly by external agencies. Wentworth and Aubel (1916), working with swine, concluded that some three hereditary factors are concerned.

Inheritance of fecundity in the fowl has been studied very extensively by Pearl (1912). Barred Plymouth Rocks and Indian Game, breeds of high and of relatively low fecundity respectively, were used and the winter egg production considered. He found that there were three classes of hens: (1) those which laid no eggs during the winter period; (2) those which laid less than 30; (3) those which laid more than 30. 6 per cent. of the Indian Game and 54 per cent. of the Plymouth Rocks belonged to class (3). F_1 and F_2 generations and back-crosses were raised and trap-nested, and as a result of this investigation Pearl concluded that there exists a "fecundity" factor determining the winter production of less than 30 eggs. This autosomal factor, called by Pearl L_1, is dominant to its allelomorph l_1 present in fowls which belong to class (1) which lay no eggs during the winter period. The duplex condition L_1L_1 is similar in its effect to the simplex. In addition there is an X-borne factor L_2 which alone results in a winter egg production of less than 30 eggs. But the "double dose" of L_1 is not equal to $L_1 + L_2$, for the simultaneous presence and action of L_1 and L_2 results in a production of over 30 eggs during the winter period. Genes for high and low fecundity exist and behave in inheritance as do the genes for the multitude of structural characters of Drosophila. The following genetic constitutions were recognised during the course of the experiment:—

Barred Rock ♀ ♀.	Gametes.				
1. $L_1l_1(L_2X)Y$	$L_1(L_2X)$	$l_1(L_2X)$	L_1Y	l_1Y	Over 30
2. $L_1L_1(L_2X)Y$	$L_1(L_2X)$		L_1Y		"
3. $l_1l_1(L_2X)Y$	$l_1(L_2X)$		l_1Y		Under 30
4. $L_1l_1(l_2X)Y$	$L_1(l_2X)$	$l_1(l_2X)$	L_1Y	l_1Y	"
5. $L_1L_1(l_2X)Y$	$L_1(l_2X)$		L_1Y		"
6. $l_1l_1(l_2X)Y$	$l_1(l_2X)$		l_1Y		None

Indian Game ♀♀.					
1. $L_1L_1(l_2X)Y$	$L_1(l_2X)$		L_1Y		Under 30
2. $L_1l_1(l_2X)Y$	$L_1(l_2X)$	$l_1(l_2X)$	L_1Y	l_1Y	”
3. $l_1l_1(l_2X)Y$	$l_1(l_2X)$		l_1Y		None
Barred Rock ♂♂.					
1. $L_1L_1(L_2X)(L_2X)$	$L_1(L_2X)$				
2. $L_1L_1(L_2X)(l_2X)$	$L_1(L_2X)$	$L_1(l_2X)$			
3. $L_1l_1(L_2X)(L_2X)$	$L_1(L_2X)$	$l_1(L_2X)$			
4. $L_1l_1(L_2X)(l_2X)$	$L_1(L_2X)$	$L_1(l_2X)$	$l_1(L_2X)$	$l_1(l_2X)$	
5. $l_1l_1(L_2X)(L_2X)$	$l_1(L_2X)$				
6. $l_1l_1(L_2X)(l_2X)$	$l_1(L_2X)$	$l_1(l_2X)$			
7. $L_1L_1(l_2X)(l_2X)$	$L_1(l_2X)$				
8. $L_1l_1(l_2X)(l_2X)$	$L_1(l_2X)$	$l_1(l_2X)$			
9. $l_1l_1(l_2X)(l_2X)$	$l_1(l_2X)$				
Indian Game ♂♂.					
1. $L_1L_1(l_2X)(l_2X)$	$L_1(l_2X)$				
2. $L_1l_1(l_2X)(l_2X)$	$L_1(l_2X)$	$l_1(l_2X)$			
3. $l_1l_1(l_2X)(l_2X)$	$l_1(l_2X)$				

From the breeder's point of view the mating involving the genotypes $L_1L_1(L_2X)Y \times L_1L_1(L_2X)(L_2X)$ would be the ideal, but it would require infinite patience and resource to distinguish between hens of the constitutions $L_1L_1(L_2X)Y$, $L_1l_1(L_2X)Y$, and cocks $L_1L_1(L_2X)(L_2X)$, $L_1l_1(L_2X)(L_2X)$, $L_1L_1\ (L_2X)(l_2X)$, $(L_1l_1)L_2X)(l_2X)$.

Among the Barred Rocks every possible genetic constitution was represented, but among the Indian Game the gene L_2 was not possessed by any individual.

Since this symbol L_2 is largely used in poultry literature, it is desirable that an exact understanding of what it really signifies should be gained. In the first place, it must not be forgotten that it was used by Pearl in the interpretation of the results of a certain experiment. These results were yielded by a particular experimental mating, involving certain particular birds. They are not necessarily the results which any other sort of mating with any other birds would yield. Certain Indian Game and certain Plymouth Rocks, used as experimental material, under certain experimental conditions yielded results to which a certain interpretation was applied and this interpretation when carefully examined proved to be satisfactory in this particular case. There can be no question of basing upon this particular case a generalisation that can be applied to all strains of all breeds under any environmental conditions. This particular piece of experimentation must be regarded as being a noteworthy contribution to our knowledge of the inheritance of fecundity in the fowl, but it has not made that knowledge complete. There is great need for further experiment. The general fact that "fecundity" as a character is inherited can be accepted, but the mode of inheritance of high fecundity has not yet been conclusively demonstrated. In Pearl's material there appeared to be sex-linked component, in other material it appears to be autosomal. The difficulty in studying the inheritance of such a character as this is first that it is necessary to define standards which cannot be entirely satisfactory; the number of eggs laid during the three or four winter months, for example, and secondly, that husbandry confounds the geneticist—a good poultryman could get many more birds through the test than could a bad one.

For the present the poultry breeder must recognise that the geneticist has not yet solved this riddle.

It is convenient to approach this question of the inheritance of grades of fertility from the angle of the inheritance of sterility.

In Drosophila there is considerable evidence derived from breeding experiments that certain definite genes affect the fertility of the individual. The sex-linked wing-characters "rudimentary" and "fused" are almost invariably associated with sterility: the male (XY) is fertile, the female (XX) sterile, the development of the ova being abnormal; the sterility is based on infecundity. To maintain rudimentary or fused stocks the heterozygous female must be employed and in such the number of mature ova is much less than in the wild type fly; fecundity is diminished. It is a matter of common observation that any combination of recessive characters in Drosophila is associated with a decreased fecundity, and this fact must play its part in the elimination of recessive mutants in nature. It has not yet been shown that in the case of domesticated animals a combination of recessive characters is likewise associated with unfavourable physiological qualities.

The work of Bridges (1916) on non-disjunction has shown that specific chromosome aberration lead to complete sterility. It will be remembered that the XO male is sterile.

Sterility is common in the offspring of an interspecific cross. In the case of the bird the following have been recorded among others:—

♀ Parents		♂	♂♂	Offspring	♀♀
Turtur orientalis	×	*Columba livia* . . .	13	Sterile	1
Streptopelia risoria	×	*Zenaidura carolinensis* .	16	,,	0
Gallus domesticus	×	*Phasianus colchicus* . .	100	,,	0
Phasianus revesi	×	,, *torquatus*	. 161	,,	6
,, ,,	×	,, *versicolor*			

The results of some cattle crosses—

Bos taurus (the domestic cow)	× *Bos indicus* (zebu)	gives	♂♂	fertile,	♀♀	offspring.
Bos taurus	× *Bibos gruniens* (yak)	,,	♂♂	sterile,	♀♀	fertile.
Bos taurus	× *Bibos gaurus* (gaur)	,,	,,	,,	,,	,,
Bos taurus	× *Bibos frontalis* (gayal)	,,	,,	,,	,,	,,
Bos taurus	× *Bison americanus*	,,	,,	,,	,,	,,
Bibos sondaicus (banteng)	× *Bos indicus*	,,	,,	,,	,,	,,

Brentana (1914) describes hybrids from a peacock × guinea-fowl mating. These more closely resembled the peacock, save that there was a noticeable absence of the characteristic head furnishings, and a considerable reduction of the tail. The plumage was dark fawn with black stripes in the neck region, paler fawn with black specks on the chest, abdomen, and flanks. They were sterile.

Spillman (1913) gives an account of a reputed sheep × goat hybrid born twin to a perfectly normal lamb. The body was covered with goat hair, but there was a small area on the back clothed with sheep-wool. It was a female and produced a half-grown fœtus. Spillman mentions that four other similar hybrids were known to him.

Galbusera (1920) states that he has often seen he-goat × sheep hybrids in Sardinia; in bulk, udders, and wool, they combine the characters of both parents; the female hybrids are preferred to sheep, being better milkers. He states that in order to get this cross the he-goat must have been brought up amongst sheep. The hybrids are infertile. Zebra × mare, dingo × dog hybrids are fertile.

In these interspecific crosses, if but one sex among the F_1 is sterile, that sex is the heterogametic, and the cause of this sterility is infecundity.

In the case of the hybrid pheasant, Smith and Haig Thomas (1913) have shown that both spermato- and oogenesis are abnormal, and conclude that sterility in these hybrids depends on the inability of homologous chromosomes derived from different species to conjugate normally.

Among the domesticated mammals species crosses are usually regarded as curiosities, *e.g.*, fox × dog, goose × swan, and such like, but there are cases in which such hybridisation was undertaken with the definite object of producing a creature of economic value superior to that of either parent. The mule and the cattalo are examples of this. The mule has a record of being a most satisfactory draft animal. It is the hybrid produced by the mating of a male ass and a mare: the reciprocal cross of the jennet and the stallion produces a hinny. Both mule and hinny are sterile. The hybrid is hardier and freer from disease than either parent; the case is an example of hybrid vigour. The question of the fertility of the mule is a source of everlasting debate. Instances are on record in which mules are reputed to have sired foals when mated to jennies, but as a rule these cases are not supported by critical evidence. Sanson (1888), Shailer (1895), Tegetmeier (1895), Cossar Ewart (1899), Whitehead (1908) have held that there are exceptions to the general rule that the mule is infertile. In the *Field* of 17th September 1898, an English veterinary surgeon in India recorded in great detail the birth of offspring in the case of a transport mule. Lloyd-Jones (1916) reports two cases in which the female horse × ass hybrid was fertile and produced young. It is to be noted that according to many observers, the female hybrid exhibits regular œstrous periods and that Habenstreitt found plentiful follicles but no ova in the ovary of the hybrid. In spite of this evidence, however, mule breeders as a class do not believe in the fertility of the hybrid and most biologists are sceptical. Ayrault mentioned that the reported cases of fertility were based on incorrect observation and points out that in Poitou, where 50,000 mares were used annually for mule breeding, fertile mules were unknown. It is possible that many reputed fertile mules were not mules at all, but were horses, somewhat mule-like in their general characters, or that the female hybrid, actually a mule, had adopted the foal of a mare, and under these circumstances it is certain that the mule could develop an active milk secretion. Cytological evidence supports the contention that the mule is sterile. Stephan (1902) found an almost complete absence of seminiferous tubules in the testis of the male hybrid. Ivanov (1905) and Suchetet (1896) found a complete absence of functional spermatozoa in the seminal fluid, and describe the seminiferous tubules in the testis as being much reduced in size and the interstitial cells as greatly increased in number. Whitehead (1908) concluded that the testis of the mule was similar in its structure to that of the "rig," a horse in which the testis is retained in the abdominal cavity and which is sterile. Wodsedalek (1916) argues that the sterility of the mule follows from the great difference in chromosome number in the mare and the male ass. The mare has 38 chromosomes, so that each ovum will have 19; the jack probably has 65, so that each sperm will have either 32 or 33. The zygote with $19 + 32 = 51$ will become the male hybrid; the zygote with $19 + 33 = 52$ chromosomes—the female. It is not until the maturation division in gametogenesis that the abnormal number of chromosomes results in abnormal chromosome behaviour. The mule receives a different number of chromosomes from each of its parents, so that conjugation is embarrassed; but the difficulty is not morphological, for conjugation is just as difficult in the case of the gametogenesis of hybrids which receive the same number of chromosomes from each parent: the bar must be a physiological one. Development and differentiation of the individual are unremarkable, but the individual cannot produce functional gametes. Theoretically it is certainly possible that very infrequently functional gametes should result, and then mare mules bred to stallions ought readily to produce foals. It must be remembered also that practically every male mule is castrated before it has been tested for fecundity.

The species cross *Bos americanus* × *Bos taurus* is complicated by the occurrence of hydramnios during the pregnancy which results in the production of the F_1 generation and by dystocia (difficult parturition) in the case of the F_1 male which renders the birth of a male almost impossible. Moreover, if an F_1 male is born alive it is invariably sterile.

Certain breeders (Boyd, 1914), (Goodnight, 1914) have undertaken the production of the cattalo on a commercial scale. Bison bulls were mated with Hereford and Aberdeen-Angus heifers (the reciprocal cross could not be made though the reason is not stated) and in every case the pregnancy was complicated by severe hydramnios (excess of the liquor amnii, the watery fluid within the fœtal membranes), with the result that the majority of the females aborted. In fact, only about one in thirty produced a living calf, and of these a male was a rarity, for the size and shape of the male hybrid were such that the mother died in labour in the great majority of cases. It was found that the size and shape of the head of the male and the length of his neural spines were such as could not be accommodated by the birth passages of the cow and the calf or the cow or both died.

In this case lethal factors are involved, complementary lethals resulting in the production of a degree or of a kind of development of the skeleton of the offspring which renders its natural birth impossible, and in the production also of hydramnios which, in a great number of instances, ends in abortion. In this case the factors concerned in the production of the conditions leading to dystocia are sex-linked, and are not linked with those which are concerned in the production of hydramnios.

The conditions met with in the bison × cattle cross

can be interpreted in terms of the factorial hypothesis as follows:—

A and A′ are complementary autosomal factors, and together result in the production of hydramnios.

B is a dominant autosomal factor complementary to d, an X-borne recessive, and the combination Bd results in the production of certain skeletal characters which lead to dystocia.

C is a dominant autosomal factor complementary to e, an X-borne recessive, and the combination Ce results in sterility.

The series de is balanced by DE.

The bison male according to this scheme is AA BB CC (DEX)Y, the female AA BB CC (DEX)(DEX). The cattle male is A′A′bb cc (deX)Y, the female A′A′ bb cc (deX)(deX). The F_1 male will be AA′ Bb Cc (deX)Y, the female AA′ Bb Cc (DEX)(deX). There will be hydramnios in all cases. Of the fœtuses which continue to term there will be dystocia in the case of the male, but in the female, since de is balanced by DE, parturition will be possible. Similarly the female will be fertile, the male sterile. The fact that a few F_1 males are produced is to be explained by the variation in the maternal musculature, by differences in the size of the birth passages in cows of different ages and sizes, by differences in the fœtal presentation, and by differences in the management of labour.

The females of F_1 were then back-crossed to the bison or to the bull and this procedure was continued for several generations. It was found that as time went on the incidence of hydramnios became less and less, and that the proportion of dead-born calves was steadily becoming reduced. Fertile males were obtained. These facts are easily accommodated by the scheme outlined above. It will be found that a back-cross of an F_1 female to the bison sire will yield a generation in which the incidence of hydramnios is reduced by 50 per cent., as are also those of dystocia and of sterility in the case of the males. After a few years of breeding in this way several genotypes would exist, and chance selection, guided to some extent by the breeder's art, would surely in time completely remove hydramnios, dystocia, and sterility. Hydramnios characterises another species cross—*Bison americanus* and *Bos indicus*—and one case of this was treated by hysterectomy (surgical removal of the uterus) in order to obtain a living hybrid.

It would seem that in certain instances the factor of the geneticist may be endocrinal in nature, affecting the development of the tissues in such a way that conditions unfavourable to the fœtus are produced. Dystocia may be the result of an abnormal size or proportion which cannot be accommodated by the maternal birth passages, and there is much circumstantial evidence which shows that proper growth is regulated through the mechanism of the endocrine system, and that abnormality of a component member of this system is followed by abnormality in the proportions of the individual. A lethal factor may be one which affects the proper and timeous functioning of a ductless gland.

It has been shown that fertility is a character, that grades of fertility are characters, and that it is possible to "breed" high fecundity into a strain. Conversely, it is possible to bring a family to an end by deliberately neglecting the fact that the individuals that comprise it are exhibiting low grades of fertility. An instance of this is the case of Bates' Duchess family of Shorthorn cattle, which were superior animals but "shy" breeders. In fact a large proportion of the female descendants was absolutely sterile. The family was popular and at one stage in its history, when it commanded very high prices, it was an advantage that the numbers should be limited. But when once buyers came to recognise that low fecundity was a characteristic of the family, it fell from its high estate. The breeder who deliberately selects his relatively infertile individuals for further breeding is breeding for the extinction of his stock. The exact nature of this sterility has not yet been demonstrated, but that it is inherited is beyond all dispute.

Sterility may be due to structural malformations that render fruitful coitus impossible. Maldescent of the testes, severe hernia, gross imperfections of the external reproductive organs, all may result in sterility, and all these conditions may be the expression of genetic action. Undescended testes and hernia are definitely hereditary, whilst imperfection of the external reproductive organs is part of the general condition of intersexuality, which has been shown to be genetic in nature.

CHAPTER XI

HEREDITY AND DISEASE

THE geneticist is concerned not so much with the nature of a character, be it advantageous or disadvantageous to its exhibitor, as with the mode of its inheritance. But since the factorial constitution of the individual has been disclosed by the mating of "normal" with "abnormal," the geneticist and the pathologist have a certain interest in common. It is an interesting thought that if mutations have formed the stages of organic evolution, then at the time of their appearance the mutant characters might easily have been regarded by the naturalist as pathological in nature. It is difficult to estimate the real value of a mutation, and it is possible that what is looked upon as pathological to-day may come to be regarded as physiological to-morrow.

"Disease is a relative conception, and does not admit of strict definition. That which constitutes derangement of function or disturbance of metabolism in one animal or in the tissue of one animal is the normal in another. Disease itself is a perturbance which contains no elements essentially different from those of health, but elements presented in a different and less useful order."

From the genetic point of view the subject of disease can be considered under the following heads:—

(1) The inheritance of a diathesis—a predisposition to a particular group of diseases.
(2) The inheritance of an immunity, specific in relation to a particular disease.
(3) The inheritance of anatomical defects and physiological derangements.

(1) The conception of the inheritance of a predisposition

to a particular disease is a very different thing from that of the inheritance of the disease itself. The reappearance of one and the same disease in successive generations does not prove that the disease is transmissible, or that it has been transmitted. If successive generations are exposed to identical environic conditions each may contract in turn the same disease. The fœtus may be infected *in utero*, but this is synchronous infection: the causal organism was not inherited, it merely attacked two individuals through their common blood supply. It is an instance of contagion, not of inheritance. The bearers of the heritable qualities are resident upon the chromosomes, and these do not carry bacteria. But constitutional peculiarities, most probably having their origin in genetic mutations, do exist, and take the form of a lowered resistance to certain types of disease. Further, it is to be acknowledged that a virulent disease may damage the germ-cells of an individual together with the other tissues of the body, not specifically, but in a way which may impair the general physiological properties of the future zygote. In the genetic sense there are no inherited diseases. There certainly are inherited defects such as those which underlie the conditions of hæmophilia or colour-blindness, but these are not abnormal processes but inherited structural or physiological peculiarities, and it is probable that peculiarities of similar or different kinds underlie the different diatheses.

In other cases there would appear to be a transmutation of a diathesis in its inheritance, and, for example, a neuropathic tendency in the human stock may assume the form of epilepsy in one generation, and of asthma, chorea, or hysteria in the next. A diathesis is polymorphic, and its exact expression will depend on the influence of the other parent and on environment—in fact, it may not be expressed at all.

(2) Immunity to a disease may be acquired by an individual through the medium of its mother's milk, by contracting the disease and recovering from it, by being inoculated with the modified virus of the disease and by other similar measures which encourage the production of specific antitoxins in the body. However, there is little

satisfactory evidence that an immunity so acquired can be transmitted to the following generations.

On the other hand, there is considerable evidence of a sort that shows that a natural specific immunity can be a racial or even a familial characteristic. Pucci (1915), for example, records that the zebu is immune to foot-and-mouth disease, as is also the F_1 produced by the mating zebu × certain Italian and Swiss cattle. If this is so, then, theoretically, this character—specific immunity to foot-and-mouth disease—should be available for breeding into any other breed of cattle, and should be possessed by certain individuals among modern herds, in the ancestry of which the zebu is to be found.

In the Philippines it has not yet been found possible to raise pure-bred imported European and American cattle because of the incidence of disease. The zebu, however, was found to show a complete immunity to rinderpest, tick fever, and insect pests. Crosses of zebu and native cattle are also highly resistant to disease, and show a great improvement in size and conformation on the native stock. Such cross-breds exhibit to a great degree all the desirable characters of the zebu.

It is not suggested that the zebu ought to be employed in this way unless it has been shown perfectly clearly that eradication of the causal organism is impossible, and that pure-bred stock cannot be protected in other ways. The introduction of zebu blood into improved breeds cannot be undertaken lightly, since such introduction results in a lower quality of beef. The use of the zebu is certainly justified in those cases when without it there would be no beef at all.

It has been suggested that the immunity to tick fever in the case of the zebu is due to the serum excreted by the sebaceous glands of the skin being obnoxious to the tick, to the toughness of the skin, which is such that the tick cannot pierce it, and to the fact that the coat is so thin that it does not harbour ticks.

Tyzzer (1909) found that the susceptibility to transplantable tumours differed in different strains of mice. Three strains of mice were used, in one the Ehrlich tumour was successfully transplanted in 30 per cent. of cases, in the second, in 60 per cent., whereas in the third it failed to develop. The Jansen tumour developed in 40 per cent. of the first strain, but failed to do so in the case of the other two. A third kind of tumour developed only in the third strain. Tyzzer found that a tumour which readily developed in Japanese mice and failed to develop in common mice grew in F_1 individuals produced by the mating of Japanese × common mice. When the F_1 mice were back-crossed to common mice all the offspring were susceptible; when the F_2 were interbred only 2·5 per cent. were susceptible. These results show that more than three factor differences concerned with tumour susceptibility are involved; in fact, Tyzzer and Little (1920) suggest that twelve to fourteen independently inherited factors are concerned. It will be noticed that these factors for susceptibility are dominant, according to the results of these workers. The majority of cases of reputed inheritance of acquired immunity are to be explained as is the case of the mice subjected by Ehrlich to increasing doses of ricin until they became immune to doses ordinarily fatal. When these ricin-immune mice were bred to non-immune mates, the offspring showed a degree of immunity if their mother was the ricin-immune parent, but not if the immunised parent was the father. The immunity was transmitted by the female only. The explanation is that the blood of the fœtus and of the mother are in intimate relationship. The immunity in the parental and filial generations gradually disappears.

This cancer study in mice has its applications in the cancer problem of the human. The evidence derived from the study of cancer in man is suggestive but by no means conclusive. The mouse, on the other hand, has supplied evidence of the greatest scientific value. Murray (1911) has shown quite clearly that the offspring of cancerous mice are more prone to develop spontaneous cancer than are the offspring of non-cancerous parents and grandparents. Loeb and Lathrop (1921) were led to the conclusion that the tendency to develop cancer and the age at which it was developed were both heritable characters. Wells and Slye

(1923) have confirmed and extended these conclusions. As a result of their twelve years' work with a most abundant material — over 40,000 post-mortem examinations were made — these investigators have shown that cancer in the mouse occurs in many of the forms encountered in man, that the tendency to develop cancer, or the capacity to resist cancer is hereditary, that the site of the cancerous growth is determined by hereditary factors and that susceptibility to cancer behaves as a simple Mendelian recessive.

If this is so, and if for the moment any consideration of those forms of cancer which seem to be determined by extraneous stimuli—such as the skin cancers which in their origin are associated with prolonged local irritation—is avoided, it would appear to be theoretically possible for a cancer immune race to be produced. It would be necessary to segregate the cancerous and to prevent the heterozygous from mating. The difficulty, of course, would be the identification of the heterozygous.

According to Slye, cancer in mice is the exhibition of a diathesis which behaves in inheritance as a Mendelian recessive. She concludes that cancer is not transmitted as such, but rather as a tendency to occur from a given provocation, probably in the form of an over-irritation. The elimination, as far as possible, of all forms of over-irritation to the tissues of an individual of high cancer ancestry should go far to eliminate the provocation of cancer, and the eugenic control of matings so that cancer shall at least not be potential in both sides of the hybrid cross ought to eventuate in a considerable decrease in the frequency of human cancer.

In Drosophila several cases of the inheritance of tumours have been investigated. Bridges and Stark (1918) found in one culture that one-fourth of the grubs developed one or several masses of black pigment on the body; these maggots were without exception males and invariably died. In such a culture, therefore, there were twice as many females as males. Interpreted genetically, this character is sex-linked and its gene is resident upon the X-chromosome. The male possesses a single X and if this gene is resident upon it such a male will perish: therefore, no adult male can possess this gene. The female, on the other hand, has two Xs. Half the females will be normal flies and half will be heterozygous in respect of this character. A heterozygous female mated to a normal male will produce twice as many daughters as sons, for half the males will perish. By using a male with characters such as eosin eye-colour and yellow body-colour, the genes for which are resident in the X-chromosome near to that for the tumour character, it is possible to distinguish between the female heterozygous for the tumour character and the normal female, for daughters of two types will be produced, one with eosin eye-colour and yellow body—which do not carry the gene for the tumour character—and the other with wild-type coloured body and (red) eyes—which do. By taking advantage of the linkage between yellow and eosin it is possible to pick out in each generation those daughters which carry the gene for the tumour character. Such a procedure is known as "marking" the chromosome. If t represents the gene for tumour, y—yellow body, e—eosin eyes, then

(TyeX)Y	×	(TyeX)(tYEX)	
(TyeX)(TyeX)	(TyeX)(tYEX)	(TyeX)Y	(tYEX)Y
Yellow eosin ♀	Wild-type ♀ Heteroyzgous for tumour.	Yellow eosin ♂	dies

In the case of mammals, Algerian sheep are relatively immune to anthrax. The West African negro is immune to yellow fever; measles, in the case of the North American Indian, is a fatal disease. Racial immunity of this sort has been wrought out gradually. Genetic variation producing conditions conducive to immunity enables its possessors to survive and the survivors transmit this constitution, the more susceptible are weeded out and the race becomes relatively immune.

(3) For the proper study of the inheritance of defects of structure and of physiological function more and more material is becoming available. The stock-breeder has

propagated his "defectives" when these have attracted his fancy or have promised to be of use, *e.g.*, polled cattle, the earless sheep of Syria and China, tailless cats of Japan and the Isle of Man, short-legged dogs, albino rats and rabbits, polydactylous cats, fowls with cranial hernia, such as the Polish breed, and so on. A ram lamb with short crooked legs and an unusually long back appeared as a mutant in a small flock owned by Seth Wright, a Massachusetts farmer, in 1791, a time when fencing was expensive in time and money. The farmer promptly recognised the advantages of such a sheep and bred from it; the mutant character was dominant, segregation occurred in the following generations, and the Ancon breed was established by selection. Any breeder finding himself presented in this way with a favourable mutant character has only to apply himself to a simple problem in Mendelism to establish this character in his stock. It has been seen that a gene for a recessive and abnormal character may be transmitted unsuspected for many generations for all heterozygotes will exhibit the allelomorphic "normal" character. The chances that a recessive mutation will affect the race is very small indeed if the mating is free and uncontrolled, especially if the corresponding character is disadvantageous to the individual exhibiting it. Even though the character is advantageous, yet if it is recessive to the original, the chances of its spreading are extremely small. A "dominant" mutation is in a similar position, as is seen in the case of the hackleless condition in the fowl. A "hackleless" or bare-necked fowl mated to an ordinarily hackled fowl will produce chickens 50 per cent. of which will be hackled, 50 per cent. hackleless. If the hackleless birds of this generation are mated with hackled, again only 50 per cent. of their offspring will be hackleless. The dominant new character indeed, unless it has a positive advantage over the original, when both homo- and heterozygous dominant would benefit, has a smaller chance of stamping itself upon the race than the recessive, for while a recessive can be hidden, a dominant, if unfavourable, places its exhibitor at a disadvantage. Upon this question of the establishment of a new character the frequency of recurrence of a given mutation bears. The more often a particular mutation occurs the greater are the chances of its becoming established.

Detlefsen (1920) has described a herd of albino cattle which originated from two albino calves out of "grade" Holstein cows by a "full-blooded" Holstein bull, all of which were characteristically black and white. The calves were white and had pink eyes. The young albino bull mated to grade Holstein cows produced only albino offspring, about 20 in number. The albinos interbred yielded nothing but albinos. Four albino cows served by a registered Holstein bull produced 3 albinos and 1 normal. The inheritance of this albinism is peculiar. From the manner of its origin one would be led to regard it as a recessive character, yet later in different matings it behaved as though it were a dominant. A complete analysis of the character was not possible, but at any rate it is clear that it is very different from the white of the famous Chillingham and Chartley herds, the white of which is a dominant, being perhaps the extreme condition of spotting, such as is also encountered in the white bull-terrier, which it will be remembered also has pigmented areas.

A recent case of polydactylism in cattle is recorded by Roberts (1921). A normal bull mated with a polydactylous cow produced a polydactylous calf, which later mated with a normal unrelated bull, produced three polydactylous calves. The extra-toed condition is dominant to the normal. In Roberts's case the condition affected all the feet, though the extra toe was larger in the case of the hind feet. In a three-toed strain described by Bateson, which had its origin in the mating of a polydactylous cow with a normal-footed bull, the polydactylous condition appeared throughout ten recorded generations in male and female alike, but was restricted, save in one case, to the hind feet.

The solid-footed mule-footed condition, syndactylism, is common in the pig. Sir W. Menzies, of Rannoch, had such a strain for forty years, having their origin in one pair. Syndactyly behaves as a simple dominant.

In the *Proc. Zool. Soc.* of 1833, Colonel Hallam describes

a race of pigs which had no hind legs, and which bred true for this character.

Detlefsen and Yapp (1920) describe a case of congenital cataract in cattle and conclude that the condition behaves as a simple Mendelian recessive. A registered Holstein-Friesian bull, with no family history of cataract, inbred with his own stock produced several offspring with congenital cataract. By unrelated cows he produced only normal calves. 32 F_1 daughters mated to an F_1 son gave 63 calves, 55 normal and 8 with congenital cataract of the stellate type.

A peculiar notch in the margin of the ear of cattle (Jersey) behaves as a simple Mendelian dominant, according to Lush (1922). A similar but somewhat differently placed notch in the ear of the Ayrshire appears to be of the same nature.

Other mutant characters of domestic stock though of no appreciable benefit to the breeder is of considerable scientific interest. For example, the horned condition in the horse occasionally is exhibited. There are four modern horse skulls in the Natural History Museum in London, two from thoroughbreds, which show the beginnings of horns and all in the same position. In South America there is a horse with horns 3 to 4 inches long, so it is reported.

Characters of some considerable economic interest are those of the anatomical bases of hernia and of undescended testes. There is every reason to hold that these are heritable. Intersexuality and hermaphroditism in the goat and pig are definitely heritable, as is white heifer disease in the cow.

Occasionally, in the absence of a working knowledge of genetics the breeder endeavours to achieve the genetically impossible. A very striking case is seen in certain breeds of cattle in which the calf is sometimes still-born, and presents certain constant and characteristic abnormalities which have gained for such the name of "bull-dog" calves. The condition present in these cases is one very closely akin to that of achondroplasia in the human. It is a disease which affects the fœtal bones that are laid down in cartilage, those laid down in membrane escaping. The primary cause of the condition has not yet been recognised, but all authorities are agreed that abnormality of the glands of internal secretion is most probably responsible. The pregnancy which results in the production of the monstrous calves is very abnormal; there is a great excess of liquor amnii, so that at the third month of pregnancy the cow is as "big" as she should be at term; the fœtal membranes rupture and a great quantity of liquor amnii escapes; this occurs again at the fifth and at the seventh month, and sooner or later the calf is aborted (*cf.* the bison × cattle cross). Crew (1923) has brought forward evidence to show that this condition has a definite genetic basis, and is due to a retarded functioning of the pituitary during fœtal life. A very similar condition is described by Wriedt (1924) in the Norwegian Telemark cattle, and this appears to be a simple recessive. Evidence is rapidly accumulating which shows beyond doubt that such lethals and semi-lethals are very prevalent among domestic stock. A peculiar type of blindness in the Holstein-Friesian cattle is an example. Another is furnished by the same breed, for Hadley (1924) has described a semi-lethal condition in which the calf is devoid of skin on the legs, ears, and mouth, and dies within a few days or weeks after birth. Wriedt (1924) has described a genetic form of sterility in the Danish white horse, the result of the action of a lethal factor. The same authority describes a semi-lethal factor in grey-mottled dogs, such as the Great Dane and Dachshund and Norwegian Dunker Hound, which results in small eyes (microthalmia), defective pupil (coloboma), and glaucoma. Deafness in the bull-terrier is a simple recessive apparently, as is also cleft-palate in the bull-dog. The latter condition is lethal since the puppies cannot suckle. In the case of the fowl, lethals are to be found in the Frizzle, for it would seem that the homozygous frizzled bird does not appear, and in the Scots Dumpie.

In the case of the human, an example of the inheritance of a physiological character is that of colour-blindness, already referred to as an instance of a sex-linked character. It will be remembered that colour-blind women are rare because they can only have their origin in one of the three matings: (1) colour-blind man × colour-blind woman; (2) colour-blind man × a woman whose father was colour-blind; or (3) colour-blind man × a woman whose mother was heterozygous for the colour-blind character. But this is not all, for there are many grades of colour-blindness. It is possible that these differences are due either to the action of independently-heritable modifying genes or else that a multiple allelomorphic series is involved. Moreover, exceptions to the usual mode of inheritance of this character are occasionally encountered: a colour-blind man married to a perfectly normal-sighted woman may beget a colour-blind son. Such an exception can now be interpreted as a result of non-disjunction.

In certain cases of heritable defects the expression of the defect is limited to one sex. Hæmophilia—excessive bleeding on the slightest and most insignificant provocation associated with a low coagulability of the blood, and a structural weakness of the vessels—is limited almost entirely to the male. The peculiar dermal spines of the Lambert family were handed down through five generations and in the males only. In such cases the difference may result from homo- and hetero-zygosis in respect of characters, the genes for which are resident upon the X-chromosome. In the case of Drosophila it has been found that there are at least twenty-five dominant mutations which render the homozygous individual non-viable. In the heterozygous condition the lethal effect is not evidenced, and, further, it is known that in certain cases the hybrid may exhibit heterosis, and be more viable than either parental stock.

In animals it is the rule to breed only from the anatomically and physiologically sound. A deformity, a deficiency, may be a congenital acquisition, or it may be a genetic variation. It is not for the stock-breeder to test which of these possibilities is correct; but the opportunity of making this test should be offered to Research Institutions, since the abnormality may possess considerable genetical interest and its study may lead to something of economic importance. It should be borne in mind that any character that is detrimental to the life of the individual and that behaves in a Mendelian fashion in inheritance is a character in the Mendelian sense, and can only be eradicated from a stock by the application of genetical methods of breeding.

CHAPTER XII

DISPUTED BELIEFS

Telegony.

By telegony is meant the supposed influence of a sire previously mated with a female on offspring subsequently borne by that female to a different sire. Its principle is that a female is so "impregnated" by the first male to which she is bred that all the subsequent offspring, regardless of their actual father, show the influence on the mother of the first male. Popularly this phenomenon is spoken of as "infection of the germ."

A belief in telegony is widespread, and it is not necessary to travel far in order to find evidence of the hold it has upon the popular mind. In certain countries it is commonly believed that a ewe, for example, will produce better lambs if prior to her mating with a ram of her own breed she is served by a male of another species, a boar or a billy-goat. It is the deep-rooted opinion of many stock-breeders that a female of good stock once served by a male of another breed, or by a non-pedigreed male, is spoilt for further breeding. Alleged cases have been and are still being reported in all domesticated animals (both mammals and birds) and in man.

A few examples may help to define the problem. A Wyandotte hen is fertilised by a Leghorn cockerel; three months later, having been mated with a cock of her own breed for several weeks, she lays eggs which on hatching yield chickens, some of which possess the Leghorn shape and single comb. A Shorthorn cow is accidentally served by an Aberdeen-Angus bull and produces a black polled calf; she is disposed of because it is implicitly believed that even though her next calf was by a pure-bred Shorthorn, yet that calf would most certainly exhibit or hand on to its offspring certain of the characters—such as the polled condition or black coat colour—of the previous sire. A pure-bred bitch covered by a mongrel is almost invariably discarded; the fancier has not the slightest doubt that she is ruined for further breeding of pure-bred prize-winning stock. Certain Sheep-breeders' Associations refuse admission to the registers of any lamb whose mother was ever "impregnated" by mating with a ram of another breed.

This belief, more widely held than is commonly supposed, not by the stock-owners, perhaps, but certainly by the husbandmen, undoubtedly has a basis of experience. The question to be answered is whether this experience has been misinterpreted, whether the data on which this belief is fostered are based on accurate observation. To answer this question a knowledge of genetics, of the history of the breed and of the ancestry of the animals concerned is essential.

Some cases can be readily explained without any appeal to a doubtful agency. For example, in the case of the Wyandotte mentioned above, it is known that there has been a considerable infusion of the Leghorn "blood" in many of the modern strains of Wyandotte, and that a single-combed bird should occasionally occur in a rose-comb breed with this history is not surprising. Other cases offer more difficulty, but only because the history of the animals themselves and of the breed to which they belong is not available. Acknowledging that in many cases the evidence offered in support of the case is largely anecdotal and uncritical, yet there are others in which it appears almost convincing until tedious investigation is undertaken.

For example, take the classical case in which the evidence was sufficient to be accepted by Darwin, than whom there has never been a more critical yet open-minded observer. A mare of almost pure Arabian blood, belonging to Lord Morton was bred to a quagga (a form of zebra) and foaled a hybrid. Afterwards bred on two occasions to a black Arabian stallion, she foaled two colts of brown colour whose legs were striped more plainly than those of the hybrid or even than those of the quagga himself, while on the neck and other parts of the body were also well-marked stripings; the mane was short, stiff and erect, exactly as in the case of the quagga. The story was reported to the Royal Society of London by Lord Morton as a convincing case of telegony. Darwin also cites a case communicated to him by a Dr Bowerbank of a Turkish dog, black and hairless, which, having been accidentally bred to a spaniel of mixed blood with long brown hair, produced a litter of five pups, three of which were hairless, while the other two were covered by short brown hair; when bred later to a Turkish dog, equally black and hairless, she produced a litter of pups, half of which resembled their mother—*i.e.*, pure Turk—while the other half were exactly like the pups with short hair served by the spaniel. In short, Darwin admitted the fact of telegony. But much work has been done since Darwin's time, and it is now possible to investigate the problem in the light of more extensive knowledge.

In the first place, it is to be noted that the facts advanced to prove telegonic influence are never obtained from carefully controlled experiments, and that in such cases alternative explanations are not well considered. In the second place, the genotypic constitution of the animals concerned has not been determined. In order to examine fairly an alleged case of telegony it is essential that allowances should be made for variation and reversion, for the results of mating of individuals belonging to a phenotype but not to the same genotype. For instance, any white mouse would appear to be like any other white mouse, but if several white females are mated to the same agouti male, the progeny may differ very widely in the different cases. One female may produce agoutis and whites, another may produce agoutis, whites, yellows, blacks, striped agoutis, striped blacks. In the case of the white mouse there are many genotypes within the one phenotype, and here lies the explanation of possible breeding results at first sight strongly suggesting telegony.

Consider the case of Lord Morton's mare. It was the presence of the striping on the coat and the peculiar "set" of the mane which was taken as evidence of the possible influence of the quagga. Incidentally it is of interest to note that Darwin records a series of observations which suggest very strongly that quagga-like markings can be found in cases in which there is no question of any hybridisation with a quagga. He describes a brown Devonshire pony which "had on its back a very distinct stripe along the spine, light transverse rays on the inside of the legs, and four parallel bands on each shoulder." He inclines to the opinion that this striping is due to a cross between individuals of a different colour resulting in a case of "atavism." But at any rate quagga-like markings on a horse do not necessarily indicate telegony, but rather open up the question as to whether any ancestor of the modern horse was striped; whether a short stiff mane is not characteristic of certain horses as well as of the quagga. Cossar Ewart (1899) points out that the old yellow-dun horses of the forest type, which have had much to do in the origin of the modern horse, possessed a broad dorsal band and zebra-like barring on the legs as well as faint stripes on the face, neck and withers. In fact, it is probable that a remote ancestor of this forest horse was as richly striped as some modern zebras —"Even yet among mongrel ponies it is not uncommon to meet with individuals which have distinct markings very reminiscent of those of the old forest horse. Such markings are not uncommon among Arabian crosses."

Experiments carefully planned to investigate the problem of telegony were undertaken by Cossar Ewart (1896-1901), who, as nearly as possible, reconstructed the case of Lord Morton's mare. "Up to the end of the last century, Lord Morton's experiment with a male quagga and a young chestnut seven-eighths Arabian mare was regarded as affording strong evidence of telegony. Hence at the outset, I decided to repeat as accurately as possible Lord Morton's experiment. The quagga being extinct, a Burchell zebra was mated with Arab and other mares belonging to different breeds and strains. The mares after producing one or more hybrids were mated with Arab and other stallions. In the account of my experiments, illustrated by numerous figures published in the *Transactions of the Highland and Agri-*

cultural Society of Scotland for 1902, it is pointed out that though to start with I believed there was such a thing as telegony, I eventually came to the conclusion that there never has been an undoubted instance of infection in either dogs, rabbits or horses."

Ewart bred the Burchell zebra stallion Matopo to a chestnut polo pony, Valda. She produced as a result of this mating twin hybrids. The following year she produced a foal to a light chestnut thoroughbred stallion, after which she was again bred to Matopo, and produced a third hybrid foal. Subsequently she produced another foal to the service of a dark chestnut thoroughbred stallion. The three hybrid foals from this mating were all richly striped, in fact the stripes were more numerous, though less conspicuous, than those of the zebra sire. In spite of this fact, however, the two foals produced by mating Valda to the thoroughbred chestnut stallion, in no particular, either in colour or in form, resembled the hybrid foals. They were chestnut in colour without any suggestion of striping, and in liveliness of temperament or vigour of development neither of them resembled in the least the hybrid progeny. Mulatto, a black West Highland pony mare, was bred to Matopo and the result was Romulus, a beautiful, distinctly striped hybrid. Mulatto was then bred to a black Arabian stallion; to this service she produced a foal which, when examined immediately after birth, showed numerous indistinct markings, so faint, however, that their exact nature was in some doubt. Subsequently Mulatto produced another foal to the service of a dark-brown West Highland stallion which also was indistinctly marked.

In themselves these foals suggested as strongly as did those described by Lord Morton that telegony might occasionally occur. But Ewart tested the matter further by breeding two dark West Highland mares closely related to Mulatto to the same Arabian stallion which had sired the striped foal. Two foals were produced, one of which possessed the same sort of indistinct markings as those characteristic of the foals of Mulatto, while the other was much more distinctly striped. There can be no question, therefore, that the striping of Mulatto's foal was a consequence of normal hereditary processes having nothing to do with telegony.

An outline of these and other matings is as follows :—

Valda	× Matopo	1898	Hybrid twins.
	Stallion	1899	Colt without resemblance to zebra.
	Matopo	1900	Hybrid.
	Stallion	1901	Colt, no resemblance to zebra.
Mulatto	× Matopo	1896	Hybrid.
	Stallion B	1897	Colt lightly striped at birth.
	Stallion L	1899	,, ,, ,,
	Control—Stallion L × filly : striped colt.		
	,, ,, ,,		
Nora	× Stallion W	1895	Colt striped at birth, three stripes persisted.
	Matopo	1897	Hybrid.
	Stallion C	1898	Colt, no resemblance to zebra.
	Matopo	1898	Hybrid.
	Matopo	1900	Hybrid.
	Stallion S	1901	Colt, no resemblance to zebra.
Laura	× Matopo		Abortion.
	Stallion L	1898	Colt, no resemblance to zebra.
	Stallion L	1898	,, ,, ,,
	Stallion S	1900	,, ,, ,,
Rona	× Matapo	1898	Hybrid.
	Stallion M	1899	Colt, no resemblance to zebra.
Lady Douglas	× Matopo	1897	Hybrid.
	Matopo	1898	Hybrid.
	Stallion M	1900	Colt, no resemblance to zebra.
	Stallion S	1901	,, ,, ,,
Biddy	× Matopo	1897	Hybrid.
	Stallion T	1898	Kathleen : no resemblance to zebra.
	Stallion G	1898	Colt, ,, ,,
	Stallion G	1900	,, ,, ,,
Kathleen	× Stallion M	1901	Colt, no resemblance to zebra.
Tundra	× Matopo	1897	Hybrid.
	Stallion B	1898	Colt, no resemblance to zebra.
	Matopo	1898	Hybrid.
	Stallion S	1900	Colt, no resemblance to zebra.

In the case of the mares the absence of the influence of the fecundation by the zebra is morphologically indisputable : not one of the colts born after the hybrids is marked by stripes of any kind. The colts foaled by Mulatto by Stallion B and L after the birth of a hybrid alone show stripes, but the control experiment clearly establishes the fact that this striping was not necessarily due to the former association of the mother with the quagga. Nora produced a striped colt before she had even seen the quagga, but never after, although of course the hybrids she produced by Matopo were striped. Kathleen, foaled by Biddy subsequently to the birth of a hybrid, herself foaled a colt which in no way resembled a zebra. So it would appear that Kathleen was affected neither morphologically nor physiologically by the association of her mother Biddy with the zebra.

The experiments of Faltz-Fein and Ivanov (1913) confirm the conclusions arrived at by Cossar Ewart.

Litvinka	× Zebra	1897	Hybrid (aborted).
(brown mare)	Zebra	1898	„
	Zebra	1902	„
	Zebra	1905	„ (aborted).
	Stallion	1906	Colt, no resemblance to zebra.
	Zebra	1907	Hybrid.
	Stallion	1908	Colt, no resemblance to zebra.
	Stallion	1909	„ „ „
Pliakha	× Zebra	1901	Hybrid.
(piebald)	Stallion	1902-10	Nine colts, no resemblance to zebra.
	Stallion	1912	Colt, „ „ „
Armida	× Zebra	1902	Hybrid.
(bright bay)	Stallion	1904	Colt, no resemblance to zebra.
	Stallion	1906	„ „ „
	Stallion	1907	„ „ „
Priimikha	× Zebra	1905	Hybrid (artificial insemination).
(brown)	Zebra	1906	„ „ „
	Zebra	1907	„ „ „
	Stallion	1908-12	Five colts, no resemblance to zebra.
Vesta (bay)	× Zebra	1906	Hybrid.
	Stallion	1907	Colt, no resemblance to zebra.
	Stallion	1908	„ „ „
	Stallion	1912	„ „ „

Aida (piebald)	× Zebra	1907	Hybrid.
	Stallion	1908	Colt, no resemblance to zebra.
	Stallion	1909	" " "
	Stallion	1911	" " "
Zlodeika (dark brown)	× Zebra	1902	Hybrid.
	Stallion	1903-7	Four colts, no resemblance to zebra.

The experiments of Baron de Parana (1910) with zebra hybrids closely paralleled those of Cossar Ewart and likewise yielded no evidence in support of telegony. The illustrations in an article by Rommell "The Grevy Zebra as a Domestic Animal" (1913), describing the work of the U.S. Government with hybrids between different species of *Equus*, provide no evidence of any sort which support the idea of telegony. The evidence of mule breeding establishments in which thousands of mules have been bred, in every trustworthy instance is against the doctrine.

Of course, in spite of all their great weight, all that these experiments prove is that under conditions when it would most be expected, telegony is not demonstrated. They do not prove that it may not take place. But for every case of alleged telegony there are hundreds in which no reason to suggest the influence of the previous sire arises.

The difficulty of visualising any sort of mechanism by which such influence might be exerted is also against a ready acceptance of the doctrine. The spermatozoa of the previous sire might possibly remain within the genital tract of the female and become operative long after impregnation. In most European bats sexual union usually occurs in the autumn and the spermatozoa are simply stored in the uterus until ovulation and fertilisation take place in the spring. The same phenomenon is common in insects: in some queen bees the store has been known to last for two or three years, and in one case an aged queen laid fertile eggs thirteen years after the last union with a male. Hen turkeys lay fertile eggs throughout the season, though the male is removed soon after the beginning.

The spermatozoa might penetrate immature ova and survive; the ova then slowly mature and fertilisation actually might occur at such a time as to coincide with the service of the second sire.

But all authorities are now agreed that in the higher animals these suggestions are impossible and, in any case, under these conditions offspring would be born without the assistance of any second sire at all!

Romanes suggested that the sperm, after penetrating the uterus, is absorbed by the maternal organism and exercises an influence upon the ova that are not yet mature (the infection hypothesis). It is conceivable that the semen of the male does exert a physiological influence upon the female, but not an influence of such a nature as to evoke, for instance, the alleged quagga mane and stripes in the second foal of Lord Morton's mare. No specific influence of the male element has ever been demonstrated.

The mother might be influenced by the fœtus during pregnancy, and this influence might react on subsequent offspring (the saturation hypothesis). According to this theory the fœtus has in its blood special properties derived from the father and these act like a vaccine on the blood of the mother. The constitution of the offspring—partly paternal—might affect the mother's constitution and thus affect the subsequent offspring by another father. The existence of exchange between the maternal and fœtal blood is acknowledged, but the peculiarities of an animal do not promenade in its blood-stream. Gestation produces modifications in a female which are to some extent permanent. The female producing her second offspring is different to the individual she was when producing her first, and the environment of the second offspring is different from that of the first. But the difference is the same whether the father of the two offspring is one and the same individual or whether each offspring is the result of a different mating. It is the previous gestation and not the male which was associated with it that is responsible for the modification in the maternal organism.

The difficulty of the mechanism is one that cannot, as yet at any rate, be overcome, and it is reasonable to seek other interpretations. It is held by those who do not believe in telegony that the phenomena are simply illustrations of reversion. This view amounts to denying telegony in the strict sense, for in it there is no causal nexus between the previous sire and the subsequent offspring who resemble him. They happen to resemble him because he resembled one of their ancestors.

Or it may be that the subsequent offspring have accidentally varied in the direction of resemblance to the previous sire. The resemblance is mere coincidence.

The matter can be approached from the statistical side, for if the female can be influenced at later reproductions by a male who has been associated with her in earlier ones, then in a permanent union of a pair there should be found an increasing influence of the paternal type—that is, if the alleged telegony is not due to some abnormal persistence of the spermatozoa of earlier unions. Karl Pearson has shown that as regards stature there is no evidence of any steady telegonic influence. But this is not quite the same as the precise point at issue. Careful comparisons of the families of the same mother by two successive husbands are required.

It must be mentioned here that although the belief in telegony cannot be accepted, it has to be admitted that the bearing of hybrid offspring may sometimes have detrimental effects upon the dam. Breeders of mules put their mares to horses after they have reared two or three mules in order to prevent them becoming sterile. Evidently the hybrid is a greater tax upon the resources of the dam: this is particularly well illustrated in the case of the bison × cattle hybrid, which causes a tremendous drain upon the dam's system and often even death. But this is not telegony, and has nothing to do with the transference of the characters of the previous sire; it is a consequence of disturbing the physiological balance in the dam.

It may be said in conclusion that the development of the Mendelian theory of heredity has robbed most of the old evidence for telegony of all its value.

The belief in *infection of the male* is by no means so strong as that in telegony but it also is widespread. Ewart cites the case of a breeder who refused to allow his Jersey bull to serve Shetland cows for fear that the bull would subsequently carry over Shetland traits into his Jersey herd. But if it is decided to discard telegony as applied to the female, there appears to be no warrant whatsoever for considering it in the male where an effective mechanism of operation is even less conceivable.

Since it is the custom in this country for damages to be given to a breeder whose heifer has been "ruined" as a result of sexual congress with a bull of a different breed, it is desirable to suggest that in these circumstances the owner of the bull might perhaps counterclaim for damages resulting from "infection of the male." The arbiter who believes in telegony cannot but believe also in this.

Xenia is the term used to define the phenomenon in which in the case of plants the pollen of the male parent seems to affect the tissue of the maternal ovary, the seed or even the fruit, as distinguished from the embryo itself. In the case of birds, it has been suggested that the eggs laid by the hen are influenced as to size, shape, colour, and such-like characters by the male with which she is mated—that the characters of the egg may be as those of the hens of the breed to which the cock belongs. Duerden (1918) records that when South African ostrich hens are mated to a North African cock the eggs exhibit the usual characters of the egg of the South African breed and show no evidence of any influence of the North African parent.

Maternal Impression.

The belief that the mental states, the vivid sense impressions and strong emotions of a pregnant female may so affect her unborn offspring that structural changes in the body of the offspring having some correspondence with the mother's experience result, would seem to date back beyond history. In Genesis xxx. 31-43, it is recorded that Jacob used peeled wands to influence the colour of his stock, and some stock-breeders of to-day still profess their faith in this doctrine as a part of their practice. For instance, in order to ensure black calves, some breeders will keep their cows in a black-painted stall; an Aberdeen-Angus breeder may have a high black fence around the paddock lest visual impression on the mother's part should play havoc with the colour pattern of the offspring; if such a herd is separated from a neighbouring Ayrshire herd by a wire fence only, and in it there is born a red or a black-and-white calf, this is explained and accepted as a case of maternal impression. In the case of the human mother it is widely taught that prenatal culture can influence the unborn child, that by training herself she can also train the child. The weirdly abnormal appetites, cravings and aversions of the pregnant woman are held responsible for peculiarities of colour, abnormal hairiness, and various malformations of the child. A mother has an uncontrollable craving for, or an extremely strong aversion to fish, and the child is born with ichthyosis (a hereditary skin disease in which the surface of the body is covered with fish-like scales). A woman is frightened by a club-footed man—and her child is born with a similar malformation. In a certain village was born a heifer calf with three mouths, four ears, and six nostrils. Each mouth was equipped with a set of teeth, but the animal had only one tongue and took nourishment through its central mouth. The other two opened simultaneously when it was feeding. Two dog-like ears overlapped the face, and two others stood upright on the calf's head. Its features, in fact, very much resembled those of a pug dog. The owner stated that when the cow was in calf it was worried, while grazing, by a Pekingese dog.

The question to be considered is whether this doctrine of maternal impression and prenatal culture is based on accurate observation of facts and upon correct inferences therefrom.

All are agreed that for a considerable period the unborn offspring is part and parcel of the maternal organism; the embryo receives its entire nourishment from the mother and its development depends upon that nourishment. Anything which affects the supply will certainly affect the embryo *in a general but not in a particular way*, and undoubtedly emotional states can profoundly disturb the general well-being of the mother and of the unborn offspring, for they are associated with marked changes in the general metabolism and the offspring is dependent upon the blood-stream for its nourishment. A fretting mother's general health may become so affected that her offspring will not be properly nourished and will show the results of this at birth. An atmosphere of affection and happiness will tend to ensure the birth of an anatomically and physiologically normal child. Moreover, the limits of the effects of auto-suggestion cannot yet be defined, but these are different matters to the sort of case at present under discussion. It can be said without much fear of contradiction, that there is no woman who during pregnancy did not encounter some experience of the kind which according to popular tradition causes "marks." And yet the great majority of children are born unmarked. Darwin having been told by his great friend, Sir Joseph Hooker, of a case of maternal impression in one of his relatives who had a child with a particular mole, it being accredited to a fright she had experienced when she blotted with sepia a lent valuable copy of Turner's *Liber Studiorum*, wrote in reply: "I should be very much obliged if at any future or leisure time you could tell me on what you ground your doubtful belief in imagination of a mother affecting her offspring. I have attended to several statements scattered about, but do not believe in more than accidental coincidence. W. Hunter told my father, then in a lying-in hospital, that in many thousand cases he had asked the mother before confinement whether anything had affected her imagination and recorded the answers, and absolutely not one case came right, though when the child had anything remarkable they always made the cap to fit."

Darwin, no doubt, gave the true explanation of a great many of the alleged cases. When the child is born with any peculiarities the mother, guided by tradition, hunts for some experience in the preceding months that may explain them. If she finds coincidence, then it is popularly accepted that she has also found the cause, and so a typical case of prenatal influence becomes established. A lover of art wills that her child shall excel in art and her assiduous practice during pregnany seems rewarded when to her great joy it is demonstrated that the child has artistic talent. She decides naturally enough that the effects of prenatal culture have been demonstrated. But even though she had not devoted many hours of the day to practice and of the night to dreams, even had she spent this time in cultivating thoughts of hatred towards everything artistic, would her child not have been born equally well endowed with the artistic talent? The geneticist thinks so, holding that the course of the expression of hereditary factors cannot be controlled *in any definite way* by any act or attitude of the mother. This does not imply that in the case of the human, the social inheritance—the environment in its broadest sense—cannot and does not condition the expression of the genotype in which there may be factors for mental characters. Turning to the alleged influence of maternal impression in the case of the domesticated animals, it can be stated with confidence that a fuller knowledge of the pedigree of the biblical herdsman's stock would provide a truer explanation of his results. Possibly he knew the history of the herd, had observed the variations which were frequent, and took advantage of the credulous and unobservant in order to add to his reputation. The occasional birth of a red calf in a black herd is to be taken as evidence that among the black some are heterozygous and that red was used during the formative stages in the history of the herd.

The practice of allowing for maternal impression at the time of service is rather a different matter, for in the cases so far dealt with the effect is supposed to occur fairly late in pregnancy, which rather increases the difficulty of taking the suggestion of maternal impression seriously, for the experience is encountered at a time when the development of all the main parts of the fœtus is already completed. It is known that most errors of development such as lead to the production of marked physical defects are due to some cause within the embryo itself, and that most of them become expressed during the first few weeks of intra-uterine life when the mother is not aware that she is pregnant. But in these cases of alleged maternal impression at the time of service it is certain that a full knowledge of the pedigree of the beasts concerned would remove the need to consider anything so hypothetical.

There is always the difficulty of the mechanism of this influence: there is no direct communication twixt the mother and fœtus. How then can one strain credulity and imagine how a mental impression can become accurately reflected upon the embryo offspring? This scepticism is justified. Maternal impressions are not facts but superstitions born of an unscientific attitude on the part of the popular mind towards outstanding isolated instances. Remembrances of strange coincidences are longest borne in mind, the ordinary is unremarkable and is overlooked.

Reversion.

Reversion is the term used to define the reappearance through inheritance of some character or combination of characters which was not exhibited by the generations immediately preceding, but which had been borne by a more remote though not hypothetical ancestor. An instance of what would be popularly regarded as reversion is the result of mating the miniature and vestigial forms of Drosophila. Miniature wing is a single-factor recessive mutation which arose in a normal long-winged culture: vestigial wing is another. When a vestigial-winged female is mated to a miniature-winged male the progeny all have long wings, the form characteristic of the ancestral stock. The explanation is that in the miniature-winged fly a mutation had occurred in the locus M which change in no way affected the locus V; in the vestigial race a mutation had occurred in the locus V without affecting the locus M. The vestigial fly has the constitution vvMM, the miniature the constitution VVmm, and when the two are mated the resulting constitution is VvMm, so that the characters of the original wild form are reproduced. This is the principle on which reversion in hybridisation depends, and other cases differ from the above only in the number of factor differences involved.

It is necessary to distinguish between cases of reversion and certain conditions which resemble it. If the normal development is arrested during embryonic life the individual may not be perfect in all its parts. A child is born with a harelip, for example, but this does not mean that here is a case of reversion: there has been no harelipped type in the human ancestry. The case is one of arrested development, of failure of certain embryonic stages that are essential to the proper development of the human lip. Then there are certain vestigial structures, such as the gill-clefts of mammals, the remains of the pelvis and hind limbs in the cetaceans which have not yet disappeared phylogenetically. They may be alacking for many generations and then appear but they are not instances of reversion, their appearance is still quite normal. According to the definition given, the ancestor must be real and not hypothetical. Polydactylism, for example, does not indicate that there has been in the lineage of the individual an ancestor with more than five digits: there are simpler explanations of digital abnormality than this. A man's great-great-grandfather may have been a noted drunkard, but though the man himself drinks unwisely it does not necessarily follow that this is a case of reversion. A man may become a drunkard through his own initiative, he may acquire a habit just as did his ancestor in somewhat similar circumstances.

Atavism is the term used to define the phenomenon in which by skipping a generation a particular character in the offspring is unlike the corresponding character in the parents but, instead, resembles the character in one of the grandparents. A study of any P_1, F_1, and F_2 examples will supply the factorial interpretation of this. Reversion is most commonly illustrated in the F_1 of a cross, but instances are known in which it does not appear until F_2. Such a case is that of the single comb in the Pea and Rose comb experiment in which the single comb resulted from the bringing together of two complementary factors which had become separated during the evolution of the different breeds.

The Transmission of Acquired Characters.

An acquired character is a new specific modification of the soma impressed upon the organism by a known agency in the environment or in the exercise of bodily function. The possibility of its transmission implies that this character acquired by the parent reappears in the offspring in the absence of the action of the agency which determined its production in the preceding generations. The notion of the inheritance of acquired characters grew up long before the cellular structure of organisms was recognised, dating back to the time of Aristotle at least, and when it was first recognised that the germ-cells are separated from those which give rise to the body tissue at a very early stage of development the discovery naturally proved a shock to the minds of a generation which vaguely thought of the reproductive elements as an offshoot from the parent body. The precise question at issue is whether a structural change in the body induced by some change in use or disuse or by some change in the environment can so affect the germ-cells in a specific or representative way that the offspring will, through inheritance, exhibit even in some slight degree the modification which the parent acquired.

That the influence of the somatic metabolism on the germ-cells is of a very restricted character is readily seen from a series of experiments by Castle and Phillips (Fig. 67). On 6th January 1909, the left ovary was removed from an albino guinea-pig, then about five months old, and an ovary of a pure black guinea-pig about one month old was fastened near the tip of the uterine horn, distant a centimetre or more from the site of the ovary removed. One week later, 13th January, a second operation was performed in which the right ovary of the albino was removed, and in its place was ingrafted an ovary of a second black guinea-pig of the same age as the first but of a different ancestry. After the albino had fully recovered from the second operation, she was placed with an albino male with which she remained until her death about a year later. On the 23rd of July, 198 days after the operation, she gave birth to two female young. One was black but bore a few red hairs, the other one was likewise black but had some red upon it and its right foot was white. On 15th October 1909, the grafted albino bore a third young one, a male which like those previously born, had a few red hairs interspersed with black. On 11th January 1910, the grafted albino was observed to be pregnant for the third time and this time she was very large. Unfortunately, on 2nd February, she died of pneumonia with three full-grown male young *in utero*. The skins of these animals were saved: like the other three they were black but with a few

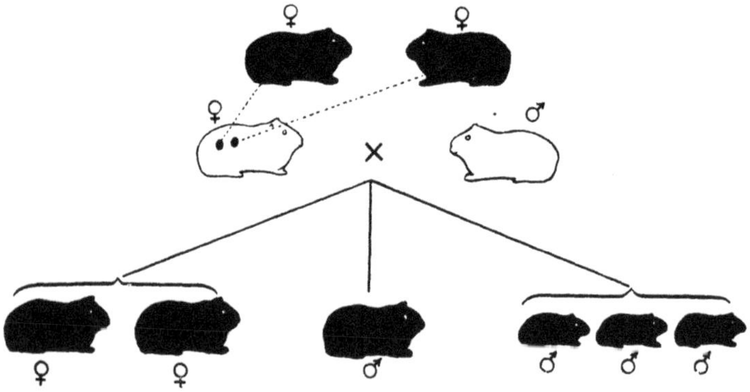

FIG. 67. (*After* Castle.)

red hairs among the black ones; they bore no white hairs. A daughter of the grafted albino was mated with the albino male, her father, and bore three young, two of which were albinos and one black with some few red hairs. If she had been the daughter of a pure black mother instead of a grafted albino, she would have been expected to have produced black and albino offspring in equal numbers. The observed result was the nearest possible agreement with this expectation. A control mating of the male albino was made with a female of pure black stock. As a result there were produced two litters of young, including five individuals, all black with red hairs interspersed. This result shows that the red hair found on the six young of the grafted albino was due not to the foster mother influence of the grafted albino but to the influence of the male parent. The young of the grafted mother were in colour exactly what the black guinea-pig which furnished the graft might have been expected to bear herself, had she been mated with the male instead of being sacrificed to furnish the graft; the white foot borne by one of the young is no exception to this statement. Spotting characterised the race of guinea-pigs from which the father came; he was himself born in a litter which contained spotted young, whereas neither the pure-bred black race that furnished the graft nor the albino race that received it was characterised by spotting. Inasmuch as the offspring of albino parents are invariably albinos, it is certain that the six pigmented offspring of the grafted albino female were all derived from ova furnished by the introduced ovarian tissue taken from a black guinea-pig. This tissue was introduced while the contained ova were still quite immature and it persisted in its new environment for nearly a year before the eggs were liberated which produced the last litter of three young. These young, like the earlier progeny, gave indication of foster-mother influence in their coloration.

Other experimental work with more favourable material has shown however that it is possible to induce permanent adaptive modifications. Jollos (1920) exposed Paramæcium to heat and to various poisons. Thousands of individuals of pedigreed stock were placed in high temperatures and in solutions of arsenious acid or of calcium salts. Each stock started with a sharply marked upper limit of resistance which differed for different stocks. By exposing stocks in temperatures or solutions above the permanently lethal limit but for sublethal periods, Jollos obtained strains the resistance of which was markedly raised. High resistance was induced by passing through a series of tests of gradually increasing severity. This raised resistance was never permanent, it was lost by steps—by the same steps as those in which it had been acquired. This work of Jollos shows clearly that adaptive changes lasting over many generations may be induced; that these changes may be or may not be hereditary and that they result when the inducing agent is applied when the germ-plasm is in a special state.

Embryologists for many years now have been familiar with the injurious effects of alcohol, radium, and of X-rays on the chromosomes, causing irregularities in their distribution which are reflected in the characterisation of the individual. There is no doubt whatsoever that the germ-cell can be injured, and that the individual arising from it will be abnormal. It is difficult yet to define how far these injuries are specific and how far general, but the experimental work of Stockard (1914) and others show that the organs affected as a result of such treatment are just those that are most subject to injury, being the most delicate parts of the organism. This being so, it is probable that the effects of such treatment are general and not specific in their action but that those parts which in development require the most perfect adjustments are the parts to show the effects first.

By the inheritance of acquired characters it is implied that the inhibition or destruction of a character is accompanied wholly or partially by the destruction of its material antecedent in the germ-plasm; and on the other hand, if a stimulus of given magnitude is required to call forth the production of a given character, the application of that stimulus to the parent implies the possibility of evoking the corresponding character in the offspring with a stimulus of smaller intensity. Concerning the first proposition no general affirmative can be seriously put forward. However, in view of Guyer and Smith's experiments it would be an act of some temerity to adopt a wholly negative attitude to the question. Guyer and Smith (1920) took the lenses of rabbits' eyes, pulped them in Ringer's physiological salt solution and injected small amounts of the resulting fluid into domestic fowl. After the lapse of some weeks the serum of the fowl's blood became "lens-sensitised," *i.e.*, it now possessed the power of destroying the lens of rabbits' eyes (and nothing else). Small quantities of this serum were then injected into pregnant rabbits. The mothers were unaffected, for in the adult the lens has practically no blood-vessels by which the serum could reach it, but in the case of the developing fœtuses the lenses were affected and the young were born with diminished or completely aborted lenses and retinæ. Some of these survived and were mated to give rise to young some of which showed the defect. Without any further exhibition of lens-sensitised serum the defect was transmitted through six generations. In two cases an affected male mated with a normal doe produced young with the defect. Guyer and Smith suggest that "the degenerating eyes are themselves directly or indirectly originating antibodies in the blood-serum of their bearers which at times affect the germ-cells. As the transmission was equally potent in the male and the female side in crosses with normal individuals, there is no reason to doubt that a genuine germinal change had been produced."

Whether the change was first produced in the soma of the embryo and, secondarily, impressed on the germinal constitution or produced concurrently in both is not clear. It is pointed out that the mothers which were injected during pregnancy on subsequent matings produced broods without eye defects. And it might be argued from this that if the lysin acted on the germ-cells of the embryo and upon its eye rudiments concurrently, it would be expected to act equally on the germ-cells of the mother, which in fact it does not do. But then if the lysin injected into the mother circulates freely in the embryo, why do not the chemical substances set free by the destruction of the lens on the alternate view equally affect the germ-cells of the mother and embryo? The failure of the destruction of the lens of the embryo to influence the germ-cells of the mother on the Lamarckian view is as difficult to interpret as the failure of the lysin to act on the germ-cells of the mother on the Weismannian view, unless a not inherently repugnant assumption is made in the case of the female, that the germ-cells are more susceptible in the embryo than in the adult. But if such an assumption is made the critical value of the experiment is at once invalidated. It is to be noted that the test which Guyer and Smith made to see if the germ-cells of the mother were affected, the mating of the mother to an unrelated and uninfected male was not a proper test. The F_1 contained no defective individuals,

But this is not remarkable if the eye defect character was, as it appears to be, a recessive.

Similar experimental work has been carried out more recently in this country by Huxley and Carr Saunders (1924). They obtained purely negative results. Guyer and Smith, however, have published further data (1924) confirming their earlier conclusions. For the present it must be understood that these results of Guyer and Smith, suggestive as they are, must not be used as the jumping-off place for generalisations concerning the inheritance of acquired characters. General principles must needs rest on a larger body of ascertained fact. The explanation offered by Guyer and Smith requires that there shall either be identity or a great degree of resemblance between the protein of the lens and the protein of the genes upon which lens formation is based. The lens protein must resemble the "lens formation" gene protein more than the protein of any other gene. This may be so, but it is difficult to imagine the chemical correspondence between many of the characters of Drosophila, for example, and their corresponding genes. And in any case this conception implies a considerable degree of preformation and preformation itself is no longer a safe foundation upon which to build a theory.

In any case, it must be conceded to Guyer and Smith that there are indications of "some constitutional identity between the substance of the mature organ in question and its material antecedent in the germ." It is of interest to note that the germinal change which Guyer and Smith were apparently able to establish behaved as a Mendelian factor.

Exact unequivocal experiments to test the question of the transmissibility of somatic modification are exceedingly difficult to devise and their results unfortunately are always capable of interpretation in more than one sense, since interpretation so often depends upon the point of view. Cunningham carried out certain work with flatfish. The young flatfish is pigmented on both sides of the body, but later when it settles on one side the pigment on that side disappears. Cunningham (1904) kept young fish in an aquarium lighted from below, and found that although the pigment disappeared from the underneath surface of the fish it later began to return. The disappearance of the pigment although exposed to light proves that the loss is hereditary; its return on continued exposure to light is interpreted by Cunningham as indicating that its disappearance was due to absence of light and had become hereditary since the process could be reversed. The evidence, is presumptive and does not amount to absolute proof. The asymmetry of the flatfish is the result of the habits acquired by its ancestors, according to the Lamarckian view. Since these ancestors lay on their sides one eye became useless, but as the result of the muscles pulling it, in time the eye came to be situated on the side of the head that is uppermost, otherwise it would have become degenerate. So runs the argument, but anything approaching conclusive experimental proof is lacking.

Kellogg (1908) starved silk-worm caterpillars for two generations, and found that the third generation even if well fed were below the size of the normal stock. But the results may have been due to insufficient embryonic nourishment and not to a specific alteration of the germ-cells.

Griffith and Detlefsen carried out an extensive experiment with rats which were rotated for several months in cages. Some of the young born outside the cage showed irregularities in their gait and when tested gave a different and specific response according to whether their parents had been rotated to the right or left. But as Detlefsen points out it is possible that the stock was exhibiting some vertebral disease.

Kammerer (1923) has more recently carried out a series of experiments dealing with this question of the inheritance of acquired characters. For example, in one of his experiments he used the two European salamanders, *Salamandra maculosa*, yellow and black, inhabiting the lowlands, oviparous, producing at birth 30 to 40 gilled offspring which live in water for six weeks before losing their gills and taking to the land; and *Salamandra atra*, black, living at high altitudes, viviparous, giving birth to only two young, which, from their birth onward are land animals. But if a pregnant black salamander is dissected a dozen or more young will be found *in utero*, and of these only two situated farther back, nearest to the openings of the oviducts, are destined to be born, for all the others during the period of the mother's pregnancy degenerate and are devoured by the hindermost two; these *in utero* possess long gills which become absorbed before birth. Kammerer kept *S. atra* under conditions in which they were gradually accustomed to more warmth and moisture, and found that the number of offspring produced at a birth increased from two to three and four, and, moreover, that these young were born at an earlier stage of their development even before their gills are absorbed, and that if these young ones are reared under these conditions of warmth and moisture they will produce even more than four young at a birth, and that these will be provided with gills and will take to the water. *S. atra*, that is, assumes the habits of *S. maculosa*, and these habits and their morphological and physiological basis are transmitted to posterity. This, of course, can be interpreted as a case of return to an ancestral racial habit in response to environmental conditions equivalent to those of the ancestors. To counter this objection Kammerer then subjected *S. maculosa* to conditions of increasing cold and dryness, and found that the young produced were fewer in number and were born in a more advanced stage of development. In three generations the young number three or four, and the gills of these were the merest stumps, and the gill clefts closed, they could take to the land at once. *S. maculosa* had assumed the habits of *S. atra*, and if *S. maculosa* has the ancestral habit of *S. atra*, those of *S. atra* cannot be those of the ancestral form of *S. maculosa*. But Kammerer is critical as to the significance of these results. He suspects that they may be the result of "parallel induction," that the external conditions applied (such as moisture) affected the germ-plasm in a "direct physical and not primarily physiological manner." As an instance of parallel induction the work of Gage (1908) may be quoted. He administered the aniline dye sudan III to fowls; the body-fat took up the stain, so did their eggs, and so did the chickens hatched therefrom.

Kammerer also experimented with the "midwife" toad, *Alytes obstetricans*, which differs from all other toads in that it pairs on land, and the male has no horny pad upon his hands, and also in that the eggs of the female are much larger and fewer than in other toads. As the eggs are laid, the male winds the egg-strings around his legs and carries them about with him for some weeks until the eggs are about to be hatched; he then goes to the water and the tadpoles with covered gills emerge, *i.e.*, the tadpoles are in a stage of development equal to that of well-grown tadpoles of other toads. Kammerer accustomed Alytes to warm, dry conditions, provided a water-tank, and found that the toads began to pair in the water, that the egg-strings became slippery and fell off the male's legs into the water. In sterile water some few of the eggs hatch out and the resulting tadpoles having attained the mature toad stage will readily pair in the water; also the eggs of the female are more like those of ordinary toads and the tadpoles which emerge from them show a much earlier stage of development, actually possessing external gills, though only one on each side as compared to the three of ordinary toad tadpoles. But if a third generation is raised under these conditions the tadpoles do have three pairs of external gills, and the males of this generation have horny thumb-pads. Kammerer has raised six and seven generations and found that the pad increased in size and definiteness up to the 5th generation, after which it remained stationary.

Kammerer himself does not regard his Alytes experiment as a critical one, however; he does not look upon the result as conclusive proof of the inheritance of acquired characters, since it is possible to interpret the pad as the result of parallel induction or even as an instance of the expression of a character conditioned by external stimuli. According to this latter view, Alytes possesses the factorial basis for pad-development, but the question as to whether the pad will or will not develop is decided by the kind of environmental stimuli which play upon the individual—

warmth encourages the toad to stay in the water, and this habit encourages the expression of the pad.

In one of the specimens exhibited in this country the "thumb-pad" was examined by Bateson (1923), who found that it was not at all like the pad of the ordinary toad, and moreover that it was situated in the wrong place. Bateson points out that the broad dark mark in this specimen ran across the palm of the hand, and that the rugosities to be effective must be on the backs and radial sides of the digits, round the base of the thumb, on the inner sides of the forearms, but not on the palms of the hands. Bateson maintains that until Kammerer's observations have been clearly demonstrated and confirmed they cannot be accepted as experimental proof of the inheritance of acquired characters. MacBride (1923), on the other hand, is satisfied that Kammerer's experimental results and interpretations are critically sound.

Environmental conditions can modify the development of inherited characters, of that there is no doubt. Experiments have demonstrated that such environmental factors as the kind of light, red or white or blue, for example; the temperature, the amount of moisture, and the kind of food, definitely *influence* the development of inherited characters. It is known that in such cases these agents actually *condition* the development of the inherited characters. For example, it is well known that the kind of food supplied to the larvæ of bees determine whether the females shall be fertile (queens) or infertile (workers). The striking differences in structure and instincts of the two classes of females are all conditioned by the food provided for the larva. Each larva inherited the capacity to react in either, according to the stimulus supplied. A characterisation may indeed entirely falsify the genotype. "Eyeless" in Drosophila is a case which illustrates this. Most individuals in a genetically homozygous eyeless stock have no eyes. As the stock gets older more and more flies that emerge have eyes, and after a time an increased number of flies have both eyes present and of nearly full size. However, when these are interbred they give the same results as do their eyeless relatives. The characterisation is subject to environmental changes but the variations are not transmitted. Reference to Johannsen's brilliant analysis in the course of his "pure-line" work of the non-inheritance of individual differences due to differences in the environment will show that whilst much individual variability is due to minor genetic factors and is inherited, much is due to environmental causes and is not inherited.

Not content with any of his previous material, Kammerer has chosen in his more recent experiments the Ascidian *Ciona intestinalis*. He cut off the two siphons and found that they grew again to become somewhat larger than before, and that repeated amputations resulted in very long tubes indeed. The offspring of such individuals had siphons longer than usual. In order to preclude the criticism that this was but another instance of parallel induction, Kammerer cut off the hinder end of the body in which the hermaphroditic sex-gland is situated at the same time as the siphons were amputated. Regeneration occurred and a new sex-gland was formed from somatic tissue, and the offspring of these individuals were longer siphoned than usual. Kammerer argues that as the new germ-plasm is developed from the soma in this case, and as the development of the new sex-gland occurs when the disturbance following the amputation of the siphons has ceased, the change in the germ-plasm can have come from nowhere but from the changed body. This experiment and its results are extremely suggestive, but it has to be recognised that the bionomics of the material are not thoroughly known. For critical results it is necessary to employ pedigree stock in which the ordinary range of variation in characterisation is known.

Munro Fox (1924) has repeated the Ciona experiments only to find that in none of the animals operated upon was there any further growth of the siphons after the original length had been reattained. He points out that it is an established fact that abnormally long siphons can be grown by keeping the animals in suspension of abundant food.

Pavlov (1923) has recently reported the results of certain

work which bear upon this question. Using mice he has studied the possibility of the effects of training in one generation being transmitted to the next. The food instinct is an inborn association between stimulations of the senses of smell and sight and certain movements and secretions. But another kind of stimulation which has no inborn relation with the food reaction may be interpolated in the instinct—for example, the mouse can be trained to associate feeding-time and food with a particular musical sound of a given rate of frequency of vibration per second. After a period of training this sound alone will produce the same reactions as did the sound plus food. Pavlov calls such artificially induced association as this "conditioned" instincts as opposed to the inborn unconditioned instincts. Pavlov trained white mice to run to their feeding-place when they heard an electric bell. Three hundred lessons were required to perfect this conditioned instinct. But their offspring required only 100 lessons, and the third generation only 30, and the fourth only 10, and the fifth only 5. If this is so, then soon a generation should be born that will run to the feeding-place on hearing the bell for the first time.

This is very suggestive, but more details are necessary before its exact value can be assessed. Possibly mice differ greatly among themselves in their responsiveness to any given stimulus; perhaps if a thousand mice were trained, one or two might learn their lesson after two lessons, one or two really dull ones after 2000 or more. Perhaps degrees of responsiveness are hereditary characters, and are transmitted so that mating of selected individuals would yield progeny which in this matter showed great advance upon the general level of the whole mouse community. The experiment should be repeated by a geneticist. Pavlov's conclusions are directly negatived by the results obtained by Vicari and MacDowell (1921), Bagg (1924). These three investgators working independently have secured no data that support the suggestions that the improvement based on training is inherited.

In the goldfish there are many extraordinary characterisations, many of them apparently pathological in nature and true-breeding. The cause of these mutations is hotly debated. Ryder (1893) holds to the opinion that they are due to disturbances during the early stages of development. It is a fact, however, that as yet similar abnormalities experimentally produced have not proved to be inherited, and it is difficult to understand how such treatment could influence the germ-cells in such a specific manner that the abnormality was perpetuated. Tornier, supported by MacBride (1924), concludes that the abnormalities are the inherited results of improper environment, such as lack of oxygen and food, which upsets the normal physiological balance of the individual. The more recent results of Hance (1924) do not support Tornier's conclusion that the goldfish supplies a good case for the inheritance of acquired characters, and the abnormalities are interpreted as mutations.

The work of Jollos, and of Sturtevant and Morgan (who have recently shown that in Drosophila mutation is, in the case of the reverse mutation bar to normal, associated with crossing-over at or about the locus of the gene which mutates) places the question of the inheritance of acquired character on another level altogether. The problem is now that of the experimental modification of the germ-plasm, and it is established that the germ-plasm can be so affected by agencies of a general noxious character so that the effects of such treatment are transmitted. It should be stated in conclusion that nothing would receive a greater welcome from every geneticist than a clear-cut demonstration of a specific acquisition being inherited intact. There is no prejudice against the possibility of the inheritance of an acquired character: but it is necessary to recognise that the "will to believe" in the inheritance of acquired characters is an understandable feature of human behaviour, and one that must be checked. It may be expected that soon means will have been devised by which specific alterations of the genotype may be produced experimentally. When this has been achieved the problem of the inheritance of acquired characters will take on a new complexion. The work of Mavor (1924) is of particular interest in this connection, for he has shown that treatment of the individual with X-rays definitely increases the proportion of non-disjunctional offspring, and that the linkage relation of two genes can be disturbed by the same agency. Refinement of technique may be expected to lead to more localised control of the chromosome mechanism, and ultimately, maybe, to specific mutation.

REFERENCES

For further information the following books should be read.

CHAPTER I.

BATESON, W. (1913) *Mendel's Principles of Heredity.* Camb. Univ. Press.

DARBISHIRE, A. D. (1911) *Breeding and the Mendelian Discovery.* Cassell.

DELAGE, Y., AND GOLDSMITH, M. (1912) *The Theories of Evolution.* Palmer.

OSBORN, H. F. (1913) *From the Greeks to Darwin.* Macmillan.

PUNNETT, R. C. (1911) *Mendelism.* Macmillan.

THOMSON, J. A. (1919) *Heredity.* John Murray.

CHAPTER II.

BABCOCK, E. B., AND CLAUSEN, R. E. (1918) *Genetics in Relation to Agriculture.* M'Graw Hill.

CASTLE, W. E. (1924) *Genetics and Eugenics.* Harvard Univ. Press.

CONKLIN, G. C. (1922) *Heredity and Environment.* Princeton Univ. Press.

PUNNETT, R. C. (1923) *Heredity in Poultry.* Macmillan.

Also the Series of Monographs on Inheritance in the Domesticated Animals, published in *Bibliographia Genetica.* Martinus Nijhoff.

CASTLE, W. E. (1925) *Heredity in Rabbits and Guinea-Pigs.* In Vol. 1.

ROBERTS, J. A. FRASER, AND CREW, F. A. E., (1925) *Genetics of the Sheep.* In Vol. 2.

CHAPTER III.

AGAR, W. E. (1920) *Cytology.* Macmillan.

COWDRY, E. V. (1924) *General Cytology.* Univ. Chicago Press.

DONCASTER, L. (1920) *An Introduction to the Study of Cytology.* Camb. Univ. Press.

WILSON, E. B. (1925) *The Cell in Development and Inheritance.* Macmillan.

CHAPTERS IV. AND V.

MORGAN, T. H. (1919) *The Physical Basis of Heredity.* Lippincott.

MORGAN, T. H. (1919) *A Critique of the Theory of Evolution.* Princeton Univ. Press.

MORGAN, T. H., STURTEVANT, A. H., MULLER, H. J., AND BRIDGES, C. B. (1923) *The Mechanism of Mendelian Heredity.* Henry Holt.

NEWMAN, H. H. (1921) *Readings in Evolution, Genetics and Eugenics.* Chicago Univ. Press.

CHAPTER VI.

DONCASTER, L. (1914) *The Determination of Sex.* Camb. Univ. Press.

GEDDES, P., AND THOMPSON, J. A. (1889) *The Evolution of Sex.* Walter Scott.

GOLDSCHMIDT, R. (1923) *The Mechanism and Physiology of Sex-Determination.* English translation by W. J. Dakin. Methuen.

MORGAN, T. H. (1914) *Heredity and Sex.* Columbia Univ. Press.

CHAPTER VII.

BELL, W. B. (1920) *The Sex-Complex.* Baillière, Tindall, and Cox.

CHAMPY, C. *Sexualité et Hormones.* Doin, Paris.

GOLDSCHMIDT, R. (1923) *The Mechanism and Physiology of Sex-Determination.* English edition. Methuen.

LIPSCHUTZ, A. (1924) *The Internal Secretions of the Sex-Glands.* Heffer.

MARSHALL, F. H. A. (1922) *The Physiology of Reproduction.* Longmans & Co.

MEISENHEIMER, I. (1922) *Geschlecht und Geschlechter im Tierreich.* Fischer, Jena.

CHAPTER IX.

EAST, E. M., AND JONES, D. F. (1919) *Inbreeding and Outbreeding: Their Genetic and Sociological Significance.* Lippincott.

CHAPTER X.

MARSHALL, F. H. A. (1922) *The Physiology of Reproduction.* Longmans & Co.

CHAPTER XII.

MACBRIDE, E. W. (1924) *An Introduction to the Study of Heredity.* The Home Univ. Library.

THOMSON, J. A. (1919) *Heredity.* John Murray.

BIBLIOGRAPHY

Abl. (1918) "Unfruchtbare Zwillinge beim Rinde," *Deut. landw. Tierz.*, No. 6.

Adametz, L. (1912) "Die Variationstypen der Karakulrassen," *Mitt. d. landwirt. Lehrkanz. f. Boden-Kultur.*, **1**, 57-90.

—— (1917) "Studien über die Mendelsche Vererbung der wichtigsten Rassenmerkmale der Karakulschafe bei Reinzucht und Kreuzung mit Rambouillet," *Biblioth. Genet.*, **1**, 1-258.

—— (1917) "Hereditary Transmission of the 'Curly Wool' character of Karakul Sheep in Crosses between the Karakul and Rambouillet Breeds," *Zeit. indukt. Abst.*, **17**, 161-202.

—— (1924) "Beobachtungen über die Vererbung morphologischer und physiologischer Merkmale und Eigenschaften bei Kreuzungen von rotscheckigen Ostfriesen mit Kuhländer-Rindern," *Zeit. Tierz. und Zuchtngb.*, **1**, 101-119.

Adler, L. (1916) "Untersuchungen über die Entstehung der Amphibienneotenie. Zugleich ein Beitrag zur Physiologie der Amphibienschilddrüse," *Pflüg. Arch.*, **164**, 1-101.

—— (1917) "Metamorphosenstudien an Batrachierlarven II. Der Einfluss überreifer Eier," *Arch. Entwickl.*, **43**, 343-361.

Agar, W. E. (1924) "Experiments with certain Plumage Colour and Pattern Factors in Poultry," *Jour. Genet.*, **14**, 265-272.

Agnoletti, G. (1920) "Increase in the Weight and Quantitative and Qualitative Changes in the Wool of Lambs having undergone the Operation of Unilateral Thyroidectomy with or without Castration," *La Clinica Veter.*, **43**, 245-269.

Aida, Tatua (1921) "On the Inheritance of Colour in a Fresh-water Fish, *Aplocheilus latipes* (Temmick and Schlegel), with special reference to Sex-linked Inheritance," *Genet.*, **6**, 554-573.

Allen, C. L. (1922) "Effect of Age of Sire and Dam on the Quality of Offspring in Dairy Cows," *Jour. Hered.*, **13**, 166-176.

Allen, Edgar (1923) "Racial and Familial Cyclic Inheritance and other evidence from the Mouse concerning the cause of Œstrous Phenomena," *Amer. Jour. Anat.*, **32**, 293-304.

Allen, Ezra (1918) "Studies on Cell Division in the Albino Rat. III. Spermatogenesis," *Jour. Morph.*, **31**, 133-186.

Allen, M. G. (1904) "The Heredity of Coat-Colour in Mice," *Proc. Amer. Acad. Arts and Sci.*, **40**, 61-163.

—— (1914) "Pattern Development in Mammals and Birds," *Amer. Nat.*, **48**, 385-412, 467-484, 550-566.

Altenburg, E., and **Müller, H. J.** (1920) "The Genetic Basis of Truncate Wing: An inconstant and modified character in Drosophila," *Genet.*, **5**, 1-59.

Ancel and **Bouin** (1904) (1) "Action générale de la glande interstitielle sur l'organisme." (2) "L'apparition des caractères sexuels secondaires est sous la dépendance de la glande interstitielle." (3) "L'infantilisme et la glande interstitielle du testicule." *C. R. Acad. Sci.*, **138**, 110, 168, 231.

Ancel, P., and **Vintemberger, P.** (1924) "L'acceptation du mâle et le rut chez la lapine," *C. R. Soc. Biol.*, **90**, 437-439.

Anderson, W. S. (1913) "Coat-Colour in Horses," *Amer. Nat.*, No. 562, **47**, 615-624.

—— (1914) "The Inheritance of Coat-Colour in Horses," *Kent. Agric. Exp. Sta. Bull.*, No. 180, 121-145.

—— (1914) "Coat-Colour in Horses," *Jour. Hered.*, **5**, 482-488.

—— (1921) "Progress in Horse Breeding," *Jour. Hered.*, **12**, 134-137.

—— (1922) "Sterility in Relation to Animal Breeding," *Kent. Sta. Bull.*, No. 244, 203-234.

Anthony, R. (1899) "Heredity in Manx Cat," *Bull. Soc. Anthrop.*, **10**, 303-310.

Arkell, T. R. (1911) "Breeding Experiments with Sheep," *Rpt. Amer. Breed. Ass.*, **7**, 256-260.

—— (1912) "Further Report on Inheritance of Horns and Wool Covering in Sheep," *Rpt. Amer. Breed. Ass.*, **8**, 361-368.

—— (1912) "Some Data on the Inheritance of Horns in Sheep," *New Hamp. Agric. Exp. Sta. Bull.* No. **16**, 3-35.

—— and **Davenport, C. B.** (1912) (1) "The Nature of the Inheritance of Horns in Sheep," *Sci.*, **35**, 927; (2) "Horns in Sheep as a Typical Sex-limited Character," *Sci.*, **35**, 375-377.

Assheton, R. (1910) "Variation and Mendel. Some observations on the Crossing of Wild Rabbits with Certain Tame Breeds," *Guy's Hospit. Rpt.*, **64**, 313-342.

Auld, R. C. (1889) "Some Cases of Solid-Hoofed Hogs and Two-toed Horses," *Amer. Nat.*, **23**, 447-449.

Bachhuber, L. J. (1916) "The Behaviour of the Accessory Chromosomes and of the Chromatoid Body in the Spermatogenesis of the Rabbit," *Biol. Bull.*, **30**, 294-310.

Bagg, H. J. (1922) "Disturbances in Mammalian Development produced by Radium Emanation," *Amer. Jour. Anat.*, **30**, 132-161.

—— and **Little, C. C.** (1888-1924) "Hereditary Structural Defects in the Descendants of Mice exposed to Röentgen-ray Irradiation," *Amer. Jour. Anat.*, **33**, 119-145.

Baltzer, F. (1910) "Über die Beziehung zwischen dem Chromatin und der Entwicklung und Vererbungsrichtung bei Echinodermenbastarden," *Arch. f. Zellf.*, **5**, 497-621.

—— (1914) "Die Bestimmung des Geschlechts nebst einer Analyse des Geschlechts-dimorphismus bei Bonellia," *Mitt. Zool. Stat. Neap.*, **22**.

—— (1914) "Die Bestimmung und der Dimorphismus des Geschlechts bei Bonellia," *Sitzb. Phys-med. Ges. Würzburg.*

Bamber, Ruth C. (1922) "The Male Tortoiseshell Cat," *Jour. Genet.*, **12**, 209-216.

Barfurth, D. (1908) "Experimentelle Untersuchungen über die Vererbung der Hyperdactylie bei Hühnern. I. Der Einfluss der Mutter," *Arch. Entwickl.*, **26**, 631-650.

—— (1909) "II. Der Einfluss des Vaters," *Arch. Entwickl.*, **27**, 653-661.

—— (1911) "III. Kontrollversuche und Versuche am Landhuhn," *Arch. Entwickl.*, **31**, 479-511.

Barfurth, D. (1911) "IV. Die Flügelhöcker des Hühnchens, eine rudimentäre Hyperdactylie," *Arch. Entwickl.*, **33**, 255-273.

—— (1914) "V. Weitere Ergebnisse und Versuch ihrer Deutung nach den Mendelschen Regeln," *Arch. Entwickl.*, **40**, 279-309.

Barrington, A., and **Pearson, K.** (1906) "On the Inheritance of Coat-Colour in Cattle. I. Shorthorn Crosses and Pure Shorthorns," *Biometrika*, **4**, 427-464.

—— **Lee, A.**, and **Pearson, Karl** (1905) "On the Inheritance of Coat-Colour in Greyhound," *Biometrika*, **3**, 245-298.

Barrows, W. M., and **Phillips, J. M'I.** (1915) "Colour in Cocker Spaniels," *Jour. Hered.*, **6**, 387-397.

Bartens, R. (1914) "Vererbungsstudien über Exterieurmerkmale im englischen Vollblutspferd," *Flugs. No.* 32, *Deut. Ges. f. Züchtngsk.*, 1-42.

Bartolucci, A. (1916) "The Guernsey Breed of Cattle in Italy," *Indust. latt. and zootecn.*, **14**, 68-69, 117-119.

Bascom, K. F. (1923) "The Interstitial Cells of the Gonads of Cattle, with Especial Reference to their Embryonic Development and Significance," *Amer. Jour. Anat.*, **31**, 223-259.

Bateson, W. (1894) *Materials for the Study of Variation, treated with Special Regard to Discontinuity in the Origin of Species.* Macmillan.

—— (1902) "Note on the Resolution of Compound Characters by Cross-Breeding," *Proc. Camb. Phil. Soc.*, **12**, 50-54.

—— (1903) "The Present State of Knowledge of Colour-Heredity in Mice and Rats," *Proc. Zool. Soc. Lond.*, **2**, 71-99.

—— (1914) "Address to the Zool. Sect."—Australia, Part I., Melbourne, 19 pp.; Part II., Sidney, 18 pp., *Rep. Brit. Ass. Advanc. Sci.*

—— (1916) *Problems of Genetics*, 2nd Edition, 1-258. New Haven.

—— (1919) "Linkage in Silk-Worm: A Correction," *Nature*, **104**, 315.

—— (1923) "Dr Kammerer's Alytes," *Nature*, **111**, 738-739.

—— and **Punnett, R. C.** (1905) "A Suggestion as to the Nature of the 'Walnut' Comb in Fowls," *Proc. Camb. Phil. Soc.*, **13**, 165-168.

—— —— (1908) "The Heredity of Sex," *Sci.*, **27**, 785-787.

—— —— (1911) "The Inheritance of the Peculiar Pigmentation of the Silky Fowl," *Jour. Genet.*, **1**, 185-203.

—— —— (1911) "On the Inter-relations of Genetic Factors," *Proc. Roy. Soc., B.*, **84**, 1-8.

—— and **Saunders, E. R.** (1902) "Reports to the Evolution Committee of the Royal Society. Report I.," *Roy. Soc.*, 1-160.

—— **Saunders, E. R.**, and **Punnett, R. C.** (1905) "Reports to the Evolution Committee of the Royal Society. Report II.," *Roy. Soc.*, 1-130.

—— **Saunders, E. R.**, and **Punnett, R. C.** (1906) "Reports to the Evolution Committee of the Royal Society. Report III.," *Roy. Soc.*, 1-38.

Baur, E., und Kronacher, C. (1919) "Gibt es konstante intermediäre Rassenbastarde in der Schafzucht?" *Deut. landw. Presse*, **46**, 713-714.

Beard, J. (1897) "Rhythm of Reproduction in Mammalia," *Anat. Anz.*, **14**, 97-102.

—— (1902) "The Determination of Sex in Animal Development," *Zool. Jahrb.*, **16**, 703-764.

—— (1904) "A Morphological Continuity of Germ-Cells as the Basis of Heredity and Variation," *Rev. Neurol. and Psychiat.*, **2**, 1-217.

Beddard, F. (1903) "Exhibition of a Hairless Specimen of the Common Rat," *Proc. Zool. Soc. Lond.*, **2**, 336.
Beer, de, G. R. (1924) "Note on a Hermaphrodite Trout," *Anat. Rec.*, **27**, 61-62.
Bell, A. Graham (1904) "The Multi-Nippled Sheep of Beinn Bhreagh, *Sci.*, **19**, 767-768.
—— (1912) "Sheep Breeding Experiments in Beinn Bhreagh," *Sci.*, **36**, 378-384.
—— (1914) "Fertility in the Sheep," *Jour. Hered.*, **5**, 47-57.
—— (1923) "Saving the Six-Nippled Breed," *Jour. Hered.*, **14**, 99-111.
Bellamy, A. W. (1923) "Sex-linked Inheritance in the Teleost, *Platypoccilus maculatus*" (Günth), *Anat. Rec.*, **24**, 419.
Belling, J. (1918) "Lethal Factors and Sterility," *Jour. Hered.*, **9**, 161-165.
Benoit, J. (1923) "Sur la structure histologique d'un organe de nature testiculaire developpée spontanément chez une poule ovariotomisée," *C. R. Acad. Sci.*, **177**, 1243-1246.
—— (1923) "A propos du changement expérimental de sexe par ovariotomie chez la poule," *C. R. Soc. Biol.*, **89**, 1326-1328.
—— (1924) "Sur la signification de la glande génitale rudimentaire droite chez la poule," *C. R. Acad. Sci.*, **178**, 341-344.
—— (1924) "Action de la castration sur le plumage chez le coq domestique," *C. R. Soc. Biol.*, **90**, 450-453.
—— (1924) "Sur un nouveau cas d'inversion sexuelle expérimentale chez la poule domestique," *C. R. Acad. Sci.*, **178**, 1640-1642.
Berner, O. (1923) "Virilisme surrénal chez une poule," *Rev. franç. d'endocr.*, **1**, 474-492.
Berthold (1849) "Transplantation der Hoden," *Arch. f. Anat. and Physiol.*, **42.**
Bidder, F. (1878) "Uber den Einfluss des Alters der Mutter auf das Geschlecht des Kindes," *Geburtsh. Gegn.*, **2.**
Bissonnette, T. H. (1924) "The Development of the Reproductive Ducts and Canals in the Free-Martin with comparison of the Normal," *Amer. Jour. Anat.*, **33**, 207-246.
Blaauw, T. E. (1920) "Experiments in Crossing Pea-Fowls," *Rev. d'hist. nat. appl.*, pt. 2, 46-48.
Blakeslee, A. F., and **Warner, D. E.** (1915) "Correlation between Egg-laying Activity and Yellow Pigment in the Domestic Fowl," *Amer. Nat.*, **49**, 360-368.
Blakeslee, A., **Harris, J.**, **Warner, D.**, and **Kirkpatrick, W.** (1917) "Pigmentation and other Criteria for the Selection of Laying Hens," *Bull.* No. 92, *Storrs Agric. Exp. Sta.*, 95-194.
Blanchard, N. (1903) "On Inheritance (Grandparent and Offspring) in Thoroughbred Racehorses," *Biometrika*, **2**, 229-233.
Blaringham, L., and **Prevot, A.** (1912) "Hybrides de Cobayes sauvages (Cavia Cutleri, C. aperia) et de Cobayes domestiques (C. cobaya)," *C. R. Acad. Sci.*, **155**, 1259.
Bluhm, A. (1921) "Uber einen Fall von experimenteller Verschiebung des Geschlechtsverhältnisses bei Säugetieren," *Sitzb. Preuss. Akad. Wiss.*, 549-556.
—— (1923) "Weitere Versuche zur Verschiebung des Geschlechtsverhältnisses bei Säugetieren," *Zeit. indukt. Abst.*, **30**, 307-308.
Blunck, H., and **Speyer, W.** (1924) "Kopftausch und Heilungsvermögen bei Insekten," *Zeit. wiss. Zool.*, **123**, 156-208.

Boas, J. (1917) "Zur Beurteilung der Polydaktylie des Pferdes," *Zool. Jahrb., Anat. Bd.*, No. 4, 49-104.

Boerner (1913) "Pfau × Perlhuhnkreuzungen," *Wild u. Hund.*, **19**, 297-298.

Bond, C. J. (1913-14) "On a Case of Unilateral Development of Secondary Male Characters in a Pheasant, with Remarks on the Influence of Hormones in the Production of Secondary Sex Characters," *Jour. Genet.*, **3**, 205-217.

—— (1913-14) "Some Points of Genetic Interest in Regeneration of the Testis after Experimental Orchectomy in Birds," *Jour. Genet.*, **3**, 131-140.

—— (1919) "On Certain Factors concerned in the Production of Eye-Colour in Birds," *Jour. Genet.*, **9**, 69-82.

—— (1920) "On the Left-sided Incidence of the Supernumerary Digit in Heterodactylous Fowl," *Jour. Genet.*, **10**, 87-91.

Bonhote, J. L. (1905) "Some Notes on the Hybridising of Ducks," *Proc. IV. Inter. Ornith. Cong.*, 235-264.

—— (1909) "On Hybrid Ducks," *Proc. Zool. Soc. Lond.*, 598-599.

—— (1911) "On the Inheritance of the Web-footed Character in the Pigeon," *Proc. Zool. Soc. Lond.*, 14-19.

—— (1912) "Waltzing Character in *Mus rattus*," *Proc. Zool. Soc. Lond.*, pt. 1, 6-7.

—— and **Smalley, F.** (1909) "On Colour and Colour Pattern Inheritance in Pigeons," *Proc. Zool. Soc. Lond.*, 601-619.

Bonnet, R. (1888) "Die stummelschwänzige Hunde, etc.," *Anat. Anz.*, **3**, 584-606.

Bonnier, Gert. (1924) "On Alleged Seasonal Variations of the Sex-Ratio in Man," *Zeit. indukt. Abst.*, **32**, 97-107.

Boring, A., and **Morgan, T. H.** (1918) "Lutear Cells and Hen-Feathering," *Jour. Gen. Physiol.*, **1**, 127-131.

—— and **Pearl, R.** (1914) "The Odd Chromosome in the Spermatogenesis of the Domestic Chick," *Jour. Exp. Zool.*, **16**, 53-84.

—— —— (1918) "Sex Studies. XI. Hermaphrodite Birds," *Jour. Exp. Zool.*, **25**, 1-48.

Boveri, Th. (1910) "Die Potenzen der Ascarisblastomeren bei abgeänderten Furchung, *Zeit. f. R. Hertwig*, **3**, 131-214.

Bouin and **Ancel** (1904-6) "Recherches sur le rôle de la glande interstitielle," *C. R. Acad. Sci.*, **137, 138, 142.**

Boyd, M. M. (1906) "Breeding of Polled Herefords," *Amer. Breed. Ass.*, **2.**

—— (1908) "Short Account of the Experiments of Crossing the American Bison with Domestic Cattle," *Amer. Breed. Ass.*, **4**, 324-331.

—— (1914) "Crossing Bison × Cattle (The Cattalo)," *Jour. Hered.*, **5**, 187-197.

Brandt, A. (1889) "Anatomisches und Allgemeines über die sogenannte Hahnenfedrigkeit bei Vögeln," *Zeit. wiss. Zool.*, **48**, 101-190.

Brentana, D. (1914) "Peacock × Guineafowl Hybrids," *Il Moder. Zooi.*, ser. 5, yr. 3, 1001-1009.

Bridges, C. B. (1913) "Partial Sex-linkage in the Pigeon," *Sci.*, **37**, 112-113.

—— (1915) "A Linkage Variation in Drosophila," *Jour. Exp. Zool.*, **19**, 1-21.

—— (1916) "Non-disjunction as Proof of the Chromosome Theory of Heredity," *Genet.*, **1**, 1-163.

—— (1917) "An Intrinsic Difficulty for the Variable Force Hypothesis of Crossing-Over," *Amer. Nat.*, **51**, 370-373.

—— (1917) "Deficiency," *Genet.*, **2**, 445-465.

Bridges, C. B. (1918) "Maroon: A Recurrent Mutation in Drosophila," *Proc. Nat. Acad. Sci.*, **4**, 316-318.

—— (1919) "The Developmental Stages at which Mutation occurs in the Germ Tract," *Proc. Soc. Exp. Med.*, **17**, 1-2.

—— (1921) "Triploid Intersexes in *Drosophila melanogaster*," *Sci.*, **54**, 252-254.

—— (1921) "Genetical and Cytological Proof of Non-disjunction of the IV Chromosome of *Drosophila melanogaster*," *Proc. Nat. Acad. Sci.*, **7**, 186-192.

Broca, P. (1859) "Sur les principaux hybrides du genre *Equus*, sur l'hérédité des caractères chez les metis, et sur la fécondité des mules," *Jour. de Physiol.*, **2**, 250-258.

—— (1859) "Résumé des faits relatifs aux croisements des chiens, des loups, des chacals, et des renards," *Jour. de Physiol.*, **2**, 390-396.

Broomhead, W. W. (1913) "Truthahn × Huhn," *Geflüg. Welt.*, **5**, 300.

Brown, Ed. (1916) "Fecundity of Hens and its Relation to Size of Egg," *Jour. Board. Agric.*, **22**, 230-233.

Brown-Séquard (1889) "Du rôle physiologique et therapeutique d'un suc extrait de testicule," *Arch. de physiol.*, ser. 5, **1**, 739-746.

Bruce, R. (1908) "Interesting Facts on Colour Inheritance in Shorthorn Cattle," *Breed. Gaz.*, **54**, 113.

Bullock, W. E. (1915) "Heterologous Transplantation: Mouse Tumours in Rats," *Lancet*, 1-10.

Burch, D. S. (1921) "Pure Bred Sires lead rapidly to Improvement in Female Stock: Current Results in Federal State Campaign for Better Bred Livestock Furnish Striking Facts about Breeding," *Jour. Hered.*, **12**, 45-48.

Bush-Brown, H. K. (1911) "Horses and Horse Breeding," *Amer. Breed. Mag.* **2**, 85-97, 175-188; (1913) *ibid.*, **4**, 21-27.

—— (1920) "Heredity in Horses," *Jour. Hered.*, **11**, 215-227.

Bush, J. W. (1919) "A Supposed Sheep × Goat Hybrid," *Jour. Hered.*, **10**, 357.

Camden (1911) "Lincoln-Romney Cross-Breeding in New Zealand," *Pasturalist's Rev.*, **21**, 1000.

Camek, J. (1920) "Investigations on the Hair of Different Breeds of Cattle," *Jour. Agric. Sci.*, **10**, 12-21.

Cameron, J. (1924) "Colours in Shorthorns," *Shorth. Breed. Guide*, 42.

Campbell, M. H. (1924) "Inheritance of Black and Red Coat-Colours in Cattle," *Genet.*, **9**, 419-441.

Carothers, E. E. (1913) "Mendelian Ratio in Relation to certain Orthopteran Chromosomes," *Jour. Morph.*, **24**, 447-506.

—— (1917) "Segregation and Recombination of Homologous Chromosomes as found in two Genera of Cicrididæ (Orthoptera)," *Jour. Morph.*, **28**, 445-493.

—— (1921) "Genetical Behaviour of Heteromorphic Homologous Chromosomes of Circotettix (Orthoptera)," *Jour. Morph.*, **35**, 457-484.

Carrol, W. E. (1917) "Selecting Dairy Bulls by Performance," *Utah Agric. Exp. Sta.* (Bull. No. 153).

Carr-Saunders, A. M. (1922) "Note on Inheritance in Swine," *Sci.*, **55**, 19.

Castle, W. E. (1903) "The Heredity of 'Angora' Coat in Mammals," *Sci.*, **18**, 760-761.

—— (1905) "Heredity of Coat Characters in Guinea-pigs and Rabbits," *Carn. Inst. Publ.*, No. 23, 1-78.

Castle, W. E. (1906) "The Origin of Polydactylous Race of Guinea-pigs," *Carn. Inst. Publ.*, No. 49, 15-29.
—— (1906) "Yellow Mice and Gametic Purity," *Sci.*, **24**, 275-281.
—— (1907) "On a Case of Reversion induced by Cross-Breeding and its Fixation," *Sci.*, **25**, 151-153.
—— (1907) "Colour Varieties of the Rabbit and of other Rodents: Their Origin and Inheritance," *Sci.*, **26**, 287-291.
—— (1908) "A New Colour Variety of the Guinea-pig," *Sci.*, **28**, 250-252.
—— (1909) "Studies of Inheritance in Rabbits," *Carn. Inst. Publ.*, No. 114, 1-68.
—— (1911) *Heredity in Relation to Evolution and Animal Breeding.* Appleton.
—— (1912) "On the Origin of Pink-eyed Guinea-pig with Coloured Coat," *Sci.*, **35**, 508-510.
—— (1912) "On the Origin of an Albino Race of Deer-Mouse," *Sci.*, **35**, 346-348.
—— (1912) "On the Inheritance of Tri-coloured Coat in Guinea-pig and its Relation to Galton's Law of Ancestral Heredity," *Amer. Nat.*, **46**, 437-440.
—— (1912) "Are Horns in Sheep a Sex-limited Character?" *Sci.*, **35**, 574-575.
—— (1913) "Reversion in Guinea-pig and its Explanation," *Carn. Inst. Publ.*, No. 179, 1-10.
—— (1914) "Some New Varieties of Rats and Guinea-pigs and their Relation to Problems of Colour Inheritance," *Amer. Nat.*, **48**, 65-73.
—— (1914) "Yellow Varieties of Rats," *Amer. Nat.*, **48**, 254.
—— (1915) "Mr Müller on the Constancy of Mendelian Factors," *Amer. Nat.*, **49**, 37-42.
—— (1916) "Size Inheritance in Guinea-pig Crosses," *Proc. Nat. Acad. Sci.*, **2**, 252-264.
—— (1919) "Inheritance of Quantity and Quality of Milk Production in Dairy Cows," *Proc. Nat. Acad. Sci.*, **5**, 428-434.
—— (1919) "Piebald Rats and Selection: A Correction," *Amer. Nat.*, **53**, 370-376.
—— (1919) "Siamese: An Albinistic Colour Variation in Cats," *Amer. Nat.*, **53**, 265-268.
—— (1919) "Studies of Heredity in Rabbits, Rats, and Mice," *Carn. Instit. Publ.*, No. 288, 1-56.
—— (1920) "Genetics of the Dutch Rabbit: A Reply," *Jour. Genet.*, **10**, 293-299.
—— (1921) "More Linked Genes in Rabbits," *Sci.*, **54**, 634-636.
—— (1921) "Genetics of the 'Chinchilla' Rabbit," *Sci.*, **53**, 387.
—— (1922) "Genetic Studies of Rabbits and Rats," *Carn. Instit. Publ.*, No. 320. 1-55.
—— (1922) "Genetics of the Vienna White Rabbit," *Sci.*, **55**, 269-270, 429-430.
—— (1924) "Linkage of Dutch, English, and Angora in Rabbits," *Proc. Nat. Acad. Sci.*, **10**, 107-108.
—— (1924) "Some Varieties of White Rabbits," *Jour. Hered.*, **15**, 211-219.
—— (1924) "Genetics of the Multi-Nippled Sheep," *Jour. Hered.*, **15**, 75-85.
—— (1924) "Genetics of the Japanese Rabbit," *Jour. Genet.*, **14**, 225-230.
—— and **Fish, H. D.** (1915) "The Black-and-Tan Rabbit and the Significance of Multiple Allelomorphs," *Amer. Nat.*, **49**, 88-96.
—— and **Forbes, A.** (1906) "Heredity of Hair-length in Guinea-pigs and its Bearing on the Theory of Pure Gametes," *Carn. Inst. Publ.*, No. 49, 1-14.

Castle, W. E., and **Hadley, P. B.** (1915) "The English Rabbit and the Question of Mendelian Unit-Character Constancy," *Amer. Nat.*, **49**, 23-27.

—— and **Little, C. C.** (1909) "The Peculiar Inheritance of Pink Eyes among Coloured Mice," *Sci.*, **30**, 313-314.

—— —— (1910) "On a Modified Mendelian Ratio among Yellow Mice," *Sci.*, **32**, 868-870.

—— and **Phillips, J. C.** (1911) "On Germinal Transplantation in Vertebrates," *Carn. Inst. Publ.*, No. 144, 1-26.

—— —— (1913) "Further Experiments on Ovarian Transplantation in Guinea-pigs," *Sci.*, **38**, 783-786.

—— —— (1914) "Piebald Rats and Selection: [An experimental test of the effectiveness of Selection and the Theory of Gametic Purity in Mendelian Crosses]," *Carn. Inst. Publ.*, No. 195, 1-54.

—— and **Wachter, W. L.** (1921) "Genetics of Hereford Cattle," *Jour. Hered.*, **12**, 37-39.

—— —— (1924) "Variations of Linkage in Rats and Mice," *Genet.*, **9**, 1-12.

—— and **Wright, S.** (1915) "Two Colour Mutations of Rats which show Partial Coupling," *Sci.*, **42**, 193-195.

—— —— (1916) "Studies of Inheritance in Guinea-pigs and Rats," *Carn. Inst. Publ.*, No. 241, 1-192.

—— and **Others** (1906) "The Effects of In-Breeding, Cross-Breeding, and Selection upon the Fertility and Variability of Drosophila," *Proc. Amer. Acad. Arts and Sci.*, **41**, 729-786.

—— (with **H. E. Walter, R. C. Mulleny**, and **S. Cobb**) (1909) "Studies on Inheritance in Rabbits," *Carn. Inst. Publ.*, No. 114, 1-68.

Champy, C. (1921) "Changement expérimental du sexe chez le *Triton alpestri Laur.*, *C. R. Acad. Sci.*, **172**, 1204-1207.

Chapeaurouge, de A. (1912) "Die Sage von der Galloway Kuh und deren tatsächliche Stellung zur Shorthorn Zucht," *Flugsschr.* No. 20, *Deut. Ges. Züchtngsk.*, 1-32.

Chappelier, A. (1911) "La ponte et l'œuf chez les hybrides provenant du croisement: canard de ferme ♂ et canard de Barbarie ♀," *Rapp. IV. Conf. Génét.*, 503-506.

Charon, A., Oinene, G., and **Yoneno, G.** (1921) "The Rejuvenescene of Animals: Experiments on Old Fowls and Doe Rabbits," *Jour. d'Agric. prat.*, **55**, 454-457.

Christie, W. and **Wriedt, Ch.** (1923) "Die Vererbung von Zeichnungen, Farben und anderen Charakteren bei Tauben," *Zeit. indukt. Abst.*, **32**, 233-298.

Cirencester Royal Agricultural College (1910) "Fecundity in Sheep," Sci. Bull. No. 2.

Clark, L. N. (1915) "The Effect of Pituitary Substance on the Egg Production of the Domestic Fowl," *Jour. Biol. Chem.*, **22**, 485-491.

Clarke, Wm. Eagle (1898) "On Hybrids between the Capercaillie and the Pheasant," *Ann. Scot. Nat. Hist.*, 17-21.

Cockayne, E. A. (1915) "Gynandromorphism and Kindred Problems," *Jour. Genet.*, **5**, 75-131.

Cole, Leon J. (1912) "A Case of Sex-linked Inheritance in the Domestic Pigeon," *Sci.*, **36**, 190-192.

—— (1914) "Studies on Inheritance in Pigeons. I. Hereditary Relations of the Principal Colours," *R. I. Agric. Exp. Sta.* (Bull. No. 158), 312-380.

Cole, Leon J. (1919) "A Defect of Hair and Teeth in Cattle probably hereditary," *Jour. Hered.*, **10**, 303-306.

— (1920) "Inheritance of Milk and Meat Production in Cattle," *Wisc. Agric. Exp. Sta.* (Bull. No. 319), 53-54.

— (1922) "Chantecler Poultry: A New Breed," *Jour. Hered.*, **13**, 147-152.

— and **Bachhuber, L. J.** (1914) "The Effect of Lead on the Germ-Cells of the Male Rabbit and Fowl as indicated in their Progeny," *Proc. Soc. Exp. Biol. Med.*, **12**, 24-29.

— and **Davis, C. L.** (1914) "The Effect of Alcohol on the Male Germ-Cells, studied by means of Double Mating," *Sci.*, **39**, 476-477.

— and **Jones, Sarah** (1920) "The Occurrence of Red Calves in Black Breeds of Cattle," *Wisc. Agric. Exp. Sta.* (Bull. No. 313), 1-35.

— and **Kelley, F. J.** (1919) "Studies on Inheritance in Pigeons. III. Description and Linkage Relations of Two Sex-linked Characters," *Genet.*, **4**, 183-203.

— and **Kirkpatrick, W. F.** (1915) "Sex Ratios in Pigeons, together with Observations on the Laying, Incubation and Hatching of the Eggs," *R. I. Agric. Exp. Sta.* (Bull. No. 162), 463-512.

— and **Lippincott, W. A.** (1919) "The Relation of Plumage to Ovarian Condition in a Barred Plymouth Rock Pullet," *Biol. Bull.*, **36**, 167-182.

— and **Steele, D. G.** (1922) "A Waltzing Rabbit," *Jour. Hered.*, **13**, 291-294.

Collins, H. H. (1923) "Variations in Coat-Colour within a Single Sub-Species of Mice of the Genus *Peromyscus*," *Anat. Rec.*, **24**, 379-380.

Conrow, Sara B. (1915) "Taillessness in the Rat," *Anat. Rec.*, **9**, 783.

— (1917) "Further Observations on Taillessness in the Rat," *Anat. Rec.*, **12**, 155-159.

Conte, A. (1909) "Une variation brusque: les poules à cou nu," *C. R. Soc. Biol.*, **66**, 255-257.

Coombs, R. D. (1917) "Bull Terrier Breeding," *Jour. Hered.*, **8**, 314-319.

Copeman, S. M., and **Parsons, F. G.** (1904) "Observations on the Sex of Mice," Preliminary Paper, *Proc. Roy. Soc. B.*, **73**, 32-48.

Corner, George W. (1923) "The Problem of Embryonic Pathology in Mammals, with Observations upon Intra-uterine Mortality in the Pig," *Amer. Jour. Anat.*, **31**, 523-545.

Correns, C. (1900) "G. Mendel's Regel über der Verhalten der Nachkommenschaft der Rassenbastarde," *Ber. Deut. Bot. Ges.*, **17**, 158-168.

Cousins, H. H. (1912) "Jerseys at the Hope Stock Farm: Crossing with Zebus," *Bull. Dept. Agric. Jamaica*, **2**, 42-49.

Crampe (1883) "Zucht-Versuche mit zahmen Wanderratten: Resultate der Zucht in Verwandschaft," *Landw. Jahrb.*, **12**, 389.

— (1884) "Zucht-Versuche mit zahmen Wanderratten: Resultate der Kreuzung der zahmen Ratten mit wilden," *Landw. Jahrb.*, **13**, 699.

Crew, F. A. E. (1921) "A Description of certain Abnormalities of the Reproductive System found in Frogs, and a Suggestion as to their Possible Significance," *Proc. Roy. Phys. Soc. Edin.*, **20**, 236-252.

— (1921) "Sex-Reversal in Frogs and Toads: A Review of the Recorded Cases of Abnormality of the Reproductive System with an Account of a Breeding Experiment," *Jour. Genet.*, **11**, 141-181.

— (1921) "On the Fleeces of Certain Primitive Species of Sheep," *Ann. Appl. Biol.*, **8**, 164-169.

Crew, F. A. E. (1921) "The Cause of the Aspermatic Condition of the Undescended Testis." (Thesis, Edinburgh Univ.)
—— (1922) "A Histological Study of the Undescended Testicle of the Horse," *Jour. Comp. Path.*, **35**, 62-69.
—— (1922) "A Suggestion as to the Cause of the Aspermatic Condition of the Imperfectly Descended Testis," *Jour. Anat.*, **61**, 98-106.
—— (1922) "Ovarian Disease and the Secondary Sexual Characters in the Domestic Hen," *Veter. Jour.*, 62-68.
—— (1922) "The Fertility of Twins and the Free-Martin in Cattle," *Scot. Jour. Agric.*, **5**, 204-209.
—— (1922) "A Case of Developmental Intersexuality in *Bos domesticus*," *Veter. Jour.*, 178-184.
—— (1922) "A Black Leghorn which Turned White," *Jour. Hered.*, **13**, 299-303.
—— (1923) "Genetics and Stock-Breeding," *Scot. Jour. Agric.*, **6**, 341-344.
—— (1923) "Three Cases of Developmental Intersexuality in the Pig," *Veter. Jour.*, 306-311.
—— (1923) "Studies in Intersexuality. I. A Peculiar Type of Developmental Intersexuality in the Male of Domesticated Mammals," *Proc. Roy. Soc. B.*, **95**, 90-109. II. "Sex-Reversal in the Fowl," *Proc. Roy. Soc. B.*, **95**, 256-278.
—— (1923) "The Significance of an Achondroplasia-like Condition met with in Cattle," *Proc. Roy. Soc. B.*, **95**, 228-255.
—— (1923) "The Cocky-Feathered Hen," *Nat. Poult. Jour.*, 579-580.
—— (1924) "Hermaphroditism in the Pig," *Jour. Obstet. and Gynæc.*, **31**, 369-386.
—— (1924) "The Sex-Ratio and the Question of its Control," *Inter. Rev. Agric.*, **2**, 554-570.
—— (1924) "Blue and White Colour in Swine," *Jour. Hered.*, **15**, 395-396.
—— and **Dighton, Adair** (1923) "Developmental Intersexuality in the Domesticated Goat," *Veter. Jour.*, 135-139.
—— and **Panikkar, M. R. V.** (1922) "A Description of the Abnormal Reproductive System of a Pig," *Veter. Jour.*, 95-100.
—— —— (1922) "A Description of a Cryptorchid Goat with Abnormal Genitalia," *Veter. Jour.*, 133-139.
Cuénot, L. (1899) "Détermination du sexe chez les animaux," *Bull. Sci. de France Belg.*, **32**, 462-535.
—— (1902) "La loi de Mendel et l'hérédité de pigmentation chez les souris," 1re note, *Arch. de Zool. Exp. et Gén.*, **3**, 27.
—— (1903-1904) (*a*) "L'hérédité de la pigmentation chez les souris," 2me note, *Arch. de Zool. Exp. et Gén.*, **1**, 33-41; (*b*) *Ibid.*, 3me note, *Arch. de Zool. Exp. et Gén.*, **2**, 45-56.
—— (1904) "Un paradoxe héréditaire chez les souris," *Réun. Biol. de Nancy*, 1050-1052.
—— (1905) "Les races pures et leurs combinaison chez les souris, 4me note, *Arch. de Zool. Exp. et Gén.*, **3**, 124-132.
—— (1907) "L'hérédité de la pigmentation chez les souris," 5me note, *Arch. de Zool. Exp. et Gén.*, **6**, 1-13.
—— (1911) "La loi de Mendel et l'hérédité de pigmentation chez les souris," 7me note. "Les determinants de la couleur chez les souris," *Arch. de Zool. Exp. et Gén.*, **8**, 40-56.
—— (1911) "L'hérédité chez les souris," *Verh. naturf. Ver.*, **49**, 214-223.

Cunningham, J. T. (1892) "The Evolution of Flat-Fishes," *Nat. Sci.*, **1**, 191-199.
—— (1895) "The Evolution of Flat-Fishes," *Nat. Sci.*, **6**, 169-177, 233-239.
—— (1903) "Observations and Experiments on Japanese Long-Tailed Fowl," *Proc. Zool. Soc. Lond.*, **1**, 227-250.
—— (1912) "Mendelian Experiments on Fowls," *Proc. Zool. Soc. Lond.*, **16**, 241-259.
—— (1919) "Results of a Mendelian Experiment on Fowls, including the Production of a Pile Breed," *Proc. Zool. Soc. Lond.*, 173-202.
—— and **McMunn, C. A.** (1893) "On the Coloration of the Skins of Fishes, especially of *Pleuronectidæ*," *Phil. Trans. Roy. Soc.*, **184**, 765-812.
Cutler, D. W. (1918) "On the Sterility of Hybrids between the Pheasant and the Gold Campine Fowl," *Jour. Genet.*, **7**, 155-165.
—— and **Doncaster, L.** (1915) "On the Sterility of the Tortoiseshell Tom Cat," *Jour. Genet.*, **5**, 65-74.

Damme, van C. (1911) "Notes on the Mule-Breeding Industry in Poitou," *Bull. Agric. du Congo Belge*, **2**, 197-202.
Danforth, C. H. (1919) "An Hereditary Complex in the Domestic Fowl," *Genet.*, **4**, 587-596.
Darbishire, A. D. (1902-1903) (*a*) "Note on the Results of Crossing Japanese Waltzing Mice with European Albino Races," 101-104; (*b*) 2nd Report, 165-174; (*c*) 3rd Report, 282-285.—*Biometrika*, **2**.
—— (1913) "Mendelism," *Trans. High. and Agric. Soc. Scotl.*, **25**, 145-159.
Darwin, Charles (1868) *The Variation of Animals and Plants under Domestication.* John Murray.
—— (1910) *The Origin of Species by Means of Natural Selection.* John Murray.
Davenport, C. B. (1900) "Review of von Guaita's Experiments in Breeding Mice," *Biol. Bull.*, **2**, 121-128.
—— (1904) "Colour Inheritance in Mice," *Sci.*, **19**, 110-114.
—— (1905) "The Origin of Black Sheep in the Flock," *Sci.*, **22**, 674-675.
—— (1906) "Inheritance in Poultry," *Carn. Inst. Publ.*, No. 52.
—— (1907) "Dominance of Characteristics in Poultry," *Roy. Hort. Soc. Rep. of Confer. on Genet.*, 1-2.
—— (1908) "Inheritance in Canaries," *Carn. Instit. Publ.*, No. 95, 1-26.
—— (1909) "Inheritance of Characteristics in Domestic Fowl," *Carn. Inst. Publ.*, No. 121, 1-100.
—— (1910) "The New Views about Reversion," *Proc. Amer. Phil. Soc.*, **49**, 291-296.
—— (1910) "Inheritance of Plumage Colour in Poultry," *Proc. Soc. Exp. Biol. and Med.*, **7**, 168.
—— (1911) "Another Case of Sex-limited Heredity in Poultry," *Proc. Soc. Exp. Biol. and Med.*, **9**, 1-2.
—— (1912) "Sex-limited Inheritance in Poultry," *Jour. Exp. Zool.*, **13**, 1-18.
—— (1914) "The Bare-Necks," *Jour. Hered.*, **5**, 374.
—— (1916) "Heredity of Albinism," *Jour. Hered.*, **7**, 221-223.
—— (1913) "Caprine Free-Martins," *Veter. Jour.*, 62-70.
Davies, C. J. (1912) "Heredity in Goats," *Mendel. Jour.*, Sept.
—— (1913) "Pigments carried by Cattle," *Live Stock Jour.*, 62, 85-86.
Davies, H. P. (1920) "Were the Black-and-White Holsteins originally Red-and-White?" *Jour. Hered.*, **11**, 155.

Dawson, R. (1923) *The Causation of Sex in Man* (3rd edition). H. K. Lewis.

Dechambre, P. (1914) "Short-Faced Abyssinian Mules," *Bull. Soc. Nat. d'Acclimat.*, **61**, 129-132.

Dendy, Arthur (1909) "On the Principles of Heredity as Applied to the Production of New Forms of Plants and Animals," *Jour. Roy. Soc. Arts.*, **57**, 525-534.

Detlefsen, J. A. (1912) "The Fertility of Hybrids in a Mammalian Species Cross," *Amer. Breed. Magaz.*, **3**, 261-265.

—— (1914) "Genetic Studies on a Cavy Species Cross," *Carn. Inst. Publ.*, No. 205, 1-134.

—— (1916) "Pink-Eyed White Mice carrying the Colour Factor," *Amer. Nat.*, **50**, 46-49.

—— (1920) "A Herd of Albino Cattle in Minnesota, U.S.A.," *Jour. Hered.*, **11**, 378.

—— (1921) "A New Mutation in the House Mouse," *Amer. Nat.*, **55**, 468-473.

—— (1923) "A Lethal Type in Mice, which may live a few days after Birth," *Anat. Rec.*, **24**, 417.

—— (1923) "Linkage of Dilute Colour and Dark Eye in Mice," *Anat. Rec.*, **26**, 396.

—— and **Carmichael, W. J.** (1921) "Inheritance of Syndactylism, Black and Dilution in Swine," *Jour. Agric. Res.*, **20**, 595-604.

—— and **Clements, L. S.** (1924) "Linkage of a Dilute Colour Factor and Dark-Eye in Mice," *Genet.*, **9**, 247-260.

—— and **Roberts, E.** (1918) "On a Black Cross in Mice involving Three Allelomorphic Pairs of Characters," *Genet.*, **3**, 573-598.

—— —— (1919) "Linkage of Genetic Factors in Mice," *Anat. Rec.* **17**, 338.

—— —— (1921) "Studies on Crossing-Over. I. The Effect of Selection on Cross-Over Values," *Jour. Exp. Zool.*, **32**, 333-354.

—— and **Yapp, W. W.** (1920) "Congenital Cataract in Cattle," **56**, 277-280.

Devauchelle, I. (1919) "Observations on the Formation of Sex in Bees," *L'Apiculture*, **63**, 285-288.

Dighton, Adair (1922) "The Sex Ratio," *The Sport. Chron.* (Sept. 23rd).

—— (1923) "Coat-Colour in Greyhounds," *Proc. Zool. Soc. Lond.*, 1-9.

Döderlein, L. (1887) "Ueber schwanzlose Katzen," *Zool. Anz.*, **10**, 606-608.

Doncaster, L. (1904) "On the Inheritance of Tortoiseshell and Related Colours in Cats," *Proc. Camb. Phil. Soc.*, **13**, 35-38.

—— (1905) "The Inheritance of Coat-Colour in Rats," *Proc. Camb. Phil. Soc.*, **13**, 2815-22.

—— (1907) "Inheritance and Sex in *Abraxas grossulariata*," *Nature*, **76**, 248.

—— (1908) "Sex-Inheritance in the Moth *Abraxas grossulariata* and its Variation *Lacticolor*," *Roy. Soc.*, *4th Rpt. Evol. Com.*, 53-57.

—— (1912) "Notes on Inheritance of Colour and other Characters in Pigeons," *Jour. Genet.*, **2**, 89-98.

—— (1912) "Sex-limited Inheritance in Cats," *Sci.*, **36**, 144.

—— (1913) "A Possible Connexion between Abnormal Sex-limited Transmission and Sterility," *Proc. Camb. Phil. Soc.*, **17**, 307-309.

—— (1913) "On Sex-limited Inheritance in Cats, and its Bearing on the Sex-limited Transmission of Certain Human Abnormalities," *Jour. Genet.*, **3**, 11-23.

—— (1913) "On an Inherited Tendency to Produce Purely Female Families in *Abraxas grossulariata*, and its Relation to an Abnormal Chromosome Number," *Jour. Genet.*, **3**, 1-10.

Doncaster, L. (1914) "Chromosomes, Heredity and Sex: A Review of the Present State of the Evidence with Regard to the Material Basis of Hereditary Transmission and Sex-Determination," *Q. J. M. S.*, **59**, 487-521.

—— (1914) "On the Relations between Chromosomes, Sex-limited Transmission and Sex-Determination in *Abraxas grossulariata*," *Jour. Genet.*, **4**, 1-21.

—— (1915-17) "Gametogenesis and Sex-Determination in the Gall-Fly, *Neuroterus lenticularis*," *Proc. Roy. Soc. B.*, **89**, 183-198.

—— (1920) "The Tortoiseshell Tomcat—A Suggestion," *Jour. Genet.*, **9**, 335-337.

—— and **Marshall, F. H. A.** (1910) "The Effects of One-sided Ovariotomy in the Sex of the Offspring," *Jour. Genet.*, **1**, 70-72.

—— and **Raynor, G. H.** (1904) "Note on Experiments on Heredity and Sex-Determination in *Abraxas grossulariata*," Section D., *Brit. Ass. Advanc. Sci.*

—— —— (1906) "On Breeding Experiments with Lepidoptera," *Proc. Zool. Soc. Lond.*, **1**, 125-133.

Douville (1912) "Surdite congénitale et albinisme partiel chez le chien," *Rec. méd. vétér.*, **89**, 391-399.

Drinkwater, H. (1922) "The Inheritance of Acquired Characters and of Maternal Impressions," *B. M. J.*, pt. 1, 167.

Dry, F. W. (1924) "The Genetics of the Wensleydale Breed of Sheep. I. The Occurrence of Black Lambs," *Jour. Genet.*, **14**, 203-218.

Duck, Russell W. (1921) "Mendelism in Fur Sheep Crosses," *Jour. Hered.*, **12**, 410-413.

—— (1922) "Mendelism in Fur Sheep Crosses. II. The Zygotic Cause of Red Lambs when Fur Sheep are Crossed on Longwools or their Grade Offspring," *Jour. Hered.*, **13**, 63-68.

—— (1923) "Colour of Shorthorn Cattle," *Jour. Hered.*, **14**, 65-75.

Duerden, J. E. (1918) "Absence of Xenia in Ostrich Eggs," *Jour. Hered.*, **9**, 243-245.

—— (1919) "Crossing the North African and South African Ostrich," *Jour. Genet.*, **8**, 155-194.

—— (1920) "Inheritance of Callosities in the Ostrich," *Amer. Nat.*, **54**, 289-312.

—— (1922) "The Origin of Feathers from the Scales of Reptiles," *S. Afric. Jour. Sci.*, **19**, 263-268.

—— and **Essex, R.** (1922) "Degeneration in the Limbs of South African Serpentiform Lizards (Chamæsaura)," *S. Afric. Jour. Sci.*, **19**, 269-275.

Duncker, H. (1923) "Die Erblichkeit der Scheitelhauben bei Kanarienvögeln," *Jour. f. Ornith.*, **73**, 421-450.

—— (1924) "Einige Beobachtungen über die Vererbung der weissen Farbe bei Kanarienvögeln," *Zeit. indukt. Abst.*, **32**, 363-376.

Dunn, L. C. (1916) "The Genetic Behaviour of Mice of the Colour Varieties 'Black-and-Tan' and 'Red,'" *Amer. Nat.*, **50**, 664-675.

—— (1919) "Anomalous Ratios in a Family of Yellow Mice suggesting Linkage between the Genes for Yellow and for Black," *Amer. Nat.*, **53**, 558-560.

—— (1920) "Independent Genes in Mice," *Genet.*, **5**, 344-361.

—— (1920) "The Sable Variety of Mice," *Amer. Nat.*, **54**, 247-261.

—— (1920) "Types of White Spotting in Mice," *Amer. Nat.*, **54**, 465-495.

—— (1920) "Linkage in Mice and Rats," *Genet.*, **5**, 325-343.

—— (1921) "Unit Character Variation in Rodents," *Jour. of Mammal.*, **2**, 125-140.

—— (1922) "A Gene for the Extension of Black Pigment in Domestic Fowls," *Amer. Nat.*, **56**, 463-466.

Dunn, L. C. (1922) "Inheritance of Plumage Colour in Crosses of Buff and Columbian Fowls," *Amer. Nat.*, **56**, 242-255.

—— (1923) "Colour Inheritance in Fowls. The Genetic Relationship of the Black, Buff, and Columbia Coloration in the Domestic Fowl," *Jour. Hered.*, **14**, 23-32.

—— (1923) "Experiments on Close Inbreeding in Fowls. Preliminary Report," *Storrs Agric. Exp. Sta.* (Bull. No. 111), 139-172.

—— (1923) "The Problem of Hatchability from the Standpoint of Genetics," *Sci. Agric.* (Sept.)

—— (1923) "A Lethal Gene in Fowls," *Amer. Nat.*, **57**, 345-349.

—— (1923) "A Method for distinguishing the Sex of Young Chicks," *Storrs Agric. Exp. Sta.* (Bull. No. 113), 245-280.

—— **Webb, H. F.**, and **Schneider, M.** (1923) "The Inheritance of Degree of Spotting in Holstein Cattle," *Jour. Hered.*, **14**, 229-240.

Durham, F. (1907) "Note on Melanins," *Jour. Physiol.*, **35**, 47-48.

—— (1908) "A Preliminary Account of the Inheritance of Coat-Colour in Mice," *Roy. Soc. 4th Rept. Evol. Com.*, 41-53.

—— (1911) "Further Experiments on the Inheritance of Coat-Colour in Mice," *Jour. Genet.*, **1**, 159-178.

—— and **Marryat, D. E. C.** (1908) "Note on the Inheritance of Sex in Canaries," *Roy. Soc. 4th Rept. Evol. Com.*, 57-60.

Durham, G. B. (1921) "Inheritance of Belting Spotting in Cattle and Swine," *Amer. Nat.*, **55**, 467-477.

Düsing, Carl (1884) "Die Regulierung des Geschlechtsverhältnisse bei der Vermehrung der Menschen, Tiere und Pflanzen," *Jen. Zeit. f. Naturw.*, **17**.

Eckles, C. H., and **Palmer, L. S.** (1917) "Influence of Parental Age on Offspring," *Jour. Agric. Res.*, **11**, 645-658.

—— and **Shaw, R. H.** (1913) "Variation in the Composition and Properties of Milk from the Individual Cow," *Bur. Anim. Indust. U.S. Dept. Agric.*, (Bull. No. 157), 1-27.

—— —— (1913) "The Influence of Breed and Individuality on the Composition and Properties of Milk," *Bur. Anim. Indust. U.S. Dept. Agric. Bull.*, No. 156, 1-27.

Egloff, J. M. (1913) "Colour Factors in the Hair of the Horse," *Amer. Breed. Mag.*, **4**, 27-31.

Ellinger, Tage (1921) "The Influence of Age on Fertility in Swine," *Proc. Nat. Acad. Sci.*, **7**, 134-138.

Embody, G. C. (1918) "Artificial Hybrids between Pike and Pickerel," *Jour. Hered.*, **9**, 253-256.

Ernest, J. A. (1916) "Spotted Asses," *Jour. Hered.*, **7**, 165-168.

Essenberg, J. M. (1923) "Sex-Differentiation in the Viviparous Teleost, *Xiphophorus helleri*, Heckel," *Biol. Bull.*, **45**, 46-96.

Euren, H. F. (1918) *The Heredity of Dual-Purpose Cattle*, 1-96. Norwich.

Evans, W. (1910) "Hybridising Gamebirds in Captivity (Pheasants)," *Amer. Breed. Mag.*, **1**, 135-137.

Ewart, J. Cossar (1899) *The Penycuik Experiments.* A. & C. Black.

—— (1900) "Cross-Breeding in Animals," *Ann. Meet. Nat. Veter. Assoc.*, Dublin.

—— (1901) "Variation: Germinal and Environmental," *Sci. Trans. Roy. Dubl. Soc.*, **7**, 353-378.

Ewart, J. Cossar (1901) "The Experimental Study of Variation," Zool. Sect. *Brit. Ass. Advanc. Sci.*
—— (1902) "Experimental Contributions to the Theory of Heredity. Reversion and Telegony. Telegony in the *Equidæ*," *Trans. Highl. and Agric. Soc. Scotl.*, **14**, 1-61.
—— (1903) "The Wild Horse (*Equus prjevalskii*, Poliakoff)," *Proc. Roy. Soc. Edin.*, **24**, 460-468.
—— (1906) "The Trapan and its Relationship with Wild and Domestic Horses," *Proc. Roy. Soc. Edin.*, **27**, 7-21.
—— (1909) "The Possible Ancestors of the Horses living under Domestication," *Proc. Roy. Soc.*, **81**, 392-397.
—— (1910) "The Principles of Breeding and the Origin of Domesticated Breeds of Animals," *Ann. Rpt. Bur. Anim. Indust. U.S. Dept. Agric.*, 125-186.
—— (1912) "Eugenics and the Breeding of Light Horses, I. and II.," *The Field*, **119**, 288, 346.
—— (1913-14) "I. Sheep of the Mouflon and Urial Types, 1-33. II. Wild Sheep of the Argali Type, 1-29.—*Trans. Highl. and Agric. Soc. Scotl.*
—— (1919) "Telegony," *Nature*, **104**, 216-217.
—— (1919) "The Intercrossing of Sheep and the Evolution of New Varieties of Wool," *Scot. Jour. Agric.*, **2**, 1-10.

Farkas, K. (1903) "Beiträge zur Energetik der Ontogenese, III.," *Pflüg. Arch.* **98**, 490-546.
Farmer, J. B., and **Digby, L.** (1914) "On Dimensions of Chromosomes considered in relation to Phylogeny," *Phil. Trans. Roy. Soc.*, **205**, 1-25.
Faure, C. (1919) "Case of Rudimentary Hermaphroditism in the Cock," *C. R. Soc. Biol.*, **82**, 519-520.
Federley, H. (1911) "Sur un cas d'hérédité gynéphore dans une espèce de papillon," *IV. Confér. de Génét.*, 469-477.
—— (1911) "Breeding Experiments with the Moth *Pygæra*," *Arch. Rass. u. Ges. Biol.*, **8**, 281-338.
—— (1912) "Das Verhalten der Chromosomen bei der Spermatogenese der Schmetterlinge, *Pygæra anachoreta*, *curtula* und *pigra* sowie einigen ihrer Bastarde," *Zeit. indukt. Abst.* **9**, 1-110.
Feldman, H. W. (1922) "A 4th Allelomorph in the Albino Series in Mice," *Amer. Nat.*, **56**, 573-574.
—— (1923) "Colour Varieties of the Black Rat," *Anat. Rec.*, **26**, 391-392.
—— (1923) "Linkage Relations of Albino Allelomorphs in Rats and Mice," *Anat. Rec.*, **26**, 391.
—— (1924) "Linkage of Albino Allelomorphs in Rats and Mice," *Genet.*, **9**, 487-492.
Finkler, W. (1923) "Kopftransplantation an Insekten," *Arch. micr. Anat. Entwickl.*, **99**, 104-133.
Finlay, G. F. (1924) "Sterility in Swine," *Nat. Counc. of Pig Breed. and Feed.*, 3-24.
—— (1925) "Studies on the Sex Differentiation in the Fowl," *Brit. Jour. Exp. Biol.*, **2**.
Firket, J. (1920) "On the Origin of Germ Cells in Higher Vertebrates," *Anat. Rec.*, 309-316.
Floriot (1913) "L'hérédité chez le cheval," *Rev. vétér. milit.*
Foges (1903) "Zur Lehre der sekundaren Geschlechtscharaktere, *Pflüg. Arch.*, **93**, 39-58.

Fogle, P. E. (1912) "Transmission of Colour and Colour Markings in Hereford × Shorthorn Crosses," *Amer. Breed. Mag.*, **3**, 201-204.

Foreman, E. C. (1922) "Inheritance ot Higher Fecundity and the Mode of Transmission," *Michig. Sta. Rpt.*, 231-232.

Fouchard, P., and **Houmeau, A.** (1913) "Mule Breeding in Poitou," *La vie agric. rurale*, **2**, 188-195.

Fox, H. Munro (1923) "Experiments with *Ciona*," *Nature*, **112**, 653.

—— (1924) "Note on Kammerer's Experiments with *Ciona* concerning the Inheritance of an Acquired Character," *Jour. Genet.*, **14**, 89-91.

Frateur, J. L. (1914) "Contribution à l'étude du barrage de la plume chez la volaille. Hérédité de la couleur coucou chez le coucou de Malines," *Inst. Zoot.*, No. 14, 1-12.

Fröhlich, G. (1912) "Ueber den Einfluss der Verwandschaftszucht auf die Fruchtbarkeit bei weissem Edelschwein," *Fühlings landw. Zeit.*, **61**, 529.

—— (1913) "Vererbung der Farben beim Schwein," *Jour. f. Landw.*, **61**, 217-235.

Führer, Ludwig (1912) "Studien zur Monographie des Steinschafs," *Mitt. d. landw. Lehrkanz. k. k. Hochsch. f. Bodenkult.*, **1**, 91-114.

Funquist, H. (1920) "The Inheritance of the Muzzle Colour in the Cattle Breed of Stjernsund," *Hereditas*, **1**, 343-363.

—— and **Roman, Nils** (1923) "Vererbung 'weisser Abzeichen' bei Rindern," *Hereditas*, **4**, 65-80.

Gage, S. H. and **S. P.** (1908) "Sudan III deposited in the Egg and transmitted to the Chick," *Sci.*, **39**, 494-495.

Gaines, W. L. (1922) "Inheritance of Fat-Content of Milk in Dairy Cattle," *Proc. Amer. Soc. Anim. Prod.*

Galbusera, S. (1920) "Crosses between Ewe and He-Goat, between Ram and Goat and between Sow and Wild Boar in Sardinia," *La Clinica veter.*, **48**, 385-386.

Galloway, A. R. (1909) "Canary Breeding: A Partial Analysis of Records from 1891-1909," *Biometrika*, **7**, 1-42.

—— (1910) "Canary Breeding—A Rejoinder," *Biometrika*, **7**, 401-403.

Galton, Francis (1875) "A Theory of Heredity," *Contemp. Rev.*, 80-95.

—— (1889) *Natural Inheritance.*

Gates, R. R. (1915) *The Mutation Factor in Evolution with Particular Reference to Œnothera.* Macmillan.

—— (1921) "The Genetics of Sex," *Nature*, 571-572.

—— (1921) "The Inheritance of Acquired Characters," *Nature*, 89.

Gemmill, J. F. (1896) "On Some Cases of Hermaphroditism in the Limpet (*Patella*), with Observations regarding the Influence of Nutrition on Sex in the Limpet," *Anat. Anz.*, **12**, 392-395.

George, J. A. "Les Races bovines," *Librairie agric. d. l. maison rust.*

Ghigi, A. (1919) "Sulla fertilia degli ibridi fra Columba leuconota e piccion domestici," *Riv. Ital. di Ornit.*

—— (1921) "Les ancêtres sauvages de la volaille et des pigeons domestiques," *Trav. 1er Congr. mond. d'avicult.*, **1**, 97.

—— (1922) "L'hybridisme dans la genèse des races domestiques d'oiseaux," *Genetica*, **4**, 364-374.

—— (1923) "Osservazioni sull' eredita nel Pollame compiute nell' anno 1922," *Rivist. Ciol.*, **5**, 9-15.

Goldschmidt, R. (1912) "Zuchtversuche mit Enten., I.," *Zeit. indukt. Abst.*, **9**, 161-191.

—— (1916) "Experimental Intersexuality and the Sex Problem," *Amer. Nat.*, **50**, 705-718.

—— (1916) "A Preliminary Report on Further Experiments in Inheritance and Determination of Sex," *Proc. Nat. Acad. Sci.*, **2**, 53-58.

—— and **Others** (1920) "Untersuchungen über Intersexualität," *Zeit. indukt. Abst.*, **23**, 1-199.

—— (1921) "The Determination of Sex," *Nature*, 780-784.

—— (1922) "Ueber Vererbung im Y-Chromosom," *Biol. Zentralb.*, **42**, 481-487.

—— and **Pariser, K.** (1923) "Triploide Intersexe bei Schmetterlingen," *Biol. Zentralb.*, **43**, 446-452.

—— and **Poppelbaum, H.** (1914) "Erblichkeitsstudien an Schmetterlingen II.," *Zeit. indukt. Abst.*, **11**, 280-316.

Gonzales, B. M. (1923) "Experimental Studies on the Duration of Life. VIII. The Influence upon Duration of Life of Certain Mutant Genes of *Drosophila melanogaster*," *Amer. Nat.*, **57**, 289-325.

Goodale, H. D. (1909) "Sex and its Relation to the Barring Factor in Poultry," *Sci.*, **29**, 1004-1005.

—— (1910) "Breeding Experiments in Poultry," *Proc. Soc. Exp. Biol. and Med.*, **7**, 178-179.

—— (1910) "Some Results of Castration in Ducks," *Biol. Bull.*, **20**, 35-66.

—— (1911) "Studies on Hybrid Ducks, I.," *Jour. Exp. Zool.*, **10**, 241-254.

—— (1913) "Castration in Relation to the Secondary Sexual Characters of Brown Leghorn," *Amer. Nat.*, **47**, 159-169.

—— (1916) "Note on the Behaviour of Capons when Brooding Chicks," *Jour. Anim. Behav.*, **6**, 319-324.

—— (1916) "Gonadectomy in Relation to the Secondary Sexual Characters of Some Domestic Birds," *Carn. Inst. Publ.*, No. 243, 1-52.

—— (1916) "Egg Production and Selection," *Amer. Nat.*, **50**, 479-485.

—— (1916) "Further Development in Ovariotomised Fowls," *Biol. Bull.*, **30**, 286-294.

—— (1916) "A Feminised Cockerel," *Jour. Exp. Zool.*, **20**, 421-428.

—— (1916) "A Study of Broodiness in the R. I. R. Breed of Domestic Fowl," *Anat. Rec.*, **11**, 553-554.

—— (1917) "Crossing-Over in the Sex Chromosome of the Male Fowl," *Sci.*, **46**, 213.

—— (1918) "Winter Cycle of Egg Production in the Rhode Island Red Breed of the Domestic Fowl," *Jour. Agric. Res.*, **12**, 547-574.

—— (1918) "Feminised Male Birds," *Genet.*, **3**, 276-295.

—— (1919) "Interstitial Cells in the Gonads of Domestic Fowl," *Anat. Rec.*, **16**, 247-250.

—— and **Morgan, T. H.** (1913) "Heredity of Tricolour in Guinea-pigs," *Amer. Nat.*, **57**, 321-348.

—— **Sandborn, R.**, and **White, D.** (1920) "Broodiness in Domestic Fowl: Data concerning its Inheritance in the Rhode Island Red Breed," *Mass. Agric. Exp. Sta.* (Bull. No. 199), 93-116.

Goodnight, C. (1914) "My Experience with Bison Hybrids," *Jour. Hered.*, **5**, 197-199.

Goodrich, H. B. (1916) "The Germ-Cells of *Ascaris incurva*," *Jour. Exp. Zool.*, **21**, 61-100.

Gortner, R. A. (1910) "Spiegler's White Melanin as Related to Dominant or Recessive White," *Amer. Nat.*, **44**, 497-502.

Gould, H. N. (1917) "Studies on Sex in the Hermaphrodite Mollusc *Crepidula plana*. II. Influence of Environment on Sex," *Jour. Exp. Zool.*, **23**, 1-70.

Gowen, J. W. (1918) "Studies in Inheritance of Certain Characters between Dairy and Beef Breeds in Cattle, I. and II." I. *Maine Agric. Exp. Sta.* (Bull. No. 272). II. *Jour. Agric. Res.*, **15**, 1-58.

—— (1919) "A Biometrical Study of Crossing-Over. On the Mechanism of Crossing-Over in the Third Chromosome of *Drosophila melanogaster*," *Genet.*, **4**, 205-250.

—— (1920) "Inheritance of Milk Yield and Butter-Fat Percentage in Crosses of Dairy and Beef Breeds of Cattle," *Jour. Hered.*, **11**, 300-316, 365-376.

—— (1920) "Studies on Milk Secretion. V. On the Variation and Correlation of Milk Secretion with Age. VI. On the Variations and Correlations of Butter-Fat Percentage with Age in Jersey Cattle," *Genet.*, **5**, 11-187, 249-324.

—— and **Covell, H. R.** (1921) "Studies on Milk Secretion. IX. On the Performance of the Progeny of Holstein-Friesian Sires," *Maine Agric. Exp. Sta.* (Bull. No. 399), 121-252.

Gräfenberg, E. (1923) "Sex Specificity of Female Blood," *Arch. Gynäkol.*, **117**, 52-53.

Greenman, M. J., and **F. L. Duhring** (1923) *Breeding and Care of the Albino Rat for Research Purposes.* Philadelphia: Wistar Institute, 1-107.

Griffith, C. R. (1922) "Are Permanent Disturbances of Equilibration Inherited?" *Sci.*, **56**, 676-678.

Guaita, von, G. (1898) "Versuche mit Kreuzungen von verschiedenen Rassen der Hausmaus," *Ber. naturf. Ges.*, **10**, 317-332.

—— (1900) "Versuche mit Kreuzungen von verschiedenen Rassen der Hausmaus, II.," *Ber. naturf. Ges.*, **11**, 131-138.

—— (1902) "Versuche mit Kreuzungen von verschiedenen Rassen der Hausmaus," (Inaug. Dissert.), 1-24.

Gugnoni, Cesare (1917) "Heredity, Causes, and Importance of White Marks on the Coats of Equine Animals," *Giorn. d'Ippolog.*, **30**.

Günther, H. (1923) "Letaldispositionen und Sexualdispositionen," *Naturw. Korrsp.*, **1**, 19 (46).

Guyer, M. F. (1909) "Atavism in Guinea-Chicken Hybrids," *Jour. Exp. Zool.*, **7**, 723-745.

—— (1909) "On the Sex of Hybrid Birds," *Biol. Bull.*, **16**, 193-198.

—— (1909) "La Livrée du Plumage chez les Hybrids de Pintade et de Poule," *Bull. Mus. d'hist. nat.*, No. 1, 1-3.

—— (1912) "Modifications in the Testes of Hybrids from the Guinea and the Common Fowl," *Jour. Morph.*, **23**, 45-55.

—— and **Smith, E. A.** (1920) "Studies on Cytolysins. II. Transmission of Induced Eye Defects," *Jour. Exp. Zool.*, **31**, 171-215.

—— —— (1924) "Further Studies on Inheritance of Eye Defects Induced in Rabbits," *Jour. Exp. Zool.*, **38**, 449-474.

Hadley, F. B. (1925) *Inheritance of a Congenital Epithelial Defect of Calves.* Quoted by L. J. Cole, *Rev. Scot. Cattle Breed. Conf.*, 45. Oliver & Boyd.

Hadley, Philip B. (1913) "The Presence of the Barred Plumage Pattern in the White Leghorn Breed of Fowls," *Amer. Nat.*, **47**, 418-428.

—— (1913-14) "Studies on Inheritance in Poultry. I. The Constitution of the White Leghorn Breed, 151-216. II. The Factor for Black Pigmentation in the White Leghorn Breed," 449-459, *R. I. Agric. Exp. Sta.* (Bull. Nos. 155, 161).

—— (1915) "The White Leghorn," *Journ. Hered.*, **6**, 147-151.

—— and **Caldwell, D. W.** (1920) "Studies on the Inheritance of Egg-Weight. I. Normal Distribution of Egg-Weight," *R. I. Agric. Exp. Sta.* (Bull. No. 181), 1-64.

Haeckel, E. (1876) *Generelle Morphologie.* Berlin.

Haecker, V. (1912) "Ueber Kreuzungsversuche mit Himalaya und Black-and-Tan Kaninchen," *Mitt. Naturf. Ges.*, **2**, 1-4.

—— and **Kuttner, O.** (1915) "Ueber Kaninchenkreuzungen. II. Zur Frage der Unreinheit der Gameten," *Zeit. indukt. Abst.*, **14**, 49-70.

Hagedoorn, A. L. (1908) "Origin of Two New Retrogressive Varieties by one Mutation in Mice," *Univ. Calif. Publ. Physiol.*, No. 12, **3**, 87-90.

—— (1909) "Mendelian Inheritance of Sex," *Arch. Entwickl.*, **28**, 1-34.

—— (1909) "Inheritance of Yellow Colour in Rodents," *Univ. Calif. Publ. Physiol.*, No. 14, **3**, 95-99.

—— (1912) "On Tricolour Coat in Dogs and Guinea-pigs," *Amer. Nat.*, **46**, 682-683.

—— (1912) "The Genetic Factors in the Development of the House-Mouse which Influence the Coat Colour," *Zeit. indukt. Abst.*, **6**, 97-136.

—— (1914) "Repulsion in Mice," *Amer. Nat.*, **48**, 699-700.

—— and **A. C.** (1922) "Species Crosses in Rats," *Zeit. indukt. Abst.*, **29**, 97-121.

Haldane, J. B. S. (1919) (1) "The Probable Errors of Calculated Linkage Values, and the Most Accurate Method of determining Gametic from certain Zygotic Series," 291-298. (2) "The Combination of Linkage Values, and the Calculation of Distance between the Loci of Linked Factors," 299-309. *Jour. Genet.*, **8**.

—— (1921) "Sex-linked Inheritance in Poultry," *Sci.*, **54**, 663.

—— (1922) "Sex-Ratio and Unisexual Sterility in Hybrid Animals," *Jour. Genet.*, **12**, 101-110.

—— (1924) "A Mathematical Theory of Natural and Artificial Selection," *Trans. Camb. Phil. Soc.*, **23**, 19-41.

—— **Sprunt, A. D.**, and **Haldane, N. M.** (1915) "Reduplication in Mice," *Jour. Genet.*, **5**, 133-136.

Hammerschlag (1912) "Zuchtversuche mit japanischen Tanzmäusen und europäischen Laufmäusen," *Arch. Entwickl.*, **33**, 339-344.

Hammond, J. (1914) "On Some Factors controlling Fertility in Domestic Animals," *Jour. Agric. Sci.*, **6**, 263-277.

—— (1921) "Further Observations on the Factors controlling Fertility and Fœtal Atrophy," *Jour. Agric. Sci.*, **11**, 337-366.

—— (1922) "The Relative Growth and Development of Various Breeds and Crosses of Pigs," *Jour. Agric. Sci.*, **12**, 387-423.

—— (1923) "Changes in the Reproductive Organs of the Cow during the Sexual Cycle and Pregnancy," *Quart. Jour. Exp. Physiol.*, Suppl. vol., 134-136.

—— and **Marshall, F. H. A.** (1923) "The Corpus luteum of the Domestic Rabbit and the Change in the Reproductive Organs in relation to Lactation," *Quart. Jour. Exp. Physiol.*, Suppl. vol., 137-138.

Hammond, J., and **Saunders, H. G.** (1913) "Some Factors affecting the Milk Yield," *Jour. Agric. Sci.*, **13**, 74.

Hance, R. T. (1917) "The Diploid Chromosome Complexes of the Pig (*Sus scrofa*) and their Variations," *Jour. Morph.*, **30**, 155-222.

—— (1924) "Heredity in Goldfish," *Jour. Hered.*, **15**, 177-182.

—— (1924) "The Somatic Chromosomes of the Chick and their Possible Sex Relation," *Sci.*, **59**, 424-425.

Harman, Mary T. (1916) "A Gynandromorph Cat," *Anat. Rec.*, **11**, 476-479.

—— (1917) "Another Case of Gynandromorphism," *Anat. Rec.* **13**, 425-436.

Harms, W. (1923) "Die physiologische Geschlechtsumstimmung," *Verh. deut. zool. Ges.*, **28**, 37-38.

Harper, E. H. (1905) "Studies in the Inheritance of Colour in Percheron Horses," *Biol. Bull.*, **9**, 265-280.

Harris, J. A. (1915) "Physical Conformation of Cows and Milk Yield," *Jour. Hered.*, **6**, 348-350.

—— (1916) "Variation, Correlation and Inheritance of Fertility in the Mammals," *Amer. Nat.*, **50**, 626-636.

—— (1916) "Statistical Studies of the Number of Nipples in the Mammals," *Amer. Nat.*, **50**, 696-704.

—— and **Blakeslee, A. F.** (1918) "The Correlation between Egg-Production during Various Periods of the Year in the Domestic Fowl," *Genet.*, **3**, 27-72.

—— and **Goodale, H. D.** (1922) "The Correlation between the Egg-Production of the Various Periods of the Year in the Rhode Island Red Breed of Domestic Fowl," *Genet.*, **7**, 446-465.

—— and **Lewis, H. R.** (1922) "The Correlation between First and Second Year Egg-Production in the Domestic Fowl," *Genet.*, **7**, 274-318.

—— —— (1923) "The Correlation between the Time of Beginning and the Time of Cessation of Laying in the First and Second Laying Year in the Domestic Fowl," *Genet.*, **8**, 37-74.

—— **Blakeslee, A. F.**, and **Warner, D. E.** (1917) "The Correlation between Body Pigmentation and Egg-Production in the Domestic Fowl," *Genet.*, **2**, 36-77.

—— **Kirkpatrick, W.**, **Blakeslee, A.**, **Warner, D.**, and **Card** (1921) "The Egg-Record of Limited Periods as Criteria for Predicting the Egg-Production of the White Leghorn Fowl," *Genet.* **6**, 265-309.

Harrison, J. W. H. (1916-17) "Studies in the Hybrid *Bistoninæ*, I. and II.," *Jour. Genet.*, **6**, 95-162, 269-314.

—— (1919) "Studies on the Hybrid *Bistoninæ*, IV. Concerning Sex-Ratio and Related Problems," *Jour. Genet.*, **9**, 1-38.

—— (1922) "Interspecific Sterility," *Nature*, **110**, 312.

—— and **Doncaster, L.** (1914) "On Hybrids between Moths of the Geometrid Sub-Family *Bistoninæ*," *Jour. Genet.*, **3**, 229-248.

Hart, E. B., and **Steenbock, H.** (1918) "Hairless Pigs: The Cause and Remedy," *Wisc. Agric. Exp. Sta.*, (Bull. No. 297), 1-11.

Hartman, Carl (1920) "The Free-Martin and its Reciprocal: Opossum, Man, Dog," *Sci.*, **52**, 469-471.

—— (1922) "A Brown Mutation in the Opossum (*Didelphis virginian*) with Remarks upon the Grey and the Black Phases in this Species," *Jour. Mammal*, **3**, 146-149.

Hartman, Carl, and **Hamilton, W. F.** (1922) "A Case of True Hermaphroditism in the Fowl, with Remarks on Secondary Sex Characters," *Jour. Exp. Zool.*, **36**, 185-199.

Harvey, E. Brown (1916) "Chromosome Number in the Metazoa," *Jour. Morph.*, **28**, 1-64.

—— (1920) "A Review of the Chromosome Number in the Metazoa, Pt. II.," *Jour. Morph.*, **34**, 1-68.

Hatai, S. (1912) "On the Appearance of Albino Mutations in Litters of the Common Norway Rat," *Sci.*, **35**, 875-876.

Hayden, C. C. (1922) "A Case of Twinning in Dairy Cattle," *Jour. Hered.*, **13**, 22-24.

Haynes, W. (1913) "Prepotency in Airedale Terriers," *Sci.*, **38**, 404-405.

—— (1914) "In-Breeding in Dogs," *Jour. Hered.*, **5**, 368-369.

—— (1915) "Effect of the Popular Sire," *Jour. Hered.*, **6**, 494-496.

Hays, F. A. (1918) "II. The Influence of Excessive Sexual Activity of Male Rabbits on the Nature of their Offspring," *Jour. Exp. Zool.*, **25**, 571-613.

—— (1921) "Effect of Excessive Use of Male Rabbits in Breeding," *The Breed. Gaz.*, **89**, 66.

—— (1923) "The Tortoiseshell Cat," *Jour. Hered.*, **14**, 369-370.

—— (1924) "In-Breeding the Rhode Island Red Fowl, with Special Reference to Winter Egg Production," *Amer. Nat.*, **58**, 43-59.

—— and **Sandborn, Ruby** (1924) "The Inheritance of Fertility and Hatchability in Poultry," *Mass. Agric. Exp. Sta.* (Techn. Bull., No. 6), 21-42.

Hays, Grace P. (1917) "A Case of a Syndactylous Cat," *Jour. Morph.*, **30**, 65-82.

Heape, W. (1899) "Note on the Fertility of Different Breeds of Sheep, with Remarks on the Prevalence of Abortion and Barrenness therein," *Proc. Roy. Soc., B.*, **65**, 99-111.

—— (1899) "Abortion, Barrenness, and Fecundity in Sheep," *Jour. Roy. Agric. Soc.*, **10**, 217-248.

—— (1907) "Note on the Influence of Extraneous Forces upon the Proportion of the Sexes produced by Canaries," *Proc. Camb. Phil. Soc.*, **14**, 201-205.

—— (1907) "Notes on the Proportion of Sexes in Dogs," *Proc. Camb. Phil. Soc.*, **14**, 121-151.

Hegner, R. W. (1914) *The Germ-Cell Cycle in Animals.* New York.

Heller, L. L. (1915) "Reversion in Sheep," *Jour. Hered.*, **6**, 480.

Herbst, Curt. (1909) "Vererbungsstudien. VI. Die cytologischen Grundlagen der Verschiebung der Vererbungsrichtung nach der mütterlichen Seite," *Arch. Entwickl.*, **27**, 266-308.

Heron, D. (1910) "Inheritance in Canaries: A Study in Mendelism," *Biometrika*, **7**, 403-408.

Hertwig, Paula (1923) "Der bisherige Stand der erbanalytischen Untersuchungen an Hühnern," *Zeit. indukt. Abst.*, **30**, 183-254.

Hertwig, R. (1912) "Uber den derzeitigen Stand des Sexualproblem," *Biol. Zentralb.*, **32**, 65, 129.

Hillardt, A. (1913) "Vererbung der Schwanzlosigkeit bei Hunden," *Wien. landw. Zeit.*, **63**, 97.

Hink, August (1915) "Researches on the Transmission of Epilepsy in Animals," *Deut. tierärtz. Woch.*, **41**, 351-352.

Hofacker (1828) *Uber die Eigenschaften welche sich bei Menschen und Tieren auf die Nachkommenschaft vererben, mist besonderer Rücksicht auf die Pferdezucht.* Tübingen.

Hogben, L. T. (1919-20) "Studies on Synapsis. II. Parallel Conjugation and the Prophase Complex in Periplaneta, with Special Reference to the Premiotic Telophase," *Proc. Roy. Soc., B.*, **91**, 305-329.

Hoge, M. A. (1915) "The Influence of Temperature on the Development of a Mendelian Character," *Jour. Exp. Zool.*, **18**, 241-298.

Hooper, J. J. (1919) "Inheritance of Colour in Jersey Cattle," *Jour. Dairy Sci.*, **2**, 290-292.

—— (1921) "Colour of Cross-Bred Calves," *Jour. Hered.*, **12**, 480.

—— (1921) "Studies of Dairy Cattle," *Kent. Agric. Exp. Sta.* (Bull. No. 224), 91-161.

—— and **Nutter, J. W.** (1924) "Sex of Over-Term Calves," *Jour. Hered.*, **15**, 462.

Horlacher, L. J., and **Good, E. S.** (1922) "Breeding Experiments with Kentucky Mountain Ewes," *Kent. Agric. Exp. Sta.* (Bull. No. 243), 139-199.

Horning, B., and **Torrey, H.** (1922) "Hen Feathering induced in Male Fowls by Feeding Thyroid," *Anat. Rec.*, **23**, 132.

Hover, J. M. (1916) "Finding the Prepotent Sire," *Jour. Hered.*, **7**, 173-178.

Huff, F. (1921) "Der Einfluss der Inzucht auf die Leistungen des Vollblutpferdes," *Fühlings landw. Zeit.*, **70**, 47-61.

Hunt, R. E. (1921) "Selecting Holstein-Friesian Sires for High Yearly Production," *Jour. Hered.*, **12**, 369-384.

Hunt, W. D. (1923) "The Laws of Heredity and the Breeding of Farm Animals," *N. Z. Jour. Agric.*, **27**, 103-111.

Hurst, C. C. (1905) "Experimental Studies on Heredity in Rabbits," *Linn. Soc. Jour.*, **29**, 283-324.

—— (1905) "Experiments with Poultry," *Roy. Soc. 2nd Rpt. Evol. Com.*, 131-154.

—— (1906) "On the Inheritance of Coat-Colour in Horses," *Proc. Roy. Soc. B.*, **77**, 388-394.

—— (1907) "Mendelian Characters in Plants and Animals," *Roy. Hort. Soc. Rpt. on Confer. Genet.*, 1-16.

—— (1909) *Mendelism and Sex*, 1-34.

—— (1911) "The Application of Genetics to Horse-Breeding" (Sub-Sect. K), *Brit. Ass. Advanc. Sci.*

—— (1912) "Mendelian Experiments with Thoroughbred Horses," *Bloodst. Breed. Rev.*, **1**, 86-90.

—— (1921) "The Genetics of Egg Production in White Leghorns and White Wyandottes, and its Application to Poultry Breeding," *Trans. 1st World Poult. Cong.*, **1**, 3-22.

—— (1923) "The Genetics of Fecundity in Domestic Hens," *Eugenics, Genetics, and the Family*, **1**, 212-217. Williams & Wilkins, Baltimore.

Huxley, J. S. (1920) "Note on an Alternating Preponderance of Males and Females in Fish, and its possible Significance," *Jour. Genet.*, **10**, 265-276.

—— (1921) "Linkage in *Gammarus chevreuxi*," *Jour. Genet.*, **11**, 229-233.

—— (1923) "Late Fertilisation and Sex-Ratio in Trout," *Sci.*, 291-292.

Hyde, R. R. (1913) "Inheritance of the Length of Life in *Drosophila ampelophila*," *Rpt. Indiana Acad. Sci*, 113-123.

—— (1914) "Fertility and Sterility in *Drosophila ampelophila*," *Jour. Exp. Zool.*, **17**, 141-171, 173-212, 343-372.

—— (1924) "In-breeding, Out-Breeding, and Selection with *Drosophila melanogaster*," *Jour. Exp. Zool.*, **40**, 181-216.

Ibsen, H. L. (1916) "Tricolour Inheritance. I. The Guinea-pigs. II. The Basset Hound. III. Tortoiseshell Cat," *Genet.*, **1**, 287-311, 367-377, 377-387.
—— (1919) "The Triple Allelomorphic Series in Guinea-pigs," *Genet.*, **4**, 597-606.
—— (1919) "Synthetic Pink-Eyed Self-White Guinea-pig," *Amer. Nat.*, **53**, 120-130.
—— (1920) "Linkage in Rats," *Amer. Nat.*, **54**, 61-67.
—— (1922) "Some Genetic Experiments with Guinea-pigs and Rats," *Amer. Soc. Anim. Product.*, 99-101.
—— (1923) "Evidence of the Independent Inheritance of Six Pairs of Allelomorphs in Guinea-pigs, *Anat. Rec.*, **26**, 392-393.
—— and **Schaumburg, L.** (1923) "Sex-Ratios in Guinea-pigs," *Anat. Rec.*, **24**, 412-413.
—— and **Steigleder, E.** (1917) "Evidence for the Death *in utero* of the Homozygous Yellow Mouse," *Amer. Nat.*, **51**, 740-752.
Ivanov, E. I. (1905) "Untersuchungen uber die Ursachen der Unfruchtbarkeit von Zebroiden," *Biol. Zentralb.*, **28**, 789-804.
—— (1911) "Die Fruchtbarkeit der Hybriden des *Bos taurus* und des *Bison americanus*," *Biol. Zentralb.*, **31**, 21-24.
—— (1911) "Zur Frage der Fruchtbarkeit der Hybriden des Hauspferdes, der Zebroiden, und der Hybriden vom Pferde und *Equus Przewalskii*," *Biol. Zentralb.*, **31**, 24-28.
—— (1913) "Sur la fecondité de *Bison bonasus* x *Bos taurus*," *C. R. Soc. Biol.*, **75**, 376-378.
—— (1922) "Artificial Fertilisation in Stock Breeding," *Jour. Agric. Sci.*, **12**, 244-256.
—— (1924) "De la fécondation artificielle des mammifères et des oiseaux," *C. R. Acad. Sci.*, **178**, 1854-1956.
—— and **Philipchenko, J.** (1916) "Beschreibungen von Hybriden zwischen Wisent und Hausrind," *Zeit. indukt. Abst.*, **16**, 1-48.

Jäger (1879) "Zur Pangenesis," *Kosmos*, **4**.
Janssens, F. A. (1905) "Evolution des auxocytes mâles du *Batraceps attenuatus*," *La Cellule*, **22**, 377-435.
—— (1909) "La théorie de la chiasmotypie. Nouvelle interprétation des cinèsis de maturation," *La Cellule*, **25**, 389-411.
—— (1919) (1) "A propos de la chiasmotypie et de la théorie de Morgan, 917-920. (2) Une formule simple exprimant ce qui se passe en réalité lors de la 'chiasmotypie' dans les deux cinèses en maturation, 930-934," *C. R. Soc. Biol.*, **82**.
Jenks, A. E. (1916) "Spotted Asses," *Jour. Hered.*, **7**, 165-169.
Jennings, H. S. (1908) "Heredity, Variation and Evolution in Protozoa," *Jour. Exp. Zool.*, **5**, 577-632.
—— (1909) "Heredity and Variation in the Simplest Organisms," *Amer. Nat.*, **43**, 321-337.
—— (1911) "Pure Lines in the Study of Genetics in Lower Organisms," *Amer. Nat.*, **45**, 79-89.
Jewell, F. H. (1921) "Sex-Ratios in Fœtal Cattle," *Biol. Bull.*, **41**, 259-271.
Johannsen, W. (1903) *Ueber Erblichkeit in Populationen und in reinen Linien*, 1-68. Jena.

Johannsen, W. (1911) "The Genotype Conception of Heredity," *Amer. Nat.*, **45**, 129-159.

Jollos, V. (1920) "Experimentelle Vererbungsstudien an Infusorien," *Zeit. indukt. Abst.*, **24**, 77-97.

Jones, E. E. (1922) "The Genetic Significance of Intra-Uterine Sex-Ratios and Degenerating Fœtuses in the Cat," *Jour. Hered.*, **13**, 237-239.

Jones, Sarah (1921) "Inheritance of Silkiness in Fowls," *Jour. Hered.*, **12**, 117-128.

—— (1922) "Studies on Inheritance in Pigeons. IV. Checks and Bars, and Other Modifications of Black," *Genet.*, **7**, 468-507.

—— and **Rouse, J. E.** (1920) "The Relation of Age of Dam to Observed Fecundity in Domesticated Animals. I. Multiple Births in Cattle and Sheep," *Jour. Dairy Sci.*, **3**, 260-290.

Journal of Heredity (1917) "Hairless Dog," *Jour. Hered.*, **8**, 519-520.

Jull, M. A. (1923) "Can Sex be Controlled?" *Proc. Amer. Soc. Animal Product.*, 92-98.

Kaltenbach, R. (1917) "Uber Eierstocktransplantation bei Rouen und Pokingenten," *Zeit. indukt. Abst.*, **17**, 251-253.

Kammerer, P. (1923) "Breeding Experiments on the Inheritance of Acquired Characters," *Nature*, **111**, 637-640.

Kansas Agricultural Experiment Station (1918) "Inheritance Investigations in Swine," *Kan. Sta. Rpt.*, 41-42.

—— (1918) "Inheritance of Colour in Andalusian Fowl," *Kan. Sta. Rpt.*, 45.

Kastle, J. H., and **Buckner, G. D.** (1912) "Assymetric Colour Resemblance in the Guinea-pig," *Amer. Nat.*, **46**, 505-511.

Keller, K. (1916) "Die Kürperform der unfruchtbaren Zwillinge beim Rinde," *Zeit. indukt. Abst.*, **16**, 103-164.

—— (1922) "Uber das Phänomen der unfruchtbaren Zwillinge beim Rind und seine Bedeutung für das Problem der Geschlechtsbestimmung," *Zentralb. Gynäk.*, **46**, 364-367.

—— and **Tandler, J.** (1916) "Uber das Verhalten der Eiläute bei Zwillingsträchtigkeit des Rindes," *Wien. tier. Monatschr.*, **111**.

—— (1917) "Zur Erforschung der Unfruchtbarkeit bei den Zwillingskälbern des Rindes," *Südd. landw. Tierz.*, **12**, 296.

Kellog, Vernon L. (1908) "Inheritance in Silkworms," *Stanf. Univ. Publ.*, No. 1, 1-89.

Kennel, von (1901) "Uber eine stummelschwänzige Hauskatze und ihre Nachkommenschaft," *Zool. Jahrb.*, **15**, 219-242.

Kiesel (1913) "Uber Mendelsche Vererbung beim Rind," *Zeit. indukt. Abst.*, **10**, 269-275.

Kildee, H. H., and **M'Candlish, A. C.** (1916) "The Influence of Environment and Breeding in Increasing Dairy Production," *Iowa Agric. Exp. Sta.* (Bull. No. 165), 381-404.

King, H. D. (1915) "On the Normal Sex-Ratio and the Size of the Litter in the Albino Rat (*Mus norvegicus albinus*)," *Anat. Rec.*, **9**, 403-420.

—— (1916) "The Relation of Age to Fertility in the Rat," *Anat. Rec.*, **11**, 269-287.

—— (1916) "Experimental In-Breeding," *Jour. Hered.*, **7**, 70-76.

—— (1919) "Studies on In-Breeding," *Wistar Inst. Biol.*, 1-175.

King, H. D. (1923) "A New Occurrence of the Black-Eyed Yellow Mutation in Rats," *Sci.*, **58**, 250-251.

—— (1924) "Litter Production and the Sex-Ratio in Various Strains of Rats," *Anat. Rec.*, **27**, 337-366.

Kingsbury, B. F. (1909) "Report of a Case of Hermaphroditism in *Sus scrofa*," *Anat. Rec.*, **3**, 278-281.

Kirkham, W. B. (1916) "Embryology of the Yellow Mouse," *Anat. Rec.*, **11**, 480-481.

—— (1919) "The Fate of Homozygous Yellow Mice," *Jour. Exp. Zool.*, **28**, 125-135.

Knauer (1900) "Die Ovarientransplantation," *Arch. f. Gynäk.*, **60**.

Knight, T. A. (1909) "On the Comparative Influence of Male and Female Parents on their Offspring," *Phil. Trans. Roy. Soc.*, **99**, 392-399.

Koltzov, N. K. (1921) "Genetische Analyse der Färbung von Meerschweinchen," *Bull. Inst. Biol. Exp.*, **1**, 87-97. Moscow.

Kopeć, S. (1922) "Physiological Self-Differentiation of the Wing-Germs grafted on Caterpillars of the Opposite Sex," *Jour. Exp. Zool.*, **36**, 469-475.

—— (1923) "On the Offspring of Rabbit Does mated with two Sires simultaneously," *Jour. Genet.*, **13**, 371-382.

—— (1924) "Studies on the Inheritance of the Weight of New-Born Rabbits," *Jour. Genet.*, **14**, 241-264.

—— (1924) "On the Influence exerted by certain Inheritance Factors on the Birth-Weight of Rabbits," *Anat. Rec.*, **27**, 95-118.

Koppe-Norden (1921) "Inzucht und Individualpotenz in der schwarzbunten Rinderzucht," *Flugsschr.*, No. 56, *Deut. Ges. Züchtngsk.*, 1-23.

Korreng, G. (1912) "Die Gamaschenweite des Rindes im Verhältniss zur Milchleistung und zum Gewicht von Herz und Lunge," *Jahrb. wiss. prakt. Tierz.*, **7**, 132-142.

Krediet, G. (1921) "Ovariotestis bei der Ziege," *Biol. Zentralb.*, **41**, 447-455.

Krieg, H. (1916) "Zebroide Streifung an russischen Pferden," *Zool. Anz.*, **47**, 185-188.

—— (1924) "Scheckungsformen argentinischer Pferde," *Zeit. indukt. Abst.*, **34**, 134-139.

Kronacher, C. (1924) "Verebungsversuche und Beobachtungen an Schweinen," *Zeit. indukt. Abst.*, **34**, 1-120.

Kröning, F. (1924) "Uber die Modifikabilität der Säugerschekung," *Zeit. indukt. Abst.*, **35**, 113-138.

Kroon, H. M. (1923) "Die Bedeutung der genetischer Eigenschaftsanalyse für die Zucht der Haustiere," *Südd. landw. Tierz.*, **18**, 37-40.

Kuhlman, A. H. (1915) "Black and White Ayrshire," *Jour. Hered.*, **6**, 314-322.

—— (1915) "Aberdeen-Angus and Jersey Crosses," *Jour. Hered.*, **6**, 68-72.

Kuiper, K. (1920) "Onderzoekingen over Kleur en Teekening bij Runderen," *Genetica*, **2**, 137-161.

—— (1921) "Colour Inheritance in Cattle," *Jour. Hered.*, **12**, 102-109.

—— (1920) "Steriele soortsbastaarden," *Genetica*, **2**, 289-299.

Kuklenski (1915) "Uber das Vorkommen und die Verteilung des Pigmentes in den Organen und Geweben bei japanischen Seidenhühnern," *Arch. mikr. Anat.*, **87**, 1-37.

Kushakevitch (1910) "Die Entwicklungsgeschichte der Keimdrüsen von *Rana esculenta*," *Festsch. f. R. Hertwig.*, **2**.

Ladebeck, E. (1923) "Die Farben einiger Hühnerrassen," *Zeit. indukt. Abst.*, **30**, 1-62.

Lamon, H. M. (1921) "Lamona: A New Breed of Poultry," *Jour. Hered.*, **12**, 3-29.

Lancefield, D. E. (1922) "Linkage Relations of the Sex-linked Characters in *Drosophila obscura*," *Genet.*, **7**, 535-584.

Lancefield, R. C., and **Metz, C. W.** (1922) "The Sex-linked Group of Mutant Characters in *Drosophila willistoni*," *Amer. Nat.*, **56**, 211-241.

Lang, A. (1910) "Ueber alternative Vererbung bei Hunden," *Zeit. indukt. Abst.*, **3**, 1-32.

—— (1910) "Erblichkeitsverhältnisse der Ohrenlänge der Kaninchen nach Castle und das Problem der intermediären Vererbung und Bildung konstanter Bastardrassen," *Zeit. indukt. Abst.*, **4**, 1-23.

Laplaud, M., and **Garnier, A.** (1924) "La masculinité et la féminité dans l'espèce ovine," *Rev. d. zoot., rev. d. elev.*, **3**, 164-168, 256-265.

Laughlin, H. H. (1911) "Inheritance of Colour in Shorthorns," *Amer. Nat.*, **45**, 705-742.

—— (1912) "On the Inheritance of Coat-Colour in Cattle," *Amer. Nat.*, **46**, 1-28.

Lécaillon, A. (1922) "Sur les caractères d'un hybride issu de l'union de *Cairina maschata* × *Chenlopes ægypticus*," *C. R. Acad. Sci.*, **174**, 68-69.

—— (1922) "Sur les caractères d'un hybride mâle provenant de l'union de *Dafila acuta* × *Anas boschas*. Fécondité des hybrides obtenus par ce croisement," *C. R. Acad. Sci.*, **174**, 885-887, 1429-1433.

—— (1923) "La tendance à l'albinisme chez les hybrides de canard pilet mâle (*Dafila acuta*) et de cane sauvage (*Anas boschas*)," *C. R. Acad. Sci.*, **176**, 464-466.

Lefèvre, G. (1916) "Sex-linked Inheritance of Spangling in Poultry," *Anat. Rec.*, **11**, 499-500.

—— (1921) "Sex-linked Inheritance in Poultry," *Miss. Agric. Exp. Sta.* (Bull. No. 189), 58-59.

—— and **Rucker, E. H.** (1923) "The Inheritance of Spangling in Poultry," *Genet.*, **8**, 367-389.

Legendre, G. (1923) "L'élimination des mauvaises pondeuses d'après l'examen de leurs caractères extérieurs," *Rev. d. Zoot.*, **2**, 147-154.

Lenhossek, von M. (1913) *Das Problem der geschlechtsbestimmenden Ursachen.* Jena.

Lenoncio, M. O. (1924) "Effect of Age on the Hatching Quality of Eggs," *The Philip Agric.*, **12**, 349.

Lespinasse, V. D. (1913) "Transplantation of the Testicle," *Jour. Amer. Med. Ass.*, **61**, 1896.

Lewer, S. H. (1912) "The Modern Magpie Pigeon in the Making," *Feath. World*, **47**, 555-557.

Lichtenstern, R. (1916) "Mit Erfolg ausgeführte Hodentransplantation am Menschen," *Münch. med. Wochensch.*, **63**, 673-675.

Lienhart (1919) "On the Possibility of Telling the Sex of Eggs," *C. R. Acad. Sci.*, **169**, 102-104.

Lillie, F. R. (1917) "The Free-Martin: A Study of the Action of Sex Hormones in the Fœtal Life of Cattle," *Jour. Exp. Zool.*, **23**, 371-452.

—— (1917) "Sex-Determination and Sex-Differentiation in Mammals," *Proc. Nat. Acad. Sci.*, **3**, 464-470.

Lillie, F. R. (1923) "Supplementary Notes on Twins in Cattle," *Biol. Bull.*, **44**, 47-78.

—— and **Bascom, R. F.** (1922) "An Early Stage of the Free-Martin and the Parallel History of the Interstitial Cells," *Sci.*, **55**, 624-625.

Linnæus (1758) *Systema Naturae*, 10th Edit.

Lippincott, W. A. (1918) "The Case of the Blue Andalusian," *Amer. Nat.*, **52**, 95-115.

—— (1921) "Further Data on the Inheritance of Blue in Poultry," *Amer. Nat.*, **54**, 289-327.

—— (1923) "Genes for the Extension of Black Pigment in the Chicken," *Amer. Nat.*, **57**, 284-287.

Lipschütz, A. (1918) "The Formation of the Secondary Sexual Characters by the Gonads," *Arch. Entwickl.*, **44**, 396-410.

—— (1921) "Quantitative Untersuchungen über die innersekretorische Funktion der Testikel," *Deut. med. Wochensch.*, **13**, 1-3.

—— (1921) "L'action specifique de la sécrétion interne des glandes sexuelles et l'hypotèse de l'asexualité de la forme embryonnaire," *Rev. Sci.*, **59**, 33-36.

—— (1922) "The So-called Compensatory Hypertrophy of the Testicle after Unilateral Castration," *Jour. Physiol.*, **56**, 451-458.

—— (1923) "Beobachtungen sur Frage einseitiger Kastrationserscheinungen," *Arch. Entwickl.*, **97**, 395-399.

—— (1923) "Zur Frage der geschlechtsspezifischen Beeinflussung der Gonade durch eine heterosexuelle Geschlechtsdrüse," *Arch. Entwickl.*, **52**, 384-385.

—— (1923) "Ueber die kompensatorischen Reaktionen der Geschlechtsdrüsen," *Skand. Arch. Physiol.*, **43**, 45-54.

—— (1923) "Castration unilatérale chez la souris blanche," *C. R. Soc. Biol.*, **89**, 1137-1138.

—— (1924) "Condition de l'uterus après la castration partielle," *C. R. Soc. Biol.*, **90**, 197-199.

—— (1924) "Signes de castration postpubérale chez le cobaye. Cornes épidermiques dans le cul-de-sac du pénis," *C. R. Soc. Biol.*, **90**, 274-276.

—— (1924) "Réactions du testicule aux incisions ne touchant pas l'épididyme," *C. R. Soc. Biol.*, **90**, 273-274.

—— and **Ibrus, A.** (1923) "Sur la quantité de tissu interstitiel dans le testicule du lapin après la castration unilatérale," *C. R. Soc. Biol.*, **88**, 1259-1261.

—— and **Krause, W.** (1923) "Recherches quantitatives sur l'hermaphroditisme expérimental," *C. R. Soc. Biol.*, **89**, 220-223.

—— —— (1923) "Temps de latence dans l'hermaphroditisme expérimentale," *C. R. Soc. Biol.*, **89**, 1135-1137.

—— and **Ottow, B.** (1920) "Sur les conséquences de la castration partielle," *C. R. Soc. Biol.*, **83**.

—— and **Voss, H. E. V.** (1924) "Existe-t-il une innervation sympathique trophique du testicule?" *C. R. Soc. Biol.*, **90**, 201-202.

—— —— (1924) "Dynamique de l'hypertrophie ovarienne (experiences sur des chattes)," *C. R. Soc. Biol.*, **90**, 199-201.

—— and **Wagner, Karl** (1922) "Ueber die Hypertrophie der Zwischenzellen. Ihr Vorkommen und ihre Bedingungen," *Pflüg. Arch.*, **197**, 348-361.

—— —— (1922) "Nouvelles observations sur la fonction endocrine des cellules interstitielles du testicule chez les mammifères," *C. R. Soc. Biol.*, **86**, 306-307.

Lipschütz, A., and **Wagner, Karl** (1922) "Nouvelles observations sur l'hypertrophie des fragments ovariens," *C. R. Soc. Biol.*, **86**, 1122-1123.

—— —— (1922) "L'hypertrophie des cellules interstitielles du testicule, est-elle une réaction compensatrice endocrine?" *C. R. Soc. Biol.*, **87**, 15-17.

—— **Bormann, F.**, and **Wagner, K.** (1922) "Ueber Eunuchoidismus beim Kaninchen in Gegenwart von Spermatozöen in dem Hodenkanälchen und unterentwickelten Zwischenzellen," *Deut. med. Wochensch.*, **48**, 320-322.

—— —— (1922) "Sur l'hypertrophie des fragments ovariens dans la castration partielle," *C. R. Soc. Biol.*, **86**, 240-242.

—— **Ottow, B.**, and **Wagner, R.** (1921) "Ueber das Minimum der Hodensubstanz, das für die normale Gestaltung der Geschlechtsmerkmale ausreichend ist," *Pflüg. Arch.*, **188**, 75-86.

—— —— (1921) "Sur le ralentissement de la masculinisation dans la castration partielle," *C. R. Soc. Biol.*, **85**, 630-632.

—— —— (1921) (*a*) "Nouvelles observations sur la castration partielle." (*b*) "Sur des modifications histologicques subies par des restes du pôle inferieur du testicule dans la castration partielle. *Ibid.* . . . pôle superieur du testicule," *C. R. Soc. Biol.*, **85**, 42-43, 86-89.

—— **Wagner, C.**, and **Bormann, F.** (1922) "Ralentissement expérimental de la masculinisation," *C. R. Soc. Biol.*, **86**, 238-240.

—— **Wagner, C.**, and **Tamm, R.** (1922) "Sur l'hypertrophie des fragments ovariens dans la castration partielle," *C. R. Soc. Biol.*, **86**, 240-242.

—— and **Others** (1922) "On the Hypertrophy of the Interstitial Cells in the Testicle of the Guinea-pig under Different Experimental Condition," *Proc. Roy. Soc.*, *B.*, **93**, 132-142.

—— and **Others** (1922) "Further Experimental Investigations on the Hypertrophy of the Sexual Glands," *Proc. Roy. Soc.*, *B.*, **93**, 83-92.

—— and **Others** (1923) "Sur la question des differences de temperature entre les deux sexes," *C. R. Soc. Biol.*, **88**, 1261-1263.

—— and **Others** (1923) "New Experimental Data on the Question of the Seat of the Endocrine Function of the Testicle," *Endocr.*, **7**, 1-18.

Little, C. C. (1911) "The 'Dilute' Forms of Yellow Mice," *Sci.*, **33**, 896-897.

—— (1911) "The Influence of Heredity and of Environment in Determining the Coat-Colours in Mice," *Sci.*, **34**, 563.

—— (1912) "Yellow and Agouti Factors in Mice not Associated," *Amer. Nat.*, **46**, 491-493.

—— (1912) "Preliminary Note on the Occurrence of a Sex-limited Character in Cats," *Sci.*, **35**, 784-785.

—— (1913) "Yellow Agouti Factors in Mice," *Sci.*, **38**, 205.

—— (1913) "Experimental Studies of the Inheritance of Colour in Mice," *Carn. Inst. Publ.*, No. 179, 17-102.

—— (1914) "'Dominant' and 'Recessive' Spotting in Mice," *Amer. Nat.*, **48**, 74-82.

—— (1914) "Coat-Colour in Pointer Dogs," *Jour. Hered.*, **5**, 244-248.

—— (1915) "The Inheritance of Black-Eyed White Spotting in Mice," *Amer. Nat.*, **49**, 727-740.

—— (1916) "The Occurrence of Three Recognised Colour Mutations in Mice," *Amer. Nat.*, **50**, 335-349.

—— (1917) "The Relation of Yellow Coat-Colour and Black-Eyed White Spotting of Mice in Inheritance," *Genet.*, **2**, 433-444.

Little, C. C. (1917) "Evidence of Multiple Factors in Mice and Rats," *Amer. Nat.*, **51**, 457-580.

—— (1918-19) "Colour Inheritance in Cats, with special reference to the Colours Black, Yellow, and Tortoiseshell," *Jour. Genet.*, **7**, 279-290.

—— (1919) "The Fate of Individuals Homozygous for Certain Colour Factors in Mice," *Amer. Nat.*, **53**, 185-187.

—— (1920) "Is the Fœtal Tortoiseshell Tom Cat a Modified Female?" *Jour. Genet.*, **10**, 301-302.

—— (1920) "Is there Linkage between the Genes for Yellow and for Black in Mice?" *Amer. Nat.*, **54**, 267-270.

—— (1920) "Factors influencing the Growth of a Transplantable Tumor in Mice," *Jour. Exp. Zool.*, **31**, 307-326.

—— (1920) "Heredity of Susceptibility to a Transplantable Sarcoma of the Japanese Waltzing Mouse," *Sci.*, **51**, 467-468.

—— (1920) "Alternative Explanations for Exceptional Colour Classes in Doves and Canaries," *Amer. Nat.*, **54**, 162-175.

—— (1920) "A Note on the Origin of Piebald Spotting in Dogs," *Jour. Hered.*, **11**, 12-15.

—— (1920) "Note on the Occurrence of a Probable Sex-linked Lethal Factor in Mammals," *Amer. Nat.*, **54**, 457-460.

—— and **Bagg, H. J.** (1923) "A Brief Description of Abnormalities observed in the Descendants of X-Rayed Mice," *Anat. Rec.*, **24**, 413-414.

—— —— (1924) "The Occurrence of Four Inheritable Morphological Variations in Mice and their possible Relation to Treatment with X-Rays," *Jour. Exp. Zool.*, **41**, 45-99.

—— and **Castle, W. E.** (1909) "The Peculiar Inheritance of Pink-Eye among Coloured Mice," *Sci.*, **30**, 313-314.

—— and **Jones, E. C.** (1919) "The Inheritance of Coat-Colour in Great Danes," *Jour. Hered.*, **10**, 309-320.

—— and **Phillips, J. C.** (1913) "A Cross Involving Four Pairs of Mendelian Characters in Mice," *Amer. Nat.*, **47**, 760-762.

Lloyd-Jones, O. (1913) "The Heredity of Colour in the Tumbler Pigeons," *Sci.*, **37**, 613.

—— (1915) "What is a Breed?" *Jour. Hered.*, **6**, 531-537.

—— (1915) "Studies on Inheritance in Pigeons. II. A Microscopical and Chemical Study of the Feather Pigments," *Jour. Exp. Zool.*, **18**, 453-495.

—— (1916) "Mules that Breed," *Jour. Hered.*, **7**, 494-502.

—— and **Evvard, J. M.** (1916) "Inheritance of Colour and Horns in Blue-Grey Cattle," *Iowa Agric. Exp. Sta.* (Bull. No. 30), 67-106.

—— —— (1919) "Studies on Colour in Swine. I. The Hereditary Relationship of the Black of the Hampshire and the Red of the Duroc-Jersey," *Iowa Agric. Exp. Sta.* (Bull. No. 53), 203-208.

—— and **Hays, F.** (1918) "The Influence of Excessive Sexual Activity of Male Rabbits," *Jour. Exp. Zool.*, **25**, 571-613.

Lochow, F. (1921) "Beiträge uber Leistungsprufung und Zucht auf Leistung beim Milchvieh," *Arb. deut. landw. Ges.*, No. 309, 1-31.

Lock, R, H. (1908) "The Present State of Knowledge of Heredity in Pisum," *Ann. Roy. Bot. Gards.*, **4**, 93-111.

Loeb, Leo (1921) "Inheritance of Cancer in Mice," *Amer. Nat.*, **55**, 510-528.

Loewy, A. (1903) "Neuere Untersuchungen zur Physiologie der Geschlechtsorgane," *Ergeb. d. Physiol.*, **2**, 130-158.

—— and **Zondek, H.** (1921) "Der Einfluss der Samenstrangunterbindung auf den Stoffwechsel," *Deut. med. Wochensch.*, **13**.

Löhner, L. (1921) "In-Breeding and the Biochemical Specificity of the Individual," *Riv. Biol.*, **3**, 129-149.

Loisel, G., (1900) "Études sur la spermatogénèse chez le moineau domestique," *Jour. d. l'Anat. et Physiol.*, **36**, 160-185.

—— (1901) "Grenouille femelle presantant tous les caractères sexuels secondaires du mâle," *C. R. Soc. Biol.*, **55**, 204-206.

—— (1905) "Études sur l'hérédité de la coloration du plumage chez les pigeons voyageurs," *C. R. Soc. Biol.*, **58**, 465-468.

—— (1906) "Recherches sur l'hérédité des caractères du pélage chez le lapin," *C. R. Soc. Biol.*, **60**, 258-259.

—— (1910) "Études experimentales de l'influence du père dans l'hérédité chez le lapin," *C. R. Soc. Biol.*, **68**, 153-156.

Lotsy, J. P. (1923) "A Peculiar Eye-Colour among Malamute Dogs," *Genet.*, **5**, 77-78.

—— and **Kuiper, K.** (1922) "A Preliminary Statement of the Results of Mr Houwink's Experiments concerning the Origin of Some Domestic Animals," I.—*Genetica*, **4**, 139-161. (1923) II.-IV.—*Ibid.*, **5**, 1-50, 149-176, 357-373. (1924) V.—*Ibid.*, **6**, 221-282.

Lush, Jay L. (1921) "Inheritance in Swine," *Jour. Hered.*, **12**, 57-71.

—— (1922) "An Hereditary Notch in the Ears of Jersey Cattle," *Jour. Hered.*, **13**, 8-13.

—— (1923) "Cross-Breeding of Swine and the Chief Results," *Breed. Gaz.*, **83**, 74.

—— (1924) "Twinning in Brahma Cattle," *Jour. Hered.*, **15**, 25-27.

—— (1924) "Double Ears in Brahma Cattle," *Jour. Hered.*, **15**, 93-96.

Lutz, F. E. (1911) "Experiments with *Drosophila ampelophila* concerning Evolution," *Carn. Instit. Publ.*, No. 143, 1-40.

—— (1913) "Experiments concerning the Sexual Difference in the Wing-Length of *Drosophila ampelophila*," *Jour. Exp. Zool.*, **14**, 267-273.

Lydekker, R. (1912) *The Ox and its Kindred.* London.

Lynch, C. (1919) "An Analysis of Certain Cases of Intra-Specific Sterility," *Genet.*, **4**, 501-533.

—— (1921) "Short Ears an Autosomal Mutation in the House Mouse," *Amer. Nat.*, **55**, 421-426.

Macalik, B. (1924) "Rapports entre la quantité de la matière grasse du lait des brebis, la teneur en graisse et la finesse de leur laine et les facultés laitières," *Le Lait*, **4**, 193-200.

MacArthur, J. W. (1923) "Genetics in Fur Farming," *O. A. C. Rev.*, **35**, 267-268.

MacBride, E. W. (1923) "Dr Kammerer's Experiments," *Nature.*

—— (1924) "The Work of Tornier as Affording a Possible Explanation of the Causes of Mutation," *Eug. Rev.*, **15**, 545-555.

MacCandlish, A. C. (1919) "Environment and Breeding as Factors in influencing Milk Production," *Jour. Hered.*, **11**, 204-214.

MacCann, L. P. (1916) "Sorrel Colour in Horses," *Jour. Hered.*, **7**, 370-372.

MacClung, C. E. (1902) "The Accessory Chromosome—Sex Determinant?" *Biol. Bull.*, **3**, 43-84.

MacCurdy, H., and **Castle, W. E.** (1907) "Selection and Cross-Breeding in Relation to the Inheritance of Coat-Pigments and Coat-Patterns in Rats and Guinea-pigs," *Carn. Inst. Publ.*, No. 70, 1-55.

MacDowell, E. C. (1914) "Size-Inheritance in Rabbits," *Carn. Inst. Publ.*, No. 196, 1-55.

—— (1916) "Piebald Rats and Multiple Factors," *Amer. Nat.*, **50**, 719-742.

—— (1922) "The Influence of Alcohol on the Fertility of White Rats," *Genet.*, **7**, 117-141.

—— (1924) "Experiments with Rats on the Inheritance of Training," *Sci.*, **59**, 302-303.

—— and **Vicari, E. M.** (1921) "Alcoholism and White Rats. I. The Influence of Alcoholic Grandparents upon Maze Behaviour," *Jour. Exp. Zool.*, **33**, 209-291.

Machens (1915) "Fruchtbarkeit und Geschlechtsverhältniss beim veradelten Landschwein," *Berl. tierärzt. Wochensch.*, **31**, 559-562.

Mackenzie, K., and **Marshall, F. H. A.** (1917) "The Inheritance of Mutton Points in Sheep," *Trans. Highl. and Agric. Soc. Scotl.*, **29**, 37-49.

Macklin, M. T. (1923) "Description of Material from a Gynandromorph Fowl," *Jour. Exp. Zool.*, **38**, 355-375.

MacPherson, H. A. (1897) "On the Interbreeding of the Red Grouse (*Lagopus scotus*) and the Black Grouse (*Lyrurus tetrix*) *Ann. Scot. Nat. Hist.*, 15-17.

Magnusson, H. (1917) "Nachtblindheit beim Hunde," *v. Graefe's Arch. f. Ophth.*, **93**, 404-410.

Maillefer, Arthur (1921) "Variations des cygnes du Léman," *Bull. Soc. Vaud.*, **54**, 149-154.

Malinowsky, E. (1920) "Die Sterilität der Bastarde im Lichte des Mendelismus," *Zeit. indukt. Abst.*, **22**, 225-235.

Malone (1918) "Spermatogenesis in the Dog," *Trans. Amer. Micr. Soc.*, **37**, 97-110.

Mankato (1912) "The Breeding of the Racehorse." I. and II. Bruce Lowe Figure System Explained and Criticised. III. The Art of In-Breeding," *The Sport. Chron.* (Feb.).

Marshall, F. H. A. (1904) (1) "Fertility in Sheep," *Trans. Highl. and Agric. Soc. Scotl.* 1-10. (2) (1905, 1908) "Fertility in Scottish Sheep," *Proc. Roy. Soc., B.*, **77**, 58-62; *Trans. Highl. and Agric. Soc. Scotl.*, 1-13.

—— (1912) "On the Effects of Castration and Ovariotomy upon Sheep," *Proc. Roy. Soc., B.*, **85**, 27-33.

—— (1908) "The Effects of Environment and Nutrition upon Fertility," *Sci. Prog.*, No. 7, 1-9.

—— and **Hammond, J.** (1914) "The Effects of Complete and Incomplete Castration upon Horn Growth in Herdwick Sheep," *Jour. Physiol.*, **48**, 171-176.

Marshall, F. R. (1914) "Holstein Milk-Yield," *Jour. Hered.*, **5**, 437-439.

—— (1916) "Corriedale Sheep," *Jour. Hered.*, **7**, 88-95.

—— (1920) "Experiments in Breeding Fine-Wool Sheep," *Nat. Wool Grower*, **10**, 15-18.

—— and **Peel** (1910) "Fatness as a Cause of Sterility," *Jour. Agric. Sci.*, **3**, 383-389.

Martin, M. S. (1914) "A Race of White Canaries," *Jour. Hered.*, **5**, 220.

Martini, C. A. (1917) "Colour Inheritance in Shorthorns" (Thesis, Iowa State Coll.).

Mascheroni, E. (1916) "Improving Italian Sheep," *Indust. latt. and zoot.*, No. 3, **14**, 35-36.

—— (1924) "Horse-Rumped Cattle at the Piedmontese Breeders' Congress," *Inter. Rev. Agric.*, **2**, 154-156.

Masur (1916) "Influence of Colour in Horses on the Cure of Mange," *Berl. tierärzt. Wochensch.*, **32**, 294.

Matthews, J. W. (1912) "Sheep and Wool for the Farmer: The Cross-Bred *versus* the Merino," *The Produc. Rev.*, No. 1, **7**, 25-33.

—— (1920) "Sheep and Wool for Farmers. Cross-Breeding Experiments: Results of Lamb-Raising Trials," *Agri. Gaz. N.S. Wales*, **31**, 761-770, 846-852.

Mavor, J. W. (1923) "An Effect of X-Rays on the Linkage of Mendelian Characters in the First Chromosome of Drosophila," *Genet.*, **8**, 355-366.

—— (1923) "An Effect of X-Rays on Crossing-Over in Drosophila," *Proc. Soc. Exp. Biol. and Med.*, **20**, 335.

—— (1924) "The Production of Non-Disjunction by X-Rays," *Jour. Exp. Zool.*, **39**, 381-432.

May, H. G. (1923) "Inheritance of Weight in Poultry: Experiments at the Rhode Island Agricultural Experiment Station," *Anat. Rec.*, **24**, 417.

Meisenheimer, J. (1909) *Experimentelle Studien zur Soma und Geschlechts-differinzierung.* Jena.

Meldert, van L. (1921) "Studies on the Hereditary Transmission of Trotting Capacity in French Trotters," *Ann. de Gembloux*, **27**, 135-155.

Mendel, Gregor (1901) "Versuche über Pflanzenhybriden," 1-46. Engelman, Leipzig.

Metz, C. W. (1914) "Chromosome Studies in the Diptera. I. A Preliminary Survey of Five Different Types of Chromosome Groups in the Genus Drosophila," *Jour. Exp. Zool.*, **17**, 45-56.

—— (1916) "Chromosome Studies on the Diptera. II. The Paired Association of Chromosomes in the Diptera, and its Significance," *Jour. Exp. Zool.*, **21**, 213-280.

—— (1916) "Mutations in Three Species of Drosophila," *Genet.*, **1**, 591-607.

—— (1918) "The Linkage of Eight Sex-linked Characters in *Drosophila virilis*," *Genet.*, **3**, 107-134.

—— (1920) "Observations on the Sterility of Mutant Hybrids in *Drosophila virilis*," *Proc. Nat. Acad. Sci.*, **6**, 421-423.

—— (1920) "Correspondence between Chromosome Number and Linkage Groups in *Drosophila virilis*," *Sci.*, **51**, 417-418.

—— (1922) "Association of Homologous Chromosomes in Tetraploid Cells of Diptera," *Biol. Bull.*, **43**, 369-373.

—— and **Bridges, C. B.** (1917) "Incompatibility of Mutant Races in Drosophila," *Proc. Nat. Acad. Sci.*, **3**, 673-678.

—— and **Lancefield, R. C.** (1921) "Non-Disjunction and the Chromosome Relationship of *Drosophila willistoni*," *Proc. Nat. Acad. Sci.*, **7**, 225-229.

—— and **Moses, M. S.** (1923) "Chromosomes of Drosophila," *Jour. Hered.*, **14**, 195-204.

Miller, J. E. (1917) "Horned Horse," *Jour. Hered.*, **8**, 303-304.

Minoura, T. (1921) "A Study of Testis and Ovary Grafts on the Hen's Egg and their Effects on the Embryos," *Jour. Exp. Zool.*, **33**, 1-61.

Moenkhaus, W. J. (1904) "The Development of the Hybrids between *Fundulus heteroclitus* and *Menidia notata*, with Especial Reference to the Behaviour of the Maternal and Paternal Chromatin," *Amer. Jour. Anat.*, **3**, 29-66.

—— (1911) "The Effects of In-Breeding and Selection on Fertility, Vigour, and Sex-Ratio in *Drosophila ampelophila*," *Jour. Morph.*, **22**, 123-154.

Mohler, John R. (1909) "Importation of Brahman Cattle into Texas," *26th Ann. Rpt. Bur. of Anim. Indust., U.S.A. Dept. Agric.*, 84.

Mohr, O. L. (1919) "Character Changes caused by Mutation of an Entire Region of a Chromosome in Drosophila," *Genet.*, **4**, 275-282.

—— (1922) "Cases of Mimic Mutations and Secondary Mutations in the X-Chromosome of *Drosophila melanogaster*," *Zeit. indukt. Abst.*, **28**, 1-22.

—— (1923) "Das Deficiency-Phänomen bei *Drosophila melanogaster*," *Zeit. indukt. Abst.*, **30**, 287-283.

—— (1923) "Modifications of the Sex-Ratio through a Sex-linked Semi-lethal in *Drosophila melanogaster*," *Studia Mendel.*, 1-22.

—— (1923) "A Genetical and Cytological Analysis of a Section Deficiency involving four Units of the X-Chromosome in *Drosophila melanogaster*," *Zeit. indukt. Abst.*, **32**, 108-232.

—— and **Sturtevant, A. H.** (1919) "A Semi-lethal in *Drosophila funebris* that causes an Excess of Males," *Proc. Soc. Exp. Biol. and Med.*, **16**, 95-96.

Molhant, A. (1923) "L'hérédité de la couleur de la robe chez le cheval," *Jour. Soc. Nat. d. Agric. de Belg.*, **5**, 369-370, 378-379.

Moore, C. R. (1919) "On the Physiological Properties of the Gonads as Controllers of Somatic and Psychical Characteristics. I. The Rat," *Jour. Exp. Zool.*, **28**, 137-159.

—— (1919) "II. Growth of Gonadectomised Male and Female Rats," *Jour. Exp. Zool.*, **28**, 459-467.

—— (1921) "III. Artificial Hermaphroditism in Rats," *Jour. Exp. Zool.*, **33**, 129-171. (1921) "IV. Gonad Transplantation in the Guinea-pig," *Ibid.*, **33**, 365-389.

—— (1924) "The Behaviour of the Germinal Epithelium in Testis Grafts and in Experimental Cryptorchid Testes (Rats and Guinea-pigs)," *Sci.*, **59**, 41-44.

—— and **Oslund, R.** (1924) "Experiments on the Sheep Testis: Cryptorchidism, Vasectomy and Scrotal Insulation," *Amer. Jour. Physiol.*, **67**, 595-607.

—— and **Quick, W. J.** (1924) "The Scrotum as a Temperature Regulator for the Testis," *Amer. Jour. Physiol.*, **68**, 70-79.

Moore, J. S. (1924) "Influence of Heredity on Sex Control," *Jers. Bull. and Dairy World*, **43**, 696-697.

Morani, M. (1924) "Influenza di razioni ricche di lecitina sulla prolificità e sul sesso," *Riv. d. Zoot.*, **1**, 116-120.

Morgan, T. H. (1908) "Some Experiments in Heredity in Mice," *Sci.*, **27**, 493.

—— (1909) "Breeding Experiments with Rats," *Amer. Nat.*, **43**, 182-185.

—— (1909) (*a*) "Recent Experiments on the Inheritance of Coat-Colour in Mice," *Amer. Nat.*, **43**, 494-510. (1911) (*b*) "The Influence of Heredity and of Environment in Determining the Coat-Colour in Mice," *Ann. N.Y. Acad. Sci.*, **21**, 87-117.

Morgan, T. H. (1911) "Notes on two Crosses between different Races of Pigeons," *Biol. Bull.*, **21**, 215-221.

—— (1911) "Moulting and Change of Colour of Coat in Mice," *Sci.*, **34**, 918.

—— (1914) "Multiple Allelomorphs in Mice," *Amer. Nat.*, **48**, 449-458.

—— (1915) "Allelomorphs and Mice," *Ibid.*, **49**, 379-382.

—— (1918) "Inheritance of Number of Feathers of the Fantail Pigeons," *Amer. Nat.*, **52**, 5-27.

—— (1919) "The Genetic and Operative Evidence relating to Secondary Sexual Characters," *Carn. Inst. Publ.*, No. 285.

—— (1920) "The Effects of Castration of Hen-Feathered Campines," *Biol. Bull.*, **39**, 231-256.

—— (1920) "The Effects of Ligating the Testes of Hen-Feathered Cocks," *Biol. Bull.*, **39**, 248-256.

—— (1920) "The Genetic Factor for Hen-Feathering in the Sebright Bantam," *Biol. Bull.*, **39**, 257-259.

—— (1920) "The Endocrine Secretion of Hen-Feathered Fowls," *Endocrin.*, **4**, 381-385.

—— (1922) "The Mechanism of Heredity," *Proc. Roy. Soc.*, *B.*, **94**, 162-197.

—— (1922) *Some Possible Bearing of Genetics on Pathology*, 1-33. Lancaster.

—— (1923) "The Bearing of Mendelism on the Origin of Species," *Sci. Monthly*, **16**, 237-247.

—— and **Bridges, C. B.** (1916) "Sex-linked Inheritance in Drosophila," *Carn. Inst. Publ.*, No. 237, 87.

—— and **Goodale, H. D.** (1912) "Sex-linked Inheritance in Poultry," *Ann. N.Y. Acad. Sci.*, **22**, 113-133.

—— **Bridges, C. B.**, and **Sturtevant, A. H.** (1919) "Contributions to the Genetics of *Drosophila melanogaster*. I. The Origin of Gynandromorphs. II. The Second Chromosome Group of Mutant Characters. III. Inherited Linkage Variation in the Second Chromosome. IV. Demonstration of Genes modifying the character 'Notch,'" *Carn. Inst. Publ.*, No. 278, 1-388.

Morosini, A. (1915) "The Control of Sex," *Nuovi Ann. d. Agric. Sicil.*, **4**, 162-169.

Morris, R. T. (1916) "A Case of Testicle Grafting with Unexpected Results," *Jour. Amer. Med. Ass.*, **67**, 741-742.

Morse, Max (1909) "The Nuclear Components of the Sex Cells of Four Species of Cockroaches," *Arch. f. Zellf.*, **3**, 483-521.

Morton, Lord (1821) "A Communication of a Singular Fact in Natural History," *Phil. Trans.*, *Roy. Soc.*, **3**, 20-22.

Mršić, W. (1923) "Die Spätbefruchtung und deren Einfluss auf Entwicklung und Geschlechtsbildung," *Arch. mikr. Anat. Entwickl.*, **98**, 129-209.

Mudge, G. F. (1908) "On Some Features in the Hereditary Transmission of the Albino Character in the Black Piebald Coat in Rats," *Proc. Roy. Soc.*, *B.*, **80**, 388-399.

—— (1908) "On Some Features in the Hereditary Transmission of the Self-Black and the 'Irish' Coat Characters in Rats," *Proc. Roy. Soc.*, *B.*, **80**, 97-121.

Muller, H. J. (1916) "The Mechanism of Crossing-Over," *Amer. Nat.*, **50**, 193-221, 284-305, 350-366, 421-434.

—— (1916) "Variation due to Change in the Individual Gene," *Amer. Nat.*, **56**, 32-50.

—— (1918) "Genetic Variability, Twin Hybrids, and Constant Hybrids in a Case of Balanced Lethal Factors," *Genet.*, **3**, 422-499.

Muller, R. (1912) "Inzuchtsversuche mit vierhörnigen Ziegen," *Zeit. indukt. Abst.*, **7**, 240-251.

—— (1914) "Ein interessanter Fall Mendelscher Vererbung der Haarfarbe bei Kaninchen," *Ill. landw. Zeit.*, No. 11, 99.

—— (1914) "Die Haarstreifung der Rinder eine Mutation," *Deut. landw. Tierz.*, **18**, 29.

—— (1918) "Further In-Breeding Experiments with Many-Horned Goats," *Arch. wiss. u. prakt. Tierheilk.*, **44**, 198-206.

—— (1921) "Further In-Breeding Experiments with Many-Horned Goats," *Deut. landw. Tierz.*, **25**, 13-14.

Murray, J. A. (1911) "Cancerous Ancestry and the Incidence of Cancer in Mice," *Imp. Cancer Res. Fund, 4th Report*, 114-130.

Mussehl, F. E. (1923-4) "Sex Ratios in Poultry," *Poultry Sci.*, No. 2, 72-73.

—— and **Halbersleben, D. L.** (1923) "Influence of the Specific Gravity of Hen Eggs on Fertility, Hatching Power, and Growth of Chick," *Jour. Agri. Res.*, **23**, 717-720.

Nabours, R. (1912) "Evidence of Alternative Inheritance in the F_2 generation from Crosses of *Bos indicus* on *Bos taurus*," *Amer. Nat.*, **46**, 428-436.

—— (1913) "Possibilities for a New Breed of Cattle for the South," *Amer. Breed. Mag.*, **52**, 38-52.

Nachtsheim, H. (1913) "Cytologische Studien über die Geschlechtsbestimmung bei der Honigbiene," *Arch. f. Zellf.*, **11**, 169-241.

—— (1922) "Swine Heredity: Swine as a Reserve Stock for Experiments in Heredity," *Zeit. f. Schweinz.*, **29**, 65-71.

—— (1922) "Inheritance in Swine," *Inter. Rev. Agric.*, **13**, 1366-1367.

—— (1922) "Mendelismus und Tierzucht," *Die Naturw.*, **10**, 635-640.

—— (1924) "Vererbungsstudien an Schweinen: Die Vererbung von Farbe und Zeichnung," *Zeit. indukt. Abst.*, **33**, 317.

—— (1924) "Vererbungsversuche an Schweinen: Die Vererbung der Zitzenzahl," *Zeit. indukt. Abst.*, **33**, 307-311.

—— (1924) "Untersuchungen über Variation und Vererbung des Gesäuges beim Schwein," *Zeit. Tierz. and Züchtgsb.*, **2**, 113-161.

Nathusius, von S. (1911) "Die bisherigen Ergebnisse der Kreuzungsversuche mit dem Gayal (*Bibos frontalis*) im Hausthiergarten des Landw. Institut der Universität Halle," *Kühn. Arch.*, **1**, 61-105.

—— (1911) "Die Züchtungen mit Bückelrindern (*Bos indicus*) aus Indien und Afrika," *Kühn Arch.*, **1**, 225-252.

—— (1912) "Hochinteressante Vererbung bei Schweinen," *Ill. Landw. Zeit.*, **33**, 618.

Navez, P. (1923) "False Ribs in Cattle: Their Unimportance from the Stock-breeding Standpoint," *Ann. d. méd. vétér.*, **68**, 344-358.

Nehring, A. (1893) "Über Kreuzungen von *Cavia aperia* und *Cavia cobaya*," *Sitzb. d. Naturf. Ges.*, No. 10, 247-252.

—— (1894) "Kreuzungen von zahmen und wilden Meerschweinchen," *Zool. Gart.*, **35**, 1-6, 39-43, 74-78.

Newell, Wilmon (1915) "Inheritance in the Honey Bee," *Sci.*, **41**, 218-219.

Newman, H. H. (1908) "A Significant Case of Hermaphroditism in Fish," *Biol. Bull.*, **15**, 207-214.

—— (1917) *The Biology of Twins (Mammals)*. Chicago.

Newman, H. H. (1923) "Hybrid Vigour, Hybrid Weakness, and the Chromosome Theory of Heredity," *Jour. Exp. Zool.*, **37**, 169-205.

—— and **Patterson, J. T.** (1909) "A Case of Normal Identical Quadruplets in the Nine-Banded Armadillo," *Biol. Bull.*, **17**, 181-188.

New South Wales (1917) "The New Zealand Sheep Returns in 1917, and the Progress of Cross-Breeding in New South Wales," *The Pastoral Rev.*, **27**, 1040-1041.

Nichols, J. E. (1924) "Fertility in the Sheep," *Jour. Minist. Agric.*, **31**, 835-843.

Niedoba, T. (1923) "Uber Vererbung von Haarrichtungen," *Wien. tierärzt. Monats.*, **10**, 3.

Nilsson-Ehle, H. (1909) *Kreuzungsuntersuchungen an Hafer und Weizen*, 1-122.

Nixon, C. (1911) "A Study of the First, Second and Third Year Egg-Production of White Leghorn Hens," *Rpt. Amer. Breed. Ass.*, **7**, 279-289.

Nonidez, J. F. (1920) "The Internal Phenomena of Reproduction in Drosophila," *Biol. Bull.*, **39**, 207-230.

—— (1920) "Studies on the Gonads of the Fowl. I. Hematopoietic Processes in the Gonads of Embryos and Mature Birds," *Amer. Jour. Anat.*, **28**, 81-107.

—— (1922) "Estudios sobre las Gónadas de la Gallina. II. El Tejido intersticial del Ovario," *Lib. en Hon. de D. Santiago, Ramón y Cajal*, **2**, 137-157.

—— (1922) "Studies on the Gonads of the Fowl. III. The Origin of the so-called Luteal Cells in the Testis of Hen-Feathered Cocks," *Amer. Jour. Anat.*, **31**, 110-124.

Noorduyn, C. L. W. (1908) "Die Erblichkeit der Farben bei Kanarienvögeln," *Arch. f. Rass. und Ges. Biol.*, 161-177.

Nussbaum, M. (1880) "Die Differenzierung des Geschlechts im Tierreich," *Arch. f. mikr. Anat.*, **18**, 1-121.

—— (1901) "Zur Entwicklung des Geschlechts beim Huhn," *Anat. Anz.*, **19**, 38-40.

Nuttal, J. S. W. (1918) "A Note on the Inheritance of Colour in One Breed of Pigeons: An Attempt to Demonstrate a Mendelian Type of Transmission," *Jour. Genet.*, **7**, 119-124.

Ohio Agricultural Experimental Station (1918) "Breeding Sows before Litters are Weaned" (Mo. Bull., **3**, 142-143).

Ohler (1913) "Stirnhörner bei einem Pferde," *Deut. landw. Tierz.*, 31.

Olson, T. M., and **Biggar, T. M.** (1922) "Influence of Pure Bred Dairy Sires," *S. Dakot. Agric. Exp. Sta.* (Bull. No. 198), 433-466.

Onslow, H. (1915) "A Contribution to our Knowledge of the Chemistry of Coat-Colour in Animals and of Dominant and Recessive Whiteness," *Proc. Roy. Soc., B.*, **89**, 36-58.

—— (1922) "A Note on the Inheritance of the 'Steel' Coat-Colour in Rabbits," *Jour. Genet.*, **12**, 91-99.

Oordt, van G. J. (1924) "Intersexualiteit bij Vertebraten," *Vakbl. v. Biol.*, **5**, 129-135.

Oslund, R. (1923-1924) "A Study of Vasectomy in Rats and Guinea-pigs," *Amer. Jour. Physiol.*, **67**, 422-443.

Painter, T. S. (1921) "The Y-Chromosome in Mammals," *Sci.*, **53**, 503-504.

—— (1922) "Studies in Mammalian Spermatogenesis. I. The Spermatogenesis of the Opossum (*Didelphys virginians*)," *Jour. Exp. Zool.*, **35**, 13-46.

Painter, T. S. (1924) "Studies in Mammalian Spermatogenesis. IV. The Sex Chromosomes of Monkeys," *Jour. Exp. Zool.*, **39**, 433-461.

—— (1924) "Studies in Mammalian Spermatogenesis. V. The Chromosomes of the Horse," *Jour. Exp. Zool.*, **39**, 229-248.

Palmer, L. S. (1915) "The Physiological Relationship between the Yellow Pigment of the Hen and the Xanthophyll of Plants," *Jour. Biol. Chem.*, **23**, 261-279.

—— (1923) "Relation of Skin-Colour and Fat-Production in Dairy Cows," *Jour. Dairy Sci.*, **6**, 83-84.

—— and **Kempster, H. L.** (1919) "The Physiological Relationship between Fecundity and the Natural Yellow Pigmentation of Certain Breeds of Fowls," *Jour. Biol. Chem.*, **39**, 313-330.

Pap, E. (1921) "Ueber Vererbung von Farbe und Zeichnung bei dem Kaninchen," *Zeit. indukt. Abs.*, **26**, 185-270.

Parana, de (1910) "Principles of Breeding and the Origin of Domestic Breeds of Animals," *26th Ann. Rep. Bur. Anim. Indust., U.S.A. Dept. Agric.*

Parker and **Bullard** (1913) "On the Size of Litters and the Number of Nipples in Swine," *Proc. Amer. Acad. Arts. and Sci.*, **49**, 399-426.

Parkes, A. S. (1923) "Head-length Dimorphism of Mammalian Spermatozoa," *Q. J. M. S.*, **67**, 617-625.

—— (1923) "Studies on the Sex-Ratio and the Related Phenomena. I. Fœtal Retrogression in Mice," *Proc. Roy. Soc.*, **95**, 551-558.

—— (1923) "Studies on the Sex-Ratio and the Related Phenomena. III. The Influence of Size of Litter," *Ann. Appl. Biol.*, **10**, 287-292.

—— (1923) "Studies on the Sex-Ratio and the Related Phenomena. IV. The Frequencies of Sex Combinations in Pig Litters," *Biometrika*, **15**, 373-381.

—— (1923-24) "Studies on the Sex-Ratio and Related Phenomena. V. The Sex-Ratio in Mice and its Variation," *Brit. Jour. Exp. Biol.*, **1**, 323-334.

Parlour, W. (1913) "Jersey-Angus Cattle," *Live Stock Jour.*, **77**, 85.

Patterson, J. T. (1920) "A New Variety of Roof Rat," *Sci.*, **52**, 249-250.

Pavlov, I. P. (1923) "New Researches on Conditioned Reflexes," *Sci.*, **58**, 359-361.

Pays-Mellier, G., and **Trouessart, E.** (1907) "Sur deux hybrides de Paon et de Poule cochinchinoise," *C. R. Acad. Sci.*, **145**, 1203-1205.

Pazzini, P. (1915) "The Improvement of the Sheep of the Middle Tiber Valley by means of Crossing with Rambouillet Merinos," *Staz. agrar. sper. ital.*, **48**, pt. 9, 649-676.

Pearl, R. "The Relation of the Results obtained in Breeding Poultry for Increased Egg Production to Problem of Selection," *13th Meet. Soc. Prom. Agric. Sci.*, 1-8

—— (1908) "Appliances and Methods for Pedigree Poultry Breeding," *Maine Agric. Exp. Sta.* (Bull. No. 159), 239-274.

—— (1910) "Breeding for Production in Dairy Cattle in the light of Recent Advances in the Study of Inheritance," *8th Ann. Rept. Comm. Agric. Sta. Maine*, 118-128.

—— (1910) "Inheritance of Hatching Quality of Eggs in Poultry," *Amer. Breed. Mag.*, **1**, 129-133.

—— (1911) "Variation in the Single Combs of Fowls," *Mendel Journal* (Feb.).

—— (1911) "Inheritance in Blood Lines in Breeding Animals for Performance, with Special Reference to the 200-Egg Hen," *Ann. Rpt. Amer. Breed. Ass.*, **6**, 317-326.

Pearl, R. (1911) "Inheritance of Fecundity in the Domestic Fowl," *Amer. Nat.*, **45**, 321-345.

—— (1911) "Data on the Relative Conspicuousness of Barred and Self-Coloured Fowls," *Amer. Nat.*, **45**, 107-117.

—— (1912) "Notes on the History of Barred Breeds of Poultry," *Biol. Bull.*, **22**, 297-308.

—— (1912) "The Mode of Inheritance of Fecundity in the Domestic Fowl," *Jour. Exp. Zool.*, **13**, 153-266.

—— (1912) "The Mendelian Inheritance of Fecundity in the Domestic Fowl," *Amer. Nat.*, **46**, 697-711.

—— (1912) "Mode of Inheritance of Fecundity in the Domestic Fowl," *Maine Agric. Exp. Sta.* (Bull. No. 205), 283-394.

—— (1913) "Genetics and Breeding," *Sci.*, **37**, 539-546.

—— (1913) "On the Correlation between the Number of Mammæ of the Dam and Size of Litter in Mammals," *Proc. Soc. Exp. Biol. and Med.*, **11**, 27-32.

—— (1913) "The Measurement of the Intensity of In-Breeding," *Maine Agric. Exp. Sta.* (Bull. No. 215), 123-138.

—— (1913) "A Contribution towards an Analysis of the Problem of In-Breeding," *Amer. Nat.*, **47**, 577-614.

—— (1914) "On the Law relating Milk Flow to Age in Dairy Cattle," *Proc. Soc. Exp. Biol. and Med.*, **12**, 18-19.

—— (1915) *Modes of Research in Genetics.* New York.

—— (1915) "Mendelian Inheritance of Fecundity in the Domestic Fowl, and Average Flock Production," *Amer. Nat.*, **49**, 306-317.

—— (1915) "Seventeen Years' Selection of a Character showing Sex-linked Mendelian Inheritance," *Amer. Nat.*, **49**, 595-608.

—— (1915) "Studies in In-Breeding. VI. Some Further Considerations regarding Cousin and Related Kinds of Mating," *Amer. Nat.*, **49**, 570-575.

—— (1915) "Further Data on the Measurement of In-Breeding," *Maine Agric. Exp. Sta.* (Bull. No. 243), 226-248.

—— (1916) "Fecundity in the Domestic Fowl and the Selection Problem," *Amer. Nat.*, **50**, 89-105.

—— (1916) "Some Effects of the Continued Administration of Alcohol to the Domestic Fowl, with Special Reference to the Progeny," *Proc. Nat. Acad. Sci.*, **2**, 675-683.

—— (1916) "On the Differential Effect of Certain Calcium Salts upon the Rate of Growth of the Two Sexes of the Domestic Fowl," *Sci.*, **44**, 687-688.

—— (1916) "The Animal Breeding Industry," *Pop. Sci. Monthly* (July), 23-30.

—— (1917) "The Selection Problem," *Amer. Nat.*, **51**, 65-91.

—— (1917) "Effect of Heavy Laying in the Fowl," *Sci.*, **46**, 220-222.

—— (1917) "Fertility and Age in the Domestic Fowl," *Proc. Nat. Acad. Sci.*, **3**, 354-356.

—— (1917) "Studies on the Physiology of Reproduction in the Domestic Fowl. XVII. The Influence of Age upon Reproductive Ability, with a Description of a New Reproductive Index," *Genet.*, **2**, 417-432.

—— (1917) "Sex-Ratio in the Domestic Fowl," *Proc. Amer. Phil. Soc.*, **56**, 416-436.

—— (1917) "The Change of Milk Flow with Age," *Maine Agric. Exp. Sta.* (Bull. No. 262).

Pearl, R. (1917) "Report of Progress on Animal Husbandry Investigations in 1916," *Maine Agric. Exp. Sta. Rpt.*

—— (1920) "A Contribution to the Genetics of the Practical Breeding of Dairy Cattle," *Proc. Nat. Acad. Sci.*, **6**, 225-233.

—— and **Boring, A.** (1914) "Some Physiological Observations regarding Plumage Patterns," *Sci.*, **39**, 143-144. "The Measurement of Changes in the Rate of Fecundity of the Individual Fowl," *Ibid.*, 383-384. "Improving Egg Production by Breeding," *Ann. Rpt. Maine Agric. Exp. Sta.*, 217-236.

—— and **Curtis, M.** (1909) "Studies on the Physiology of Reproduction in the Domestic Fowl. III. A Case of Incomplete Hermaphroditism," *Biol. Bull.*, **17**, 271-286.

—— —— (1915) "Studies on the Physiology of Reproduction in the Domestic Fowl. X. Further Data on Somatic and Genetic Sterility," *Jour. Exp. Zool.*, **19**, 45-59.

—— **Gowen, J. W.**, and **Miner, J. R.** (1919) "Studies in Milk Secretion. VIII. Transmitting Qualities of Jersey Sires for Milk Yield, Butter-Fat Percentage and Butter-Fat" (with Appendix Table), *Ann. Rpt. Maine Agric. Exp. Sta.*, 89-204.

—— and **Miner, J. R.** (1919) "Variation of Ayrshire Cows in the Quantity and Fat-Content of their Milk," *Jour. Agric. Res.*, **17**, 285-322.

—— and **Parker, Sylvia** (1921-22) "Experimental Studies on the Duration of Life," *Amer. Nat.*, **55**, **56**, 481-509, 174-178, 273-280.

—— —— (1922) "On the Influence of Density of Population upon the Rate of Reproduction in Drosophila," *Proc. Nat. Acad. Sci.*, **8**, 212-219.

—— —— (1924) "Experimental Studies on the Duration of Life. IX. New Life Tables for Drosophila," *Amer. Nat.*, **58**, 71-82.

—— **Parker, S.**, and **Gonzalez, B. M.** (1924) "Experimental Studies on the Duration of Life. VII. The Mendelian Inheritance of Duration of Life in Crosses of Wild Type and Quintuple Stocks of *D. melanogaster*," *Amer. Nat.*, **57**, 153-192.

—— and **Parshley, H. M.** (1913) "Data on Sex-Determination in Cattle," *Biol. Bull.*, **24**, 205-225.

—— and **Pearl, M. D.** (1909) "Data on Variation in the Comb of the Domestic Fowl," *Biometrika*, **6**, 420-432.

—— and **Schoppe, W. F.** (1879, 1921) "Studies on the Physiology of Reproduction in the Domestic Fowl. XVIII. Further Observations on the Anatomical Basis of Fecundity," *Jour. Exp. Zool.*, **34**, 101-118.

—— and **Surface, Frank** (1909) "Is there a Cumulative Effect of Selection?" *Zeit. indukt. Abst.*, **2**, 257-275.

—— —— (1909, 1911, 1915) "A Biometrical Study of Egg Production in the Domestic Fowl." I., II., III., *Bur. Anim. Indust.*, *U.S. Dept. Agric.* (Bull. No. 110), pt. 1, 1-341.

—— —— (1909) I. "Data on the Inheritance of Fecundity obtained from the Records of Egg Production of the Daughters of 200 Egg Hens," *Maine Agric. Exp. Sta.* (Bull. No. 166), 49-84.

—— —— (1909) II. "Data on Certain Factors influencing the Fertility and Hatching of Eggs." *Ibid.*, 105-164.

—— —— (1910) "Studies on Hybrid Poultry," *Ann. Rpt. Maine Agric. Exp. Sta.*, 84-115.

Pearl, R., and **Surface, Frank** (1910) "On the Inheritance of the Barred Colour Pattern in Poultry," *Arch. Entwickl.*, **30**, 45-61.

—— (1910) "Further Data regarding the Sex-limited Inheritance of the Barred Colour Pattern in Poultry," *Sci.*, **32**, 870-874.

—— —— (1915) "Sex Studies. VII. On the Assumption of Male Secondary Characters by a Cow with Cystic Degeneration of the Ovaries," *Ann. Rpt. Maine Agric. Exp. Sta.*, 65-80.

Pearson, K. (1911) *The Grammar of Science*, 3rd Edition. A. & C. Black, London.

Pearson, K., **Lee, A.**, and **Bramley Moore, L.** (1899) "Genetic (Reproductive) Selection. Inheritance of Fertility in Man and of Fecundity in Thoroughbred Horse," *Phil. Trans. Roy. Soc.* (A), **192**, 257-330.

Pease, M. S. (1921) "A Note on Professor Morgan's Theory of Hen-Feathering in Cocks," *Proc. Camb. Phil. Soc.*, **21**, 22-26.

Pergoli, V. (1924) "Le odierne conoscenze sull' eredità e la loro pratica applicazione zootecnica," *Giorn. Agric. del Domenica*, **34**, 60.

Peters, J. (1913) "The Inheritance of the Property of Milk Production and the Utilisation of the Results obtained by the Control Society," *Deut. landw. Tierz.*, **17**, 121-125, 133-135, 145-149.

—— (1924) "Neue Untersuchungen über die Vererbung der Milchleistunge," *Mitt. deut. landw. Ges.*, **39**, 243-252.

Pézard, A. (1914) "Developpement expérimental des Ergots et Croissance de la Crète chez les Gallinacés," *C. R. Acad. Sci.*, **158**, 513-516.

—— (1915) "Transformation expérimentale des caractères sexuels secondaires, chez les Gallinacés," *C. R. Acad. Sci.*, **160**, 260-263.

—— (1918) "Le conditionnement physiologique des caractères sexuels secondaires chez les oiseaux." (Thèse, Paris.)

—— (1919) "Secondary Sexual Characters in Birds," *Trav. Lab. Prof. E. Gley, Coll. Franc.*, **4**.

—— (1919) "Alimentary Castration in Cock submitted to an Exclusively Carnivorous Diet," *C. R. Acad. Sci.*, **49**, 1177-1179.

—— (1920) "Castration of Cocks during Puberty and Generalisation of the Parabolic Law of Regression," *C. R. Acad. Sci.*, **171**, 1081-1083.

—— (1920) "Secondary Sexual Characters and Endocrinology," *Endocr.*, **4**, 527-540.

—— (1921) "The 'All-or-Nothing' Law, or the Law of Functional Constancy in Relation to the Action of the Testicle considered as an Endocrine Gland," *C. R. Acad. Sci.*, **172**, 89-92.

—— (1921) "The Latent Period in Experiments of Testicular Transplantation and the Law of 'All-or-Nothing,'" *C. R. Acad. Sci.*, **172**, 176-178.

—— (1921) "Numerical Law of Regression of Certain Secondary Sexual Characters," *Jour. Gen. Physiol.*, **3**, 271-283.

—— (1922) "Notion de 'seuil differentiel' et explication humorale du gynandromorphisme des oiseaux bipartis," *C. R. Acad. Sci.*, **174**, 1573-1576.

—— (1922) "Modifications périodiques ou définitives des caractères sexuels secondaires et du comportement chez les Gallinacés," *Ann. Sci. Nat.*, **5**, 83-105.

—— (1922) "Notion de 'seuils differentiels' et la masculinisation progressive de certains oiseaux femelles," *C. R. Acad. Sci.*, **174**, 236-238.

—— (1922) "La loi de 'tout ou rien' et le gynandromorphisme chez les oiseaux," *Jour d. physiol. path. gén.*, **20**, 200-211.

Pézard, A. (1922) "La loi du 'tout ou rien' et le gynandromorphisme chez les oiseaux. II. Le gynandromorphisme endocrinien. III. Gynandromorphisme ou intersexualité. IV. Les disharmonies endocriniennes," *Jour. d. physiol. path. gén.*, **20**, 495-508.

—— (1923) "Tissu interstitiel et caractères sexuels secondaires des oiseaux," *C. R. Soc. Biol.*, **88**, 245-247.

—— and **Caridroit, F.** (1922) "Interpénétration surrénalo-testiculaire chez des coqs castrés incomplètement," *C. R. Acad. Sci.*, **175**, 784-787.

—— —— (1922) "L'hérédité sex-linked chez les Gallinacés. Interpretation fondée sur l'existence de la forme neutre et sur les propriétés de l'hormone ovarienne," *C. R. Acad. Sci.*, **175**, 910-912.

—— —— (1922) "The Action of the Testicular Hormone on the Relative Valency of the Allelomorphic Factors in Sheep (Dorset and Suffolk)," *C. R. Acad. Sci.*, **175**, 1099-1102.

—— —— (1923) "Gynandromorphisme chez les Gallinacées," *C. R. Acad. Sci.*, **177**, 76-79.

—— **Sand, K.**, and **Caridroit, F.** (1923) "Production expérimentale du gynandromorphisme biparti chez les oiseaux," *C. R. Acad. Sci.*, **176**, 615-618.

—— —— —— (1923) "Le gynandromorphisme biparti expérimental," *C. R. Soc. Biol.*, **89**, 1103-1104.

—— —— —— (1923) "Gynandromorphisme biparti fragmentaire d'origine mâle," *C. R. Soc. Biol.*, **89**, 1271-1282.

—— —— —— (1923) "Féminisation d'un coq adulte de race Leghorn doré," *C. R. Soc. Biol.*, **89**, 947-948.

Philipchenko, J. (1919) "L'hérédité de la pigmentation chez les canaries," *Bull. Acad. Sci. Russ.*, 1233-1251.

Philiptschenko, I. (1915) "Observations on the Skulls of Hybrids between Wild and Domesticated Horses and Cattle," *C. R. Soc. Biol.*, **78**, 636-638.

Phillippi, E. (1904) "Ein neuer Fall von Arrhenoidie," *Sitz. Ges. naturf. Freund.*, 196-197.

—— (1909) "Fortpflanzungsgeschichte der viviparen Teleosteer *Glaridichthys januarius* und *G. decem-maculatus* in ihren Einfluss und Lebensweise makroskopische und mikroskopische Anatomie," *Zool. Jahrb.*, **27**, 1-94.

Phillips, J. C. (1912) "Size Inheritance in Ducks," *Jour. Exp. Zool.*, 369-380.

—— (1913) "Reciprocal Crosses between Reeve's Pheasant and the Common Ring-Neck Pheasant producing Unlike Hybrids," *Amer. Nat.*, **47**, 701-704.

—— (1914) "A Further Study of Size Inheritance in Ducks, with Observations on the Sex-Ratio of Hybrid Birds," *Jour. Exp. Zool.*, **16**, 131-148.

—— (1916) "Two Pheasant Crosses," *Jour. Hered.*, **7**, 12-16.

—— (1921) "A Further Report on Species Crosses in Birds," *Genet.*, **6**, 366-383.

Pick, L. (1914) "Uber den wahren Hermaphroditismus des Menschen und der Säugetiere," *Arch. mik. Anat.*, **84**, 119-242.

Pictet, Arnold, and **Ferrero** (1921) "Recherches de génétique dans des croisements de Cobayes," *C. R. Séan. Soc. phys. d'hist. nat.*, **38**, 32-37, 56-60, 97-100.

—— —— —— (1922) "Hérédité de la longeur des poils chez les Cobayes," *C. R. Séan. Soc. phys. d'hist. nat.*, **39**, 57-60.

—— —— —— (1922) "Hérédité de la panachure chez les Cobayes agoutis," *C. R. Séan Soc. phys. d'hist. nat.*, **39**, 35-38.

Pictet, Arnold, and **Ferrero** (1923) "Recherches sur l'hérédité de Cobayes albinos porteur d'un facteur de coloration," *C. R. Séan. Soc. phys. hist. nat.*, **40**, 147-150.

Pitt, F. (1919-20) "Notes on the Inheritance of Colour and Markings in Pedigree Hereford Cattle," *Jour. Genet.*, **9**, 281-302.

—— (1921) "Notes on the Genetic Behaviour of Certain Characters in the Polecat, Ferret, and in Polecat × Ferret Hybrids," *Jour. Genet.*, **11**, 99-116.

—— (1921) "Inheritance of Colour and Markings in Park Cattle," *Park Cattle Herd Book*, 213-218.

Plank, van der, G. M. (1920) "Kruising van Jersey met zwartbont vee," *Genet.*, **2**, 300.

—— (1924) "Ein Beitrag zur Untersuchung der Vererbung des Steppganges," *Zeit. f. Tierz. und Züchts.*, **1**, 91-95.

Plate, L, (1910) "Die Erbformeln der Farbenrasse von *Mus musculus*," *Zool. Anz.*, **35**, 634-640.

—— (1912) "Bemerkungen über die Farbenrassen der Hausmaus und die Schreibweise der Erbformeln," *Zeit. indukt. Abst.*, **6**, 275-280.

—— (1918) "Vererbungsstudien an Mäusen," *Arch. Entwickl.*, **44**, 291-336.

Plough, H. H. (1917) "The Effect of Temperature on Crossing-Over in Drosophila," *Jour. Exp. Zool.*, **24**, 147-210.

—— (1921) "Further Studies on the Effect of Temperature on Crossing-Over," *Jour. Exp. Zool.*, **32**, 187-202.

Pocock, R. I. (1911) "On Tabby Cats, and some Features in the Inheritance of Their Coat-Pattern and Colour," *Mend. Jour.*, **1**, 53-73.

Poll, H. (1909) "Zur Lehre von den sekundären Sexualcharakteren," *Sitzb. Ges. naturf. Freund.*, No. 6, 331-358.

—— (1912) "Mischlingsstudien VII. Mischlinge von *Phasianus* und *Gallus*," *Zitsb. preuss. Akad. Wiss.*, **38**, 864-882.

—— (1920) "Mischlingsstudien VIII. Pfaumischlinge, nebst einen Beitrag zur Kern-Erbfaktoren Lehre," *Arch. mikr. Anat.*, **95**, 365-458.

—— (1921) "Die Zahlenverhältnis der Geschlechter bei Vögelmischlingen," *Jour. f. Ornith.*, 512-526.

Porcherel, A. (1921) "Colour Inheritance in Mammals and Domestic Birds," *Rev. vétér.*, **72**, 541-548, 680-689.

Prawochensky, B. (1924) "La correlation entre le modèle des chevaux et leur vitesse," *Rev. d. zoot. rev. d. élev.*, **3**, 310-316.

Prévot, M. (1911) "Relations entre la couleur, la sexualité et la productivité chez le Cobaye," *Rapp. IV. Conf. Génét., Paris*, 511-513.

Przibram, H. (1907) "Vererbungsversuche über asymmetrische Augenfärbung bei Angorakatzen," *Arch. Entwickl.*, **25**, 260-265.

Pucci, C. (1915) "Some Experiments on the Mendelian Laws of Heredity," *Il Moder. Zooiat.*, **4**, 145-153.

—— (1915) "Zebu Crosses: Experiments Carried out at the Perugia Institute of Animal Husbandry," *L'Ital. agric.*, **52**, 58-63.

Punnett, R. C. (1903) "On Nutrition and Sex-Determination in Man," *Cambr. Phil. Soc. Trans.*, **12**, 262-276.

—— (1908) "Mendelism in Relation to Disease," *Proc. Roy. Soc. Med.*, 1-27.

—— (1909) "On the Alleged Influence of Lecithin upon the Determination of Sex in Rabbits," *Proc. Camb. Phil. Soc.*, **15**, 92-93.

Punnett, R. C. (1912) (1) "Inheritance of Coat-Colour in Rabbits," *Jour. Genet.*, **2**, 222-238. (1915) (2) "Further Experiments on the Inheritance of Coat-Colour in Rabbits," *Ibid.*, **5**, 37-50.

—— (1920) "The Genetics of the Dutch Rabbit: A Criticism," *Jour. Gente.*, **9**, 303-317.

—— (1922) "Mendelism and the Poultry Industry," *Nat. Poult. Jour.* (Jan.).

—— (1922) "Research in Animal Breeding, I.-IV.," *Jour. Minist. Agric.*, **28**, 11-17, 110-116, 252-259, 326-334.

—— (1924) "On the 'Japanese' Rabbit," *Jour. Genet.*, **14**, 231-240.

—— and **Bailey, Maj.** (1914) "On Inheritance of Weight in Poultry," *Jour. Genet.*, **4**, 23-39.

—— —— (1918) "Genetic Studies in Rabbits. I. On the Inheritance of Weight," *Jour. Genet.*, **8**, 1-25.

—— —— (1918) "Genetic Studies in Poultry. I. Inheritance in Leg-Feathering," *Jour. Genet.*, **7**, 203-213.

—— —— (1920) "Genetic Studies in Poultry. II. Inheritance of Egg-Colour and Broodiness," *Jour. Genet.*, **10**, 277-292.

—— —— (1921) "Genetic Studies in Poultry. III. Hen-Feathered Cocks," *Jour. Genet.*, **11**, 37-57.

—— and **Bateson, W. E.** (1905) "A Suggestion as to the Nature of the 'Walnut' Comb in Fowls," *Proc. Camb. Phil. Soc.*, **13**, 165-168.

—— —— (1911) "The Inheritance of the Peculiar Pigmentation of the Silky Fowl," *Jour. Genet.*, **1**, 185-203.

—— and **Pease, M. S.** (1921) "Genetic Studies in Poultry. IV. On the Barred Plumage of Certain Breeds," *Jour. Genet.*, **11**, 235-240.

Pusch, G. (1919) "Interbreeding Live Stock," *Jour. Hered.*, **10**, 88-89.

Ragsdale, A. C., Turner, C. W., and **Brody, S.** (1924) "The Relation between Age and Fat-Production in Dairy Cows," *Jour. Dairy Sci.*, **7**, 189-196.

Ramm (1909) *Arten und Rassen des Rindes.*

Raspail, X. (1902) "Note sur une race de lapins albinos, issue du croisement d'une femelle de lapin russe et d'un mâle garenne," *Bull. soc. nat. acclimat.*, **49**, 170-175.

Rensch, Bernhard (1923) "Ueber die Ursachen von Riesen- und Zwergwuchs beim Haushuhn," *Zeit. indukt. Abst.*, **31**, 268-286.

Research Committee on Animal Breeding (1915) "Live Stock Genetics," *Jour. Hered.*, **6**, 21-31.

Richardsen (1914) "Vererbung des Rinderfarbung bei Farbenkreuzungen," *Deut. landw. Tierz.*, No. 6, 61.

Richardson, T. C. (1924) "The 'Pinto' Burro," *Jour. Hered.*, **15**, 73-74.

Riddle, O. (1907) "A Study of Fundamental Bars in Feathers," *Biol. Bull.*, **12**, 165-174.

—— (1908-9) "Our Knowledge of Melanin Colour Formation and its Bearing on the Mendelian Description of Heredity," *Biol. Bull.*, **16**, 316-351.

—— (1912) "Preliminary Chemical Studies on Male and Female Producing Eggs of Pigeons," *Sci.*, **35**, 462-463.

—— (1914) "A Quantitative Basis of Sex," *Sci.*, **39**, 440.

—— (1915) "Determination of Sex and its Experimental Control," *Bull. Amer. Acad. Med.*, **15**, 1-20.

Riddle, O. (1916) "Sex Control and known Correlations in Pigeons," *Amer. Nat.*, **1**, 385-410.
—— (1917) "The Cause of the Production of 'Down' and other Down-like Structures in the Plumages of Birds," *Biol. Bull.*, **14**, 163-175.
—— (1917) "The Genesis of Fault-Bars in Feathers and the Causes of the Occurrence in Nature of Light and Dark Fundamental Bars," *Biol. Bull.*, **14**, 328-370.
—— (1917) "The Theory of Sex as stated in Terms of Results of Studies on Pigeons," *Sci.*, **46**, 19-24.
—— (1918) "A Case of Ataxic Mutation in the Pigeon," *Proc. Soc. Exp. Biol. Med.*, **15**, 56-58.
—— (1918) "Further Observations on the Relative Size and Form of the Right and Left Testes of Pigeons in Health and Disease and as influenced by Hybridity," *Anat. Rec.*, **14**, 283-334.
—— (1918) "A Demonstration of the Origin of Two Pairs of Identical Female Twins from Two Ova of High Storage Metabolism," *Jour. Exp. Zool.*, **26**, 227-254.
—— (1920) "Differential Survival of Male and Female Dove Embryos in Increased and Decreased Pressures of Oxygen: A Test of the Metabolic Theory of Sex," *Proc. Soc. Exp. Biol. and Med.*, **17**, 88-91.
—— (1923) "On the Cause of Twinning and Abnormal Development in Birds," *Amer. Jour. Anat.*, **32**, 199-252.
—— (1923) "Recent Studies on the Relation of Metabolism to Sex," *Anat. Rec.*, **24**, 418.
—— (1923) "A Case of Complete Sex-Reversal in the Adult Pigeon," *Anat. Rec.*, **26**, 394.
—— and **Harris, J. A.** (1918) "Note on the Relation of Blood Fat to Sex, and on the Correlation between Blood Fat and Egg Production in the Domestic Fowl," *Jour. Biol. Chem.*, **34**, 161-170.
—— and **Lawrence, J. V.** (1916) "Studies in the Physiology of Reproduction in Birds. VI. Sexual Differences in the Fat and Phosphorus of the Blood of Fowls," *Amer. Jour. Physiol.*, **41**, 430-437.
—— and **Spohn, A.** (1912) "On a Relation found to exist between Changes in the Chemical Composition of a Membrane and its Permeability," *Sci.*, **35**, 462-463.
Ridgeway, William (1919) "The Colour of Racehorses," *Nature*, **104**, 334.
Rietz, H. L., and **Roberts, E.** (1915) "Degree of Resemblance of Parents and Offspring, with Respect to Birth as Twins for Registered Shropshire Sheep," *Jour. Agric. Res.*, **4**, 479-510.
Riley, E. H. (1910) "The New Zebra Hybrid," *Amer. Breed. Mag.*, **1**, 107-110.
Ritzema-Bos, J. (1894) "Untersuchungen uber die Folgen der Zucht in engster Blutverwandschaft," *Biol. Zentralb.*, **14**, 75-81.
Ritzman, E. G. (1916) "Mendelism of Short Ears in Sheep," *Jour. Agric. Res.*, **6**, 797-798.
—— (1920) "Breeding Earless Sheep," *Jour. Hered.*, **11**, 238-240.
—— (1923) "Report on the Sheep Breeding Experiments at the New Hampshire Station," *N. H. Sta.* (Bull. No. 208), 10-11.
—— (1923) "The Inheritance of Size and Conformation in Sheep," *New Hamp. Agric. Exp. Sta.* (Tech. Bull. No. 25), 1-36.
—— (1924) "Sheep Breeding at the New Hampshire Station," *N. H. Sta. Rpt.* (Bull. No. 212), 1-16.

Ritzman, E. G., and **Davenport, C. B.** (1917) "Family Performance as a Basis of Selection in Sheep," *Jour. Agric. Res.*, **10**, 93-97.

—— —— (1920) "A Comparison of some Traits of Conformation of Southdown and Rambouillet Sheep and of their F_1 Hybrids, with Preliminary Data and Remarks on Variability in F_2," *New Hamp. Agric. Exp. Sta.* (Tech. Bull. No. 15), 1-32.

Roberts, E. (1918-1919) "Fluctuations in a Recessive Mendelian Character and Selection," *Jour. Exp. Zool.*, **27**, 157-191.

—— (1921) "Fertility in Shropshire Sheep in the United States," *Jour. Agric. Res.*, **22**, 231-234.

—— (1921) "Polydactylism in Cattle," *Jour. Hered.*, **12**, 84-86.

Roberts, J. A. Fraser (1924) "Colour Inheritance in the Sheep. I. Black Colour and Badger-Face Pattern in Welsh Mountain Sheep," *Jour. Genet.*, **14**, 367-374.

Robertson, E. (1921) "Note on Breeding for Increase of Milk in Dairy Cattle," *Jour. Genet.*, **11**, 79-90.

Robertson, J. B. (1922) "Chromosomes and Purity of Breed. The Determination of Sex (Horse)," *The Bloodstock Breed. Rev.*, **11**, 104-112.

Robertson, W. R. B. (1917) "A Mule and a Horse as Twins, and the Inheritance of Twinning," *Kans. Univ.* (Sci. Bull. No. 10), 293-294.

Robson, Guy C. (1911) "The Effect of Sacculina upon the Fat Metabolism of its Host," *Q. J. M. S.*, **57**, 267-278.

—— (1923) "A Note on the Species as a Gene-Complex," *Ann. and Mag. Nat. Hist.*, ser. 9, **11**, 111-115.

Rommel, G. M. (1906) "The Fecundity of Poland China and Duroc-Jersey Sows," *U.S. Dept. of Agric.* (Circ. No. 95), 1-12.

—— (1913) "The Grey Zebra as a Domestic Animal," *Amer. Breed. Mag.*, **4**, 129-139.

—— and **Phillip, E. F.** (1906) "Inheritance in Female Line of Size of Litter in Poland China Sows," *Proc. Amer. Phil. Soc.*, **45**, 244-254.

Rörig (1900) "Uber Geweihentwicklung," *Arch. Entwickl.*, **10**, 525-644.

Rutherford, W. J. (1912) "Heredity of Stamina in Horses," *Mendel. Jour.*, **1**, 37-92.

Ryder, J. A. (1893) "The Inheritance of Modifications due to Disturbances of the Early Stages of Development, especially in the Japanese Domesticated Races of Gold-Carp," *Proc. Acad. Nat. Sci.*, 75-94.

Sadler (1830) *The Law of Population.* London.

Safir, S. R. (1920) "Genetic and Cytological Examination of the Phenomena of Primary Non-Disjunction in *Drosophila melanogaster*," *Genet.*, **5**, 459-487.

Salaman, R. N. (1922) "The Inheritance of Fur Types and Hair Characters in Rabbits," *Jour. Genet.*, **12**, 179-208.

Sand, K. (1918) *Experimenteller Studier over Konskarakterer hos Pattedyr*, (Hasselbalchs), 1-256.

—— (1921) "Etudes expérimentales sur les glands sexuelles chez les mammifères, I. II. III.," *Jour. physiol., path. gén.*, **19**, 305-322, 494-527.

—— (1921) "Vasectomie pratiquée chez un chien dans un but de régeneration," *C. R. Soc. Biol.*, **85**, 1201-1205.

—— (1922) "Vasektomie beim Hunde als Regenrationsexperiment," *Zeit. Sexualwiss.*, **8**, 3-8.

Sand, K. (1922-1923) "Vasoligature Employed *ad modum* Steinach with a View to Restitution in Cases of Senium and other States (Impotency, Depression)," *Acta Chir. Scand.*, **4**, 387-462.

—— (1923) "L'hermaphroditisme expérimental," *Jour. phys. path. gén.*, **20**, 472-487.

Sanson, A. (1888) *Traité de Zoötechnie*, **3-5.**

Schleip, W. (1912) "Geschlechtsbestimmende Ursachen im Tierreich," *Ergeb. und Fort. d. Zool.*, **3**, 165-328.

Schmehl, R. (1912) "Inzuchtstudien in einer deutschen Rambouillet-Stammschäferei," *Deut. Ges. Inzuchtsgk.*, **15**, 1-95.

Schmidt, J. (1922) "Diallel Crossings with the Domestic Fowl," *Jour. Genet.*, **12**, 241-245.

Schmidt, W. (1917) "Beobachtungen von Vererbungserscheinung bei Hühnern," *Südd. landw. Tierz.*, **12**, 254.

Schrader, F., and **Sturtevant, A.** (1923) "A Note on the Theory of Sex-Determination," *Amer. Nat.*, **57**, 379-381.

Schultz, W. (1915-1916) "Schwarzfärbung weisser Haare durch die Rasur und die Entwicklungsmechanik der Farben von Haaren und Federn," *Arch. Entwickl.*, **41**, 535-557. *Ibid.*, **42**, 139-167, 222-242.

—— (1919) "Versteckte Erbfaktoren der Albinos für Färbung beim Russenkaninchen im Soma dargestellt, und rein somatisch sur Wirkung gebracht," *Zeit. indukt. Abst.*, **20**, 27-40.

Schulze, Oskar (1903-1904) "Zur Frage von geschlechtsbildenden Ursachen," *Arch. mikr. Anat.*, **63**, 197-257.

Schuster, E. H. J. (1905) "Results of Crossing Grey (House) Mice with Albinos," *Biometrika*, **4**, 1-12.

Sclater, P. L. (1903) "On the Zebra-and-Pony Hybrid living in the Societies' Menagerie," *Proc. Zool. Soc. Lond.*, **1**, 1.

Seiler (1921) "Geschlechtschromosomentersuchungen an Psychiden," *Arch. f. Zellf.*, **15**, 249-268.

Seligmann, C. G., and **Shattock, S. G.** (1914) "Observations made to Ascertain whether any Relation subsists between the Seasonal Assumption of the 'Eclipse,' Plumage in the Mallard (*Anas boscas*) and the Functions of the Testicle," *Proc. Zool. Soc. Lond.*, 23-43.

Serebrovsky, A. S. (1922) "Crossing-Over involving Three Sex-linked Genes in Chickens," *Amer. Nat.*, **56**, 571-572.

Severson, B. O. (1917) "Colour Inheritance in Swine," *Jour. Hered.*, **8**, 379-381.

—— (1917) "A Study in Cross-Breeding Delaine Merino Ewes with Mutton Rams and Cross-Bred Rams of the F_1 generation," *Pennsylv. Sta. Rpt.*, 212-268.

—— (1918) "Extra Toes in Horse and Steer," *Jour. Hered.*, **9**, 39.

Sexton, E. W., and **Huxley, J. S.** (1921) "Intersexes in *Gammarus chevreuxi* and Related Forms," *Jour. Marine Biol. Ass.*, **12**, 506-556.

Shailer, N. S. (1895) *Domesticated Animals.*

Shattock, S., and **Seligmann, C. G.** (1904) "Observations upon the Acquirement of Secondary Sexual Characters, indicating the Formation of an Internal Secretion by the Testicle," *Proc. Roy. Soc.*, **73**, 49-58.

—— —— (1906) "An Example of True Hermaphroditism in the Common Fowl," *Trans. Path. Soc. Lond.*, **57**, 69-109.

—— —— (1907-1908) "An Example of Incomplete Glandular Hermaphroditism in the Domestic Fowl," *Proc. Roy. Soc. Med.*, **1**, 3-7.

Sherwood, R. M. (1922) "Correlation between External Body Characters and Annual Egg-Production in White Leghorn Fowls," *Tex. Agric. Exp. Sta. Bull.*, No. 295, 1-14.

Simpson, Q. J. (1907) "Reversion induced by Cross-Breeding," *Sci.*, **25**, 426-428.

—— (1908) "Genetics in Swine Hybrids," *Amer. Ass. Advanc. Sci.*, 4.

—— (1912) "Inheritance of Fecundity in Swine," *Amer. Breed. Ass.*, 261-266.

—— (1914) "Coat-Pattern in Mammals," *Jour. Hered.*, **5**, 329-339.

—— and **Simpson, J. P.** (1909) "Inheritance of Face-Shape in Swine," *Amer. Breed. Ass.*, **5**, 250-255.

—— —— (1912) "Analytical Hybridising," *Amer. Breed. Ass.*, **7**, 266-275.

Skoda, K. (1912) "Anatomische Untersuchung an einem Fall von Didactylie beim Pferd," *Anat. Anz.*, **41**, 417-434.

Smith, A. D. B. (1924) "The Inheritance of Coat-Colour in Cattle, with Special Reference to the Shorthorn Breed" (Thesis, Iowa State College).

Smith, G. (1906) "Rhizocephala," *Fauna et Flora d. Golfes v. Neapel*, Monograph No. 29.

—— (1910-1913) "Studies in the Experimental Analysis of Sex," 1-9, *Q. J. M. S.*, **54-58.**

—— and **Thomas, Haig** (1913) "On Sterile and Hybrid Pheasants," *Jour. Genet.*, **3**, 39-52.

Smith, S. P. (1909) "An Equine Hermaphrodite," *Amer. Vet. Rev.*, **35**, 63.

Smith, W. W. (1913) "Colour Inheritance in Swine," *Amer. Breed. Mag.*, No. 4, 113-123.

So, M., and **Imai, Y.** (1920) "The Types of Spotting in Mice and their Genetic Behaviour," *Jour. Genet.*, **9**, 319-333.

Sollas, J. B. J. (1909) "Inheritance of Colour and of Supernumerary Mammæ in Guinea-pig, with a Note on the Occurrence of a Dwarf Form," *5th Rep. Evol. Com.*, 51-79.

—— (1914) "Note on the Offspring of a Dwarf-Bearing Strain of Guinea-pigs," *Jour. Genet.*, **3**, 201-204.

Spann (1913) "Kreuzungen zwischen Allgäuer und Afrikander Rindern," *Deut. landw. Tierz.*, **17**, 18.

Spillman, W. J. (1906) "Inheritance of Coat-Colour in Swine," *Sci.*, **24**, 441-443.

—— (1907) "Colour Inheritance in Mammals," *Sci.*, **25**, 313-314.

—— (1907) "Inheritance of the Belt in Hampshire Swine," *Sci.*, **25**, 541-543.

—— (1908) "Colour Factors in Mammals," *Amer. Breed. Ass.*, **4**, 357-359.

—— (1909) "Barring in Barred Plymouth Rocks," *Poultry*, **5**, 7-8.

—— (1911) "History and Peculiarities of the Mule-Foot Hog," *Amer. Breed. Ass.*, **6**, 116-120.

—— (1913) "The Arnaud Sheep × Goat Hybrid," *Amer. Breed. Ass.*, **4**, 69-72.

Spöttel, W., and **Tänzer, E.** (1922) "On the Qualities and Hereditary Transmission of Wool Characters in Leicester × Merino Crosses," *Deut. landw. Tierz.*, **26**, 518-522.

—— —— (1923) "Rassenanalytische Untersuchungen an Schafen unter besonderer Berücksichtigung von Haut und Haar," *Arch. Naturg.*, **89**, 1-242.

Stangel, W. L. (1924) "A Fertile Mare Mule," *Breed. Gaz.*, **85**, 77.

Stanley, L., and **Kelker, G. D.** (1920) "Testicle Transplantation," *Jour. Amer. Med. Ass.*, **74**, 1501-1503.

Staples-Browne, R. (1904) "Experiments on Heredity in Web-Footed Pigeon," *Brit. Ass. Advanc. Sci.*, 595.

Staples-Browne, R. (1905) "Note on Heredity in Pigeons," *Proc. Zool. Soc. Lond.*, **2**, 550-558.

—— (1908) "On the Inheritance of Colour in Domestic Pigeons, with Special Reference to Reversion," *Proc. Zool. Soc. Lond.*, 67-104.

—— (1912) "Second Report on the Inheritance of Colour in Pigeons, together with an Account of some Experiments on the Crossing of Certain Races of Doves with Special Reference to Sex-linked Inheritance," *Jour. Genet.*, **2**. 131-162.

—— (1923) "On the Crossing of some Species of Columbidæ, and the Inheritance of certain Characters in their Hybrid Offspring," *Jour. Genet.*, **13**, 153-166.

Stark, M. B. (1918) "An Hereditary Tumour in the Fruit-Fly Drosophila," *Jour. Cancer Res.*, **3**, 279-302.

—— (1919) "An Hereditary Tumour," *Jour. Exp. Zool.*, **27**, 507-532.

—— (1919) "A Benign Tumour that is Hereditary in Drosophila," *Proc. Nat. Acad. Sci.*, **5**, 573-580.

Starkweather (1883) *The Law of Sex.* London.

Steche, O. (1912) "Beobachtungen über Geschlechtsunterschiede der Hämolymphe der Insekten," *Verh. deut. zool. Ges.*, **22**, 272-281.

Steinach, E. (1912), "Willkürliche Umwandlung von Saugetiermännchen in Tiere mit ausgeprägt weiblichen Geschlechtscharakteren und weiblicher Psyche," *Pflüg. Arch.*, **144**, 71-108.

—— (1913) "Feminierung von Männchen und Maskulierung von Weibchen," *Zentralb. Physiol.*, **27**, 717-723.

—— (1916) "Pubertatsdrüse und Zwitterbildung," *Arch. Entwickl.*, **42**, 307-332.

—— (1920) "Künstliche und naturliche Zwitterdrüsen und ihre analogen Wirkungen," *Arch. Entwickl.*, **46**, 12-28.

Stephan, P. (1902) "Sur la structure histologique du testicule des Mulets," *C. R. d. l'Aos. d'Anat.*, **4**.

Stevens, N. M. (1911) "Heterochromosomes in the Guinea-pig," *Biol. Bull.*, **21**, 155-167.

Stewart, Dorothy (1923) "The Heredity of the 'White Hooded' Albino Rat," *Anat. Rec.*, **24**, 417-418.

Stockard, C. R. (1913) "The Effect on the Offspring of Intoxicating the Male Parent and the Transmission of the Defects to Subsequent Generations," *Amer. Nat.*, **47**, 139-461.

—— (1914) "A Study of Further Generations of Mammals from Ancestors treated with Alcohol," *Proc. Soc. Exp. Biol. and Med.*, **11**, 136-139.

—— and **Papanicolaou, G.** (1916) "A Further Analysis of the Hereditary Transmission of Degeneracy and Deformities by the Descendants of Alcoholized Mammals," *Amer. Nat.*, **50**, 65-88, 144-177.

—— —— (1918) "Further Studies on the Modification of the Germ-Cells in Mammals: The Effect of Alcohol on Treated Guinea-pigs and their Descendants," *Jour. Exp. Zool.*, **26**, 119-226.

Stotsenburg, J. M. (1909) "On the Growth of the Albino Rat (*Mus norvegicus* var. *albus*) after Castration," *Anat. Rec.*, **3**, 233-244.

Stroever, A. W. (1917) "Die Vererbung der Haarfarbe beim Vollblutspferde," 1-69.

—— (1917) "Das Auftreten und die Vererbung von Mehrlingsgeburten beim Vollblutspferde," 1-21.

Strong, L. C. (1922) "A Genetic Analysis of the Factors underlying Susceptibility to Transplantable Tumors," *Jour. Exp. Zool.*, **36**, 67-134.

Strong, R. M. (1912) "Results of Hybridising Ring-Doves, including Sex-linked Inheritance," *Biol. Bull.*, **23**, 293-322.

Sturtevant, A. H. (1910) "On the Inheritance of Colour in the American Harness Horse," *Biol. Bull.*, **19**, 204-216.

—— (1911) "Another Sex-limited Character in Fowls," *Sci.*, **33**, 337-338.

—— (1912) "A Critical Examination of Recent Studies on Colour Inheritance in Horses," *Jour. Genet.*, **2**, 41-51.

—— (1912) "Review of Federley's Breeding Experiments with the Moth *Pygæra*," *Amer. Nat.*, **46**, 565-568.

—— (1912) "Is there Association between the Yellow and Agouti Factors in Mice?" *Amer. Nat.*, **46**, 368-371.

—— (1912) "An Experiment dealing with Sex-linkage in Fowls," *Jour. Exp. Zool.*, **12**, 499-518.

—— (1913) "The Himalayan Rabbit Case, with Some Consideration on Multiple Allelomorphs," *Amer. Nat.*, **47**, 234-238.

—— (1913) "The Linear Arrangement of Six Sex-linked Factors in Drosophila," *Jour. Exp. Zool.*, **14**, 43-59.

—— (1914) "The Reduplication Hypothesis as applied to Drosophila," *Amer. Nat.*, **48**, 535-549.

—— (1914) "The Behaviour of Chromosomes as studied through Linkage," *Zeit. indukt. Abst.*, **13**, 234-287.

—— (1915) "Experiments on Sex Recognition and the Problem of Sexual Selection in Drosophila," *Jour. Anim. Behav.*, **5**, 351-366.

—— (1917) "Genetic Factors Affecting the Strength of Linkage in Drosophila," *Proc. Nat. Acad. Sci.*, **3**, 555-558.

—— (1918) "An Analysis of the Effects of Selection," *Carn. Inst. Publ.*, No. 264, 1-68.

—— (1920) "Genetic Studies on *Drosophila simulans*. I. Introduction. Hybrids with *Drosophila melanogaster*," *Genet.*, **5**, 488-500.

—— (1920) "Intersexes in *Drosophila simulans*," *Sci.*, **51**, 325-327.

—— (1921) "Genetic Studies on *Drosophila simulans*. II. Sex-linked Group of Genes. III. Autosomal Genes. General Discussion," *Genet.*, **6**, 43-64, 179-207.

—— (1924) "An Interpretation of Orthogenesis," *Sci.*, **54**, 379-380.

—— **Bridges, C. B.**, and **Morgan, T. H.** (1919) "The Spatial Relation of Genes," *Proc. Nat. Acad. Sci.*, **5**, 168-173.

Suchetet, A. (1897) "Problèmes hybridologiques," *Jour. d'anat. d. physiol.*, **33**, 326-355.

Sumner, F. B. (1909) "Some Effects of External Conditions upon the White Mouse," *Jour. Exp. Zool.*, **7**, 97-155.

—— (1910) "The Reappearance in the Offspring of Artificially produced Parental Modifications," *Amer. Nat.*, **44**, 5-18.

—— (1910) "An Experimental Study of Somatic Modifications and their Reappearance in the Offspring," *Arch. Entwickl.*, **3**, 317-348.

—— (1915) "Some Studies of Environmental Influence, Heredity, Correlation, and Growth in the White Mouse," *Jour. Exp. Zool.*, **18**, 325-432.

—— (1917) "Several Colour Mutations in Mice of the Genus Peromyscus," *Genet.*, **2**, 291-300.

Sumner, F. B. (1920) "Geographic Variation and Mendelian Inheritance," *Jour. Exp. Zool.*, **30**, 369-402.

—— (1922) "Linkage in Peromyscus," *Amer. Nat.*, **56**, 412-417.

—— and **Collins, H. V.** (1922) "Further Studies of Colour Mutation in Mice of the Genus Peromyscus," *Jour. Exp. Zool.*, **36**, 289-322.

—— and **Others** (1922) "A Study of Influences which may affect the Sex-Ratio of the Deer-Mouse (Peromyscus)," *Biol. Bull.*, **43**, 123-168.

Surface, F. M. (1905) "Fecundity of Swine," *Biometrika*, **6**, 433-436.

Sutton, W. S. (1903) "The Chromosomes in Heredity," *Biol. Bull.*, **4**, 231-251.

Swingle, W. W. (1922) "Is there a Transformation of Sex in Frogs," *Amer. Nat.*, **56**, 193-211.

Tandler, J., and **Grosz, S.** (1909) "Ueber den Einfluss der Kastration auf den Organismus. I. Beschreibung eines Eunuchskelets," *Arch. Entwickl.*, **27**, 35-61.

—— —— (1913) *Die biologischen Grundlagen der sekundären Geschlechtscharaktere*, 1-173. Berlin.

Tänzer, E., und **Spöttel, W.** (1922) "Das Zackelschaf unter besonderer Berücksichtigung der Zuchten des landwirtschaftlichen Instituts der Universität Halle," *Zeit. indukt. Abst.*, **28**, 89-206.

Tegetmeier, W. B., and **Sutherland, C. L.** (1895) *Horses, Asses, Zebras, Mules and Mule-Breeding.*

Templeton, George S. (1923) "Unusual Colour Inheritance: Coat-Colour of Cross-Bred Steer, Quoman's Perfection, not that ordinarily encountered in the Angus × Hereford Cross," *Jour. Hered.*, **14**, 39-40.

Terho, T. (1923) "Zur Vererbung einiger Wollcharaktere beim Mele-Schaf," *Zeit. indukt. Abst.*, **32**, 37-60.

Texas Agricultural Experiment Station (1921) "Brahma-Hereford Cross," *Texas Sta. Rpt.*, 8-9.

Thomas, Mrs R. Haig (1910) (*a*) "On Experimental Pheasant Breeding," *Proc. Zool. Soc. Lond.*, 6-9. (1912) (*b*) "Experimental Pheasant Breeding," *Ibid.*, 539-546.

Thury (1863) *Uber das Gesetz der Erzeugung der Geschlechter.* Leipzig.

Tihomirof, A. A. (1887) "A Contribution to the Study of Hermaphroditism in Birds," *Trans. Imp. Soc. Nat. Hist.*, **52**, 1-29. Moscow.

Tjebbes, K. (1924) "Crosses with Siamese Cats," *Jour. Genet.*, **14**, 355-366.

Tomhave, W. H., and **MacDonald** (1920) "Cross-Breeding Delaine Merino Ewes with Pure Bred Mutton Rams," *Penns. Agric. Exp. Sta.* (Bull. No. 163), 1-19.

Tornier (1908) "Vorläufiges über das Enstehen der Goldfischrassen," *Sitzb. d. Ges. naturf. Freund.*, 40-45.

Torrey, H. B. (1902) "Prepotency in Polydactylous Cats," *Sci.*, **16**, 554-555.

—— and **Horning, B.** (1922) "Hen-Feathering induced in the Male Fowl by Feeding on Thyroid," *Proc. Soc. Exp. Biol. and Med.*, **19**, 275-279.

Trouessart, E. (1907) "Hybrides de Paon et de Poule cochinchinoise," *L'Acclimatation*, No. 103, 645.

—— (1920) "A Peacock × Fowl Hybrid," *Rev. d'hist. nat. appl.*, pt. 2, 100-102.

Tschermak, von A. (1910) "Uber den Einfluss der Bastardierung auf Form, Farbe und Zeichnung von Kanarieneiern," *Biol. Zentralb.*, **30**, 641-646.

—— (1912) "Uber Veränderung der Form, Farbe und Zeichnung von Kanarieneiern durch Bastardierung," *Pflüg. Arch.*, **148**, 367-395.

Tschermak, von A. (1915) "Uber Verfärbung von Hühnereiern durch Bastardierung und über Nachdauer dieser Farbänderung," *Biol. Zentralb.*, **35**, 46-63.

Tschermak, E. (1900) "Uber künstliche Kreuzungen bei Pisum sativum," *Zeit. landw. Versuchsw. Oester.*, **3**, 465-555.

Tschermak, H. (1917) "Uber das verschiedene Ergebnis reziproker Kreuzung von Hühnerrassen und über dessen Bedeutung für die Vererbungslehre," *Biol. Zentralb.*, **37**, 217-277.

Tyzzer, E. E. (1907-1908) "A Series of Spontaneous Tumours in Mice, with Observations on the Influence of Heredity on the Frequency of their Occurrence," *Jour. Med. Res.*, **17**, 155-197.

—— (1907-1908) "A Study of Heredity in Relation to the Development of Tumours in Mice," *Jour. Med. Res.*, **17**, 199-211.

—— (1909) "A Series of Spontaneous Tumours in Mice, with Observations on the Influence of Heredity on the Frequency of their Occurrence," *Jour. Med. Res.*, **21**, 479-518.

—— (1909) "A Study of Inheritance in Mice, with Reference to their Susceptibility to Transferable Tumours," *Jour. Med. Res.*, **21**, 519-573.

Uda, H. (1919) "On the Relations between Blood-Colour and Cocoon-Colour in Silkworms, with Special Reference to Mendel's Law of Heredity," *Genet.*, **4**, 395-416.

Uhlman, E. (1914) "Ein Beitrag zur Frage der Vererbarkeit von Zwillingsgeburten," *Deut. landw. Tierz.*, **18**, 163-164.

University College of North Wales (1912) "Breeding Experiments with Welsh Mountain Breeding Ewes" (Bull. No. 7).

Vacher, M. (1905) "Transmission de la couleur chez les animaux de la ferme," *Bull. Soc. nat. d'agric. de France.*

Vecchi, A. (1920) "Heredity in Rabbits," *Natura*, **11**, 143-169.

Vilmorin, Ph. de (1913) "Sur les caractèrs héréditaires des chiens anoures et brachyoures," *C. R. Acad. Sci.*, **157**, 1086-1089.

Voitellier, Ch., and **Degois, E.** (1922) "Experiments on the Industrial Crossing of Southdown Ram × Limousin Goat," *Rev. de Zoot.*, No. 8, 731-747.

Volpini, A. (1924) "Della prolificità e fecondità delle scrofe," *L'aveniro zoot. umbro.*, **4**, 6.

Voronoff, S. (1922) *Greffes testiculaires*, 1-83. Paris.

Vries, H. de (1900) "Sur les unités des caractères spécifiques et leur application à l'étude des hybrides," *Rev. gén. d. Botan.*, **12**, 257.

—— (1910-1911) *The Mutation Theory*. Translation (2 vols.). London.

Wachter, W. L. (1921) "Data concerning Linkage in Mice," *Amer. Nat.*, **55**, 412-420.

Wahl, von H. (1907) "Fruchtbare Maultiere," *Jahrb. f. wiss. und prakt. Tierz.*

Walker, K. M. (1924) "The Internal Secretion of the Testis," *Lancet*, 1-50.

Wallace, R. (1915) "Results of Crossing Karakul Sheep with European, and especially British Breeds," *Jour. Board Agric.*, **22**, 434-447.

—— (1923) *Farm Live Stock of Great Britain*, 3rd edit. Edinburgh: Oliver & Boyd.

Walther, A. R. (1911) "L'hérédité de la couleur de la robe chez le cheval," 4me *Confer Inter. de Génét.*, Paris, 491-502.

—— (1912) "Studien über Vererbung bei Pferden. I. Vererbung des schwarzen Pigments," *Zeit. indukt. Abst.*, **6**, 238-244.

—— (1913) "Die Vererbung unpigmentierter Haare (Schimmelung) und Hautstellen ('Abzeichnung') bei Rind und Pferd, als Beispiel transgressiv-fluktuirender Faktoren," *Zeit. indukt. Abst.*, **10**, 1-48.

—— (1914) "Ueber den Einfluss der Rassenkreuzung auf Gewicht, Form, Glanz und Farbe der Hühnereier," *Landwirt. Jahrb.*, **46**, 89-104.

Warner, D. E., and **Edmond, H. D.** (1917) "Blood-Fat in Domestic Fowl in Relation to Egg-Production," *Jour. Biol. Chem.*, **31**, 281-294.

Warren, D. C. (1918) "The Effect of Selection upon the Sex-Ratio in *Drosophila ampelophila*," *Biol. Bull.*, **34**, 351-371.

Watson, J. A. S. (1921) "A Mendelian Experiment in Crossing Aberdeen-Angus and West Highland Cattle: Experiments made in Great Britain," *Jour. Genet.*, **9**, 59-67.

Weber, K. (1922) "Ueber Vererbung von Albinismus," *Arch. f. Augenh.*, **92**, 40-43.

Weber, M. (1890) "Ueber einen Fall von Hermaphroditismus bei *Fringilla cœlebs*," *Zool. Anz.*, **13**, 508-512.

Weinberg, W. (1909) "Die Anlage zur Mehrlingsgeburt beim Menschen und ihre Vererbung," *Arch. f. Rass und Ges. Biol.*, **6**, 322-340.

Weismann, August (1882) *Studies in the Theory of Descent.* Sampson Low, London.

—— (1893) *The Germ-Plasm: A Theory of Heredity.* Walter Scott, London.

Welch, W. H. (1920) "Heredity as expressed by our Stallion Registration Laws," *Jour. Amer. Vet. Med. Ass.*, **57**, 33-45.

Weldon, W. F. R. (1906) "On the Inheritance of the Sex-Ratio and of the Size of the Litter in Mice," *Biometrika*, **5**, 436-449.

—— (1915) "Mice Breeding Experiments: Records of Matings," *Biometrika*, **11**, 1-60.

Wellmann, O. (1916) "Experiments with Dogs in connection with the Mendelian Laws of Heredity," *Bull. Nat. Sci.*, **48**, 315-320.

Wells, H. G. (1923) "The Influence of Heredity on the Occurrence of Cancer," *Jour. Amer. Med. Ass.*, **81**, 1017, 1103.

Wentworth, E. N. (1912) "Twins in Three Generations," *Breed. Gaz.*, **62**, 133.

—— (1912) "Inheritance of Mammæ in Swine," *Proc. Amer. Breed. Ass.*, **8**, 545-549.

—— (1912) "Segregation in Cattle," *Ibid.*, 572-580.

—— (1912) "Another Sex-limited Character," *Sci.*, **35**, 986.

—— (1913) "Inheritance of Mammæ in the Duroc-Jersey Swine," *Amer. Nat.*, **47**, 257-278.

—— (1913) "Why In-Breeding Decreases Fertility," *Breed. Gaz.*, **63**, 1154.

—— (1913) "Colour in Shorthorn Cattle," *Amer. Breed. Mag.*, **4**, 202-208.

—— (1914) "Colour Inheritance in the Horse," *Zeit. indukt. Abst.*, **11**, 10-17.

—— (1914) "Sex in Multiple Births," *Sci.*, **39**, 611.

—— (1914) "Sex-linked Factors in the Inheritance of Rudimentary Mammæ in Swine," *Iowa Acad. Sci.*, **21**, 265-268.

—— (1915) "Prepotency," *Jour. Hered.*, **6**, 17-20.

Wentworth, E. N. (1915) "Colour Inheritance in the Horse," *Jour. U.S. Caval. Ass.*, **25**, 633-642.

—— (1916) "A Sex-limited Colour in Ayrshire Cattle," *Jour. Agric. Res.*, **6**, 141-147.

—— and **Aubel, C. E.** (1916) "Inheritance of Fertility in Swine," *Jour. Agric. Res.*, **5**, 1145-1160.

—— and **Lush, J. L.** (1923) "Inheritance in Swine," *Jour. Agric. Res.*, **23**, 557-582.

—— and **Sweet** (1917) "Fertility in Southdown Sheep," *Amer. Nat.*, **51**, 662-682.

Werneke, Fr. (1916) "Die Pigmentierung der Farbenrassen von *Mus musculus* und ihre Beziehung zur Vererbung," *Arch. Entwickl.*, **42**, 72-106.

Wheeler, H. J. (1910) "A Pheasant × Bantam Hybrids," *Amer. Breed. Mag.*, **1**, 261-268.

Wheeler, R. (1913) "Feeding Experiments with Mice," *Jour. Exp. Zool.*, **15**, 209-224.

White, W. T. (1921) "Crossing Holstein and Galloways at the Kodiak Station," *Alaska Sta. Rpt.*, 46.

Whitehead, R. H. (1908) "A Peculiar Case of Cryptorchism, and its Bearing upon the Problem of the Function of the Interstitial Cells of the Testis," *Anat. Rec.*, **2**, 177-182.

Whiting, P. W. (1916) "A New Colour Variety of the Norway Rat," *Sci.*, **43**, 781.

—— (1918) "Inheritance of Coat-Colour in Cats," *Jour. Exp. Zool.*, **25**, 539-570.

—— (1919) "Inheritance of White Spotting and other Characters in Cats," *Amer. Nat.*, **53**, 473-482.

—— and **King, H. D.** (1918) "Ruby-Eyed Dilute Grey, a third Allelomorph in the Albino Series of the Rat," *Jour. Exp. Zool.*, **26**, 55-64.

Whitman, C. O. (1919) "Orthogenetic Evolution in Pigeons" (vol. i.), *Carn. Inst. Publ.*, No. 257.

Wilckens, M. (1886) "Untersuchungen uber das Geschlechtsverhältnisse und die Ursachen der Geschlechtsbildung bei Haustieren," *Landwirt. Jahrb.*, **15**.

—— (1889) "Ueber die Vererbung der Haarfarbe und deren Beziehung zur Formvererbung bei Pferden," *Landwirt. Jahrb.*, **18**, 555-576.

Wilkins, V. E. (1922) "Agricultural Research and the Farmer," *Minist. of Agric. and Fisher.*, 1-168.

Wilson, E. B. (1906) "Studies on Chromosomes. III. The Sexual Differences of the Chromosome Groups in Hemiptera, with some Consideration on the Determination and Heredity of Sex," *Jour. Exp. Zool.*, **3**, 1-40.

—— (1910) "The Chromosomes in Relation to the Determination of Sex," *Sci. Prog.*, **16**, 570-592.

—— (1911) "The Sex Chromosomes," *Arch. mikr. Anat.*, **77**, 249-271.

—— (1912) "Some Aspects of Cytology in Relation to the Study of Genetics," *Amer. Nat.*, **46**, 57-67.

—— and **Morgan, T. H.** (1920) "Chiasmatype and Crossing-Over," *Amer. Nat.*, **54**, 193-219.

Wilson, James (1908) "Transmission of Colour in Shorthorns," *Breed. Gaz.*, **54**, 86.

Wilson, James (1908) "Mendelian Characters among Shorthorn Cattle," *Sci. Proc. Roy. Dubl. Soc.*, **11**, 317-324. "Mendelian Characters among Shorthorns," *Nature*, **77**, 509.

—— (1909) "The Origin of the Dexter-Kerry Breed of Cattle," *Sci. Proc. Roy. Dubl. Soc.*, **12**, 1-17. "The Colour of Highland Cattle," *Ibid.*, 66-76. "The Scandinavian Origin of the Hornless Cattle of the British Isles," *Ibid.*, 145-164.

—— (1910) "The Inheritance of Coat-Colour in Horses," *Sci. Proc. Roy. Dubl. Soc.*, **12**, 331-348. "The Separate Inheritance of Quantity and Quality in Cows' Milk," *Ibid.*, **12**, 470-479.

—— (1911) "The Inheritance of Milk-Yield in Cattle," *Sci. Proc. Roy. Dubl. Soc.*, **13**, 89-113. (1912) "Unsound Mendelian Developments, especially as regards the Presence and Absence Theory," *Ibid.*, **13**, 399-421.

—— (1912) "The Value of Pedigree," *Live Stock Jour. Alman.*, 104-106.

Winge, O. (1920) "Über die Vererbung der Haarfarbe der Pferde," *Zeit. indukt. Abst.*, **24**, 1-32.

—— (1920) "Researches on the Inheritance of Coat-Colour in Horses in Denmark," *Nord. Jordbrugsforskning*, pt. 5, 1-30.

—— (1922) "One-sided Masculine and Sex-linked Inheritance in *Lebistes reticulatus*," *Jour. Genet.*, **12**, 145-162.

—— (1922) "A Peculiar Mode of Inheritance, and its Cytological Explanation," *Jour. Genet.*, **12**, 137-144.

—— (1922) "Crossing-Over between the X- and the Y-Chromosomes in *Lebistes*," *C. R. Trav. du Lab. Carlsberg*, **14**, 1-19.

—— (1923) "Crossing-Over between the X- and the Y-Chromosomes in *Lebistes*," *Jour. Genet.*, **13**, 201-207.

Winiwarter, von H., and **Sainmont, G.** (1909) "Nouvelles recherches sur l'ovogenèse et l'organogenèse de l'ovaire des mammifères (chat). VI. Ovogenèse de la zone corticale primitive," *Arch. Biol.*, **24**, 165-267.

Witschi, E. (1921) "Der Hermaphroditismus der Frösche und seine Bedeutung für das Geschlechtsproblem und die Lehre von der inneren Sekretion der Keimdrüsen," *Arch. Entwickl.*, **49**, 316-358.

—— (1921) "Development of Gonads and Transformation of Sex in the Frog," *Amer. Nat.*, **55**, 529-538.

—— (1922) "Chromosomen und Geschlecht bei Rana temporaria," *Zeit. indukt. Abst.*, **27**, 243-255.

—— (1923) "Ueber die genetische Konstitution der Froschzwitter," *Biol. Zentralb.*, **43**, 89-96.

Wodsedalek, J. E. (1913) "Accessory Chromosomes in the Pig," *Sci.*, **38**, 30-31.

—— (1913) "Spermatogenesis in the Pig," *Biol. Bull.*, **25**, 8-46.

—— (1914) "Spermatogenesis in the Horse," *Biol. Bull.*, **27**, 295-304.

—— (1916) "Causes of Sterility in the Mule," *Biol. Bull.*, **30**, 1-56.

—— (1920) "Studies on the Cells of Cattle, with Special Reference to Spermatogenesis, Oogonia, and Sex-Determination," *Biol. Bull.*, **38**, 290-316.

Wood, C. D. (1914) "Milk Production and Age," *Maine Agric. Expt. Stat. Rpt.*, 3-5.

Wood, T. B. (1905) "Note on the Inheritance of Horns and Face Colour in Sheep," *Jour. Agric. Sci.*, **1**, 364-365.

—— (1909) "The Inheritance of Horns and Face Colour in Sheep," *Jour. Agric. Sci.*, **3**, 145-154.

Woods, F. A. (1903) "Mendel's Laws and some Records in Rabbit Breeding," *Biometrika*, **2**, 299-306.

Woodward, T. E. (1916) "Experiments to ascertain whether the Ability to produce Milk-Fat is transmitted by the Dam or the Sire," *Hoard's Dairyman*, **51**, 146.

Wriedt, C. (1914) "Ueber die kurzohrige Schafrasse Norwegen," *Jahrb. f. wiss. und prakt. Tierz.*, **9**, 266-267.

—— (1919) "Die Maultierfüchse und ihre Beziehung zur modernern Vererbungslehre," *Jahrb. Tierz.*, **12**, 143-144.

—— (1919) "Ueber die Vererbung von Ohrenlänge beim Schafe," *Zeit. indukt. Abst.*, **20**, 262-263.

—— (1919-20) "The Brindle Colour of Cattle in Relation to Red," *Jour. Genet.*, **9**, 83.

—— (1921) "Breeding Earless Sheep," *Jour. Hered.*, **12**, 56.

—— (1923) "Drei Mutationen bei Haustieren," *Zeit. indukt. Abst.*, **30**, 300.

—— (1924) "Vererbungsfaktoren bei weissen Pferden im Gestüt Friedriksborg," *Zeit. Tierz. Züchtgsb.*, **1**, 231-242.

—— (1924) "The 'Gromet' Pattern in Sheep," *Jour. Hered.*, **15**, 125-126.

—— (1924) "Lethal Factors," *Rev. Scot. Cattle Breed. Confer.*, 50-57. Oliver & Boyd.

—— (1925) "Die Erblichkeitsverhältnisse der ohrlosen und kurzohrigen Schafe und die Verbreitung dieser Typen in Norwegen," *Zeit. indukt. Abst.*, **35**.

Wright, S. (1915) "The Albino Series of Allelomorphs in Guinea-pigs," *Amer. Nat.*, **49**, 140-148.

—— (1916) "An Intensive Study of the Inheritance of Colour and of Other Coat Characters in Guinea-pigs, with Special Reference to Graded Variation," *Carn. Inst. Publ.*, No. 241, 59-160.

—— (1917) "Colour Inheritance in Mammals, I. II. The Mouse. III. The Rat. IV. The Rabbit. V. The Guinea-pig. VI. and VII. Cattle and Horse," *Jour. Hered.*, **8**, 224-235, 373-378, 426-430, 473-475, 476-480, 521-527.

—— (1918) *Ibid.*, "VIII. Swine. IX. Dog. X. Cat. XI. Man," *Jour. Hered.*, **9**, 33-38, 89-90, 139-144, 227-240.

—— (1918) "On the Nature of Size Factors," *Genet.*, **3**, 365-374.

—— (1920) "The Relative Importance of Heredity and Environment in Determining the Piebald Pattern of Guinea-pig," *Proc. Nat. Acad. Sci.*, **6**, 320-332.

—— (1923) "The Relation between the Piebald and Tortoiseshell Colour Patterns in the Guinea-pig," *Anat. Rec.*, **26**, 393.

—— (1923) "Mendelian Analysis of the Pure Breeds of Live Stock. I. The Measurement of In-Breeding and Relationship. II. The Duchess Family of Shorthorns as Bred by Thomas Bates," *Jour. Hered.*, **14**, 339-348, 405-422.

—— (1923) "Two New Colour Factors of the Guinea-pig," *Amer. Nat.*, **57**, 42-51.

—— and **Eaton, O. N.** (1923) "Factors which determine Otocephaly in Guinea-pigs," *Jour. Agric. Res.*, **26**, 161-181.

—— and **Hunt, H. R.** (1918) "Pigmentation in Guinea-pig Hair," *Jour. Hered.*, **9**, 178-181.

Yerkes, R. M. (1913) "The Heredity of Savageness and Wildness in Rats," *Jour. Anim. Behav.*, **3**, 286-296.

Yocum, Harry B. (1915-1917) "Some Phases of Spermatogenesis in the Mouse," *Univ. Calif. Publ.*, **16**, 371-380.

—— (1924) "Luteal Cells in Gonads of the Phalarope," *Biol. Bull.*, **46**, 101-105.

Zamnini (1906) "A Case of Polydactyly in a Donkey," *Rec. de méd. vétér.*, **88.**
Zavadovsky, M. (1922) *Sex and the Development of its Characters*, 1-256. Moscow.
Zeleny, C., and **Faust, E. C.** (1915) "Size Dimorphism in the Spermatozoa from Single Testes," *Jour. Exp. Zool.*, **18**, 187-240.
—— (1922) "The Effect of Selection for Eye Facet Number in the White Bar-Eye Race of *Drosophila melanogaster*," *Genet.*, **7**, 1-115.
Ziegler, H. E. (1919) "Zuchtwahlversuche an Ratten," *Fests. Württ. Land. Hochsch.*, 385-399.
Ziek, M. (1911) "Die Hornspalten des Pferdes und ihre Vererbung" (Inaug. Dissert., Bern.).
Zimmermann, R. (1917) "Breeding Rabbits for Fur," *Berl. tierärzt. Wochensch.*, **32**, 213.

AUTHORS' INDEX

GENERAL INDEX

PRINTED BY OLIVER AND BOYD, EDINBURGH

Lightning Source UK Ltd.
Milton Keynes UK
UKHW011213281019
352454UK00002B/532/P

9 781406 796117